LIFE IN A
DEVON VILLAGE

LIFE IN A DEVON VILLAGE

Henry Williamson

Salem House
Salem, New Hampshire

First published in the United States by
Salem House, 1985. A member of the
Merrimack Publishers' Circle, 47
Pelham Road, Salem, New Hampshire
03079.

© The Estate of Henry Williamson

Series design: Lawrence & Gerry Design Group

ISBN 0-88162-121-8

Library of Congress Catalog
Card Number 85-50901

Printed in Great Britain by
Richard Clay (The Chaucer Press) Ltd,
Bungay, Suffolk

PUBLISHER'S PREFACE

Henry Williamson was born in London in 1895. He joined the army in 1914 and fought in Flanders until the summer of 1917 when he was sent home suffering from shellshock and dysentery. In 1921 he moved to Devon where he lived until 1937, when he went to farm in Norfolk until the end of the Second World War. He then returned to Devon and remained there until his death in 1977.

During the 1930s he supported Mosley and Hitler, believing stubbornly in Hitler's goodwill towards Britain. His sympathy with both the British and German fascists was founded on a belief that Hitler represented the only hope for peace in Europe, a belief which was to cost him recognition in later years.

Life in a Devon Village (first published 1945) contains the story of the early years Williamson spent in Devon, at Georgeham near Ilfracombe. He lived first at Skirr Cottage opposite the Post Office, for which he paid £4 a year, and from the autumn of 1925 at Crowberry Cottage nearby. In these two cottages he wrote the books for which he is best remembered, *Tarka the Otter* (1927) and 'The Flax of Dream' (1921-28) novels.

NOTE

LIFE IN A DEVON VILLAGE, with its companion TALES OF A
DEVON VILLAGE, is compiled from material gathered together
originally in two books written between 1919 and 1929 and
called *The Village Book* and *The Labouring Life*. Both dealt with
an observed and authenticated period that has now passed
away—the first half of the interval between the two industrial
wars of the twentieth century.

I was never fully satisfied by them; they were a collection of
varying fragments rather than unified books. During the decade
that followed publication no further editions were called for
by the public, and except for a few readers, the books were
forgotten.

To-day, after several years of hard physical work as a farmer
in another part of England, I have the opportunity to give to
each of these village books its own unity, while also searching
sharply for faults in the original transcripts. Did I exaggerate
in my writings of twenty years ago? I looked for errors in the
letter, or detail, of truth, as well as for distortions in the spirit of
truth; and found there was little to correct or alter. My essential
views had undergone no alteration during a quarter of a century,
from the un-understandings of one war to the un-understandings of another. What is plain to me now was plain to me then:
1944 life in the great world is the same as 1924 life in the little
village, where coming events were cast as shadows on the walls:
the very stones of which cry out, in the silence of the heart.

1921–1944.   H. W.

Chapter One

MY NEIGHBOUR "REVVY"

I

There was a concrete ship built on the slip by the Long Bridge in the town during the "submarine peril" of 1917—a ship which, launched amidst cheers and hand-claps and hopeful smiles, and the little foamy clash of a bottle on its bow-plates, slid into the sand of the river Taw, and stuck there, with a cracked back, until it was broken up as unserviceable a little while later. William ("Revvy") Carter, the labourer, was there at the time—he had helped to build it, being one of many who mixed gravel and cement with long-handled Devon shovels, or wheeled iron barrows of liquid cement with which its ribs were covered, for one shilling and twopence an hour—very good pay in those days. "'Twas a sad sight, vor see th' poor old ship end up like that," said William Carter. He was then about forty years old, slow with a leg-wound and unsupple with rheumatism. He was used to working out of doors in all weather. When it rained, he wore a sack on his shoulders to protect him from the heat of the rain. That had been his only wet-weather covering for nearly thirty working years, except for three of them in the army, when the sack had been replaced by a groundsheet used as a waterproof cape.

When first I had known him, Revvy was married, with a small baby boy. The war had been over nearly a year; the good job on the "big ship"—the first he had got after being invalided from the battle of the Somme—was finished, and he was out of work. He was a steady worker, but slow: the little local farmers could do without him. He lived in the middle cottage of three in a row sharing a common thatch and back and front walls. The walls were built of cob—a loamy earth trodden with cow-dung and laid with straw to bind it. They were nearly a yard thick, cool in summer and warm in winter. The roof was thatch—unbruised wheaten straw. The cottages stood below the churchyard. On stormy nights the wind roared in the elm trees high above the chimney. Then the labourer felt snug as he lay in bed with Elsie his wife, and the small baby Ernie, snug and warm with the window shut and the rough brown army blankets over him, away from the black and watery wastes of battlefields, which he never spoke about, and seldom thought about, except when the wind thundered in the chimney and seethed in the churchyard elms. Owls roosted in the rafter space above the ceiling, and in spring and summer he heard them walking on the lath-and-plaster, carrying mice and young rats to their young crouching fluffy white, amidst the bones and skulls and beetle-shards of many centuries. "I like vor hear they oyls up auver, (up over)" said William Carter to me, his new neighbour in 1921. "My missus, she calls they oyls dirty birds."

"I zeed, I zeed!" cried Ernie, by his side, "I zeed a master girt oyl looking out of your dark hole, maister! Last night, I did. Yass!"

I had not long come to live in the cottage on one side of him; and everything I saw and heard was of intense interest to me.

The third cottage, roomier and altogether superior, was inhabited by William Carter's cousins, a club-footed farmer, another William Carter, his wife, and his sister, Bessie. The three cottages were visible from the road or lane, seen across a walled-in garden; but the cottage occupied by Cousin William, called "Vanderbilt" or "Thunderbolt", and his womenfolk was larger, tidier, and separated from the others by a stone wall. Cousin Willie owned and worked seven acres of land. He was deaf, and his club feet were like leather horse-hoofs.

"Revvy" was slow in movement, with boots that appeared to drag, rough greyish hair that never seemed to be brushed or cut, and a shaven face that looked as though each bi-weekly shaving were done (as indeed it was) with a razor serrated by rust and age. He had a face that was almost ugly, he was neither short nor tall, his speech was often rapid, thick, and hard to understand; indeed, looking at him as he stood about or stooped to work in his small garden below the churchyard, with his slightly bent legs and rounded back and rough mat of hair, and hearing his unmusical croon to himself as he stooped to pluck the weeds of "lamb's-tongue" (spurrey) and groundsel from his row of peas, and then looked up softly to bellow to his baby girl held up by his wife at the bedroom window, "Where be daddy's maid to, hey? Daddy's maid, you be! I zee 'ee my li'l dear!" he suggested to me a primitive man of the age of stone or bronze.

I learned much about his life at that time. It was not a happy time for Revvy: there was no dole for the agricultural labourer then; and he existed on a very little money gotten by odd jobs. Sometimes he worked in the churchyard. When the lanes were widened, for the coming age of the motor car, he was one of the gang digging and carting iron-stone from the quarry in the Spreycombe valley. In those days charabancs with loads of visitors from Combe were beginning to pass down the sunken lane to the village and beyond; often they got stuck, there being only room for one to proceed at a time, with about a foot clearance either side. When one was going up the hill, and it met another coach coming down, there was usually a long delay, argument, and the scraping of mudguards. Unemployed men, home from the European war, were given work in widening the lanes, and thereafter Revvy left his cottage in the morning, singing, after the months of idleness.

I could not help hearing what happened in the next cottage, as I sat before my fire at night, for the dividing wall was thin and brittle, mere wattle and daub, and there was a break at the back of their inside coal-house, which was also my kitchen wall. Noises of bedtime were distinctly audible through that hole, especially since it had been enlarged to the size of the Carter cat, a low slinking thief that came in silently as a grey

9

shadow and dipped its head silently in my rabbit stew-pot, or into my milk jug, and then, with rounded belly, went upstairs to sleep on my bed. Sometimes when I was reading or trying to work, there was a hiss and a swear, a yelp, a flurry and scramble-slip on the lime-ash floor, and my spaniel pup in full cry after a grey shadow vanishing through the hole in the wall.

Often as late as 10 p.m. in summer the Carter children were still out of bed. Most village children went to bed with their parents. Revvy usually began to bellow a song about bedtime, to soothe the screaming children, who were sleep-starved and under-nourished as well. The song was often *Will the Weaver*, which continued through cries of mother, son, and daughter.

"Ye bliddy ould dawbake, you!"

"Leave th' maid alone, I tull 'ee!" roared Revvy, and then sang on. I visualised his rugged face flushing with sudden anger. I knew he was sitting on the settle by the fire, boots off, breeches unbuttoned over his calves. The settle was papered out of squares out of a wallpaper sample-book; the lovely grain of elmwood completely hidden. "I like a bit of colour," Mrs. Revvy used to say. Revvy sang on, the cat-thief on his knee, washing my milk from its whiskers. Again Mrs. Revvy's high-strained cries to Ernie. Again Revvy's bellowed,

"Put it down, I tull 'ee!"

Then Madge did something, for Mrs. Revvy would yell,

"You dirty little bitch, you!" her temper caused by over-work, close air, bad teeth, and under-nourishment. Madge promptly retorted in kind, and repeated her taunts, encouraged by Revvy's laughter. Bitch was a naughty word, a bad word, and heard on childish lips, a funny word.

Soon afterwards I heard the noise of Mrs. Revvy going up-stairs. Then the front door would open. Pause. "Coo, look at the stars! Daddy, Daddy, they'm as big as lanterns!" Pause; followed by the noises of father and son preparing themselves for an undisturbed night in bed together. In the daytime I used to swish a pail of water against our common garden-wall, but the hint was not taken.

MY NEIGHBOUR "REVVY"

The door was locked when they went in again: I used to wonder why. Then the voice of Revvy would say, "Up over timber hill"—up the stairs—"into blanket field", to Ernie in his arms. They always slept with windows closed; Revvy in bed with Ernie, his missus in bed with Madge and baby. About twice a month Ernie was shifted, asleep, into the other bed; and I found the narrowness of the lath-and-plaster wall embarrassing, and I used to lie very still, lest the embarrassment pass through to the two simple people a few feet from where I lay, with cat and dog, on my bed.

2

It was but natural that both Mrs. Carters should seek to exercise their minds, their strong instincts of curiosity, by the interchange of ideas, and conversation gave almost the only opportunity in the village for this human necessity. Church on Sunday, the September Fair "in to town", a Parish Meeting or Jumble Sale or Mothers' Outing, gave only occasional opportunities for using their mental faculties. There was no social life in the village in those days; no parish hall; no Women's Institute. Strangers were still objects of curiosity and speculation; summer visitors were not numerous, as they became within a few years—with the popularity of the motor car. It was, in the times of which I write, still the deep country. It is therefore perhaps natural that my presence in the village should have caused a little speculation and gossip. Indeed, my presence provided a mild entertainment for the family next door. At the age of twenty-four I wore raggedy clothes and let my beard grow; I spent all the day and sometimes all the night out of doors, sleeping on haystacks and making fires on the hills; I amused myself for hours building little dams in the stream, and sometimes on moonlit nights I let go the rectory pond to find eels, thereby inadvertently flooding out Farmer "Stroyle" George in Hole Farm; I fired off my gun while writing in my kitchen at midnight, at the death-watch beetles tick-tick-ticking in the ceiling joists; I started up my Norton motor cycle in there, where it was kept, while tuning the engine; and most incomprehensible of all, I spent much time watching "they dirty birds", the white owls, which nested over my bedroom ceiling, once falling through the lath-and-plaster, amidst a shower of mice bones and dust, into the bedroom.

On another occasion, coming home from cleaning the school in the early morning, Mrs. Revvy was frightened by the sight of her open front door, where it had been left locked; and instead of the nightgown'd figures of Ernie and Madge at the bedroom window above, there was empty space. With heart beating fast, Mrs. Revvy peered into her kitchen. Everything seemed as she had left it—the milk jug on the table with saucer over it to keep out the cat's head, the kettle steaming on the stove, Revvy's empty teacup on the table, the chair pushed back, the washed socks on the line by the rack. But the door of the coal-house, which was built under the stairs, was open. A heap of gravel from the stream was piled by the open door. A light glimmered in the coal-house. She cried out, "Who's there?" A voice replied, "I am." A figure lying on the coal, filling the hole with cement, using hands for trowel. He had opened the lock with a piece of bent iron, and Ernie and Madge, in their sleeping suits, and crouching in the coal, were helping.

I was tired of the everlasting noise from my neighbours, amplified by the rickety box of the coal-cupboard; and if I went into her house without permission, so did Mrs. Revvy enter mine—several score of teak logs were missing, and a little empty tun, or $4\frac{1}{2}$ gallon cask, of beer, when I had been away elsewhere, my door left unlocked. I knew where those logs had gone, but I did not mind; they had a hard struggle to make do. The barrel I found later in Revvy's outhouse, filled with seed-potatoes. I did not mind that, either; but I did object, privately, to the inconsistent mind of Mrs. Revvy when she upbraided me for entering her house to do a few necessary repairs.

"Mazed as a brish," declared Mrs. "Revvy" to Mrs. "Vanderbilt", her connexion by marriage. "I reckon he's not all there, supposed to be studyin' for the writing of a book, he says, and his garden only a passle-ole-crawsclawsmaws."

Mrs. "Thunderbolt" Carter agreed that obviously I was queer, keeping my bedroom windows open at night, winter and summer, and picking the tins and shards out of the stream, and other curious habits. I was a bit touched in the head, of that the good woman was convinced.

Mazed as a brish, winnicky, passle-ole-crawsclawsmaws, expressions of authentic Old-English speech written down eagerly in my note-book as they occurred in conversation below my open bedroom window, later in the day when the break in the coal-hole wall had been solidly filled.

The bedroom window of my cottage was about 24 inches wide and 18 inches high, the only space by which light and the conversations of villagers entered the room. Later enquiry revealed that *winnicky* meant idiotic, *mazed as a brish* meant almost the same thing, while the reference to my neglected garden—"a parcel of old crow's-claws' roots"—was based on the presence there of a kind of creeping buttercup with roots more like a white octopus than a black rook's feet.

3

In due course a third baby arrived in William Carter's household. Soon it became a minute object moving about from place to place in a lowly but rapid manner, a morsel of life sometimes entirely hidden, except for a small pale face with startled brown eyes, in a bundle of rags. It was protected, in its shiftings and crab-crawlings from cold lime-ash floor to damp stone drang, from stream-edge to garden rubbish-heap, in many layers or coverings of cloth, both wool and cotton, of various colours overlaid or dyed to the hues of ashes, soil, coal, red mud from the lane, and dark brown soil from the garden, stuck together by grease, gravy, and jam.

Sometimes the lean Carter cat would be transported, with body limp and ears flat, amidst the parcel of old clothes. It seemed very patient, allowing its tail to be pulled, and fistfuls of its flank-skin to be lifted from its body. It wore a collar around its neck, and a small bell. It had long ago made friends with my spaniel; at least, sometimes the cat was seen rubbing itself against "Ole Biell", whom Revvy used to invite into his cottage on his return from work in the afternoon.

Revvy always addressed the dog in a tender, crooning voice, while the dog's body swung with joy at seeing the slouching old fellow. Dog's eyes shone; tongue and open mouth panted with smiles. It followed Revvy into his cottage. Then the cat would arch its back and lift its front part against Ole Biell, while the dog dared to raise itself slowly, and yet in one motion, until its paws were on the table edge. A strained expression came into its eyes, rolling like those of a negro, as it glanced from the plates to the faces of Revvy and his wife.

"Doan't 'ee get naught to eat tho', be starvin' be 'ee, poor old Biell, aw, 'ees master serves 'ee bad, do'm tho?" crooned Revvy, giving the dog a rabbit bone, which it took gently, dropping on its feet to crunch it rapidly under the table. "Poor ole dog, 'ees master serves 'ee rough do'm tho?"

This for my benefit; it was Revvy's humour. Yes, dog and cat were friends—until the grey beast slunk past the open door of my cottage, watched by Bill, or Biell, with eyes now yellow-hard. Those eyes rolled sideways to meet my glance, while the tail beat slightly but swiftly, and ceased; the dog was ready to spring up and attack the marauder, stepping so nimbly and with hesitation—"Ah, thief!"—yelps of excitement, claws slipping on the lime-ash floor with ungathered power, yelps diminishing down the walled passage outside. Sometimes Biell returned with a bead of blood on his nose; but always his tail was wagging. Often I felt ashamed of setting the dog on the cat; one day I would pet it, and feed it; another day, betray its friendliness. But no real harm was done.

Revvy used to declare that his cat was a proper weather prophet. When the cat sneezed as it sat before the fire, it meant that the frost was coming; when the cat put its head between its legs, "us be going to have rough weather". When it washed its face and sat with its left flank to the hearth, the weather, sure-nuff, would improve.

The cat's behaviour, to me, indicated another set of terrestrial phenomena. Thus, when it washed its face contentedly before Revvy's fire, the milk-level in my jug would probably have been lowered recently. When the weather was fine, the door was open, for it was the main window of my kitchen; but when the weather was dirty, the door was closed, and the only ven-tilation came from the draught along the floor, felt most by the cat, who turned its back to it.

The unhappy period—the odd-job and uncertain money period—came to an end, and in the morning Revvy left his cottage without singing to himself. His life was now of plough-ing, harrowing, sowing, carting dung and swedes, working with a big horse as good-natured as himself. How he looked forward to his evening return, when Ernie would run to him with joyful cries, "Daddy! Daddy! There be my daddy coming whoam!"

Mrs. Revvy, who swept and scrubbed the schoolhouse in the early morning, bought an armchair, with velvet cushions, for Revvy's use in the evening; but whenever my spaniel chose to visit his shag-haired friend, the armchair was for the dog, and Revvy sat, boots off and breeches unbuttoned at the knees, on his old hard chair. On seeing me, who sometimes followed the dog into the human warmth of the neighbouring kitchen, the spaniel opened an eye and beat its tail-stump.

"Aw, let'n bide, zurr," said Revvy, "I like that ould dog. He's comfortable in th' chair. Her slapes yurr (sleeps here) when you be gone away; he's lonesome without maister, ban't 'ee Biell, midear?"

The family regarded the dog with smiles: Ernie, Madge, the baby, and Mrs. Revvy. There the dog slept many nights, often curled warm with the grey cat, who seemed to know that Biell was on duty only in his own kitchen.

4

The January sun was shining, after gales and floods. Revvy was looking over his garden, noting that his spring cabbages were looking greener. It had been an easy winter so far; he was deliberating whether he would put out a few broad beans. The soil was "plumm"—light, neither too wet nor too dry, and warm for the time of year.

In that soil was cottage history: shards of ancient plates, clay pipe bowls, hand-forged nails thin with rust, old green sheep-jaws, rabbit bones, coal cinders. Revvy and his missus were feeling playful in the buoyant air.

"I'll 'eave 'ee outside, I wull!"

"I don't trouble," replied his wife, standing with the baby on the threshold.

"I'll scat 'ee with a bloomin' long whip, or a stick, or something."

His wife laughed happily. The grey cat rolled on the warm earth. Soil and thatch were steaming faintly. A missel thrush (grey-thrush, holm-scritch) was singing—song rapid and serene and flowing, undistinguished; so different from the bold character of the bird. It turned several ways on its treetop as it sang —restless for spring. The pennywort leaves on the garden wall were bunched—filled with rain for the coming expedition skyward—also biting stonecrop on the slate roof of the barn opposite, ready for the bitter-yellow flowers of spring. Mosses were seeding on Stroyle George's ruinous thatch—seeds on stalks like minute red-throated kingfishers perching with beaks upheld. I heard the far sound of the sea, and a carrion crow cawing in the rectory plantation.

Revvy began to croon to himself, words of a song which I caught only in fragments, as I wrote them down,

Sober person's not a sot
Boiling water's always hot
And a donkey's not a parrot.

MY NEIGHBOUR "REVVY"

Brick walls isn't made of timber
And Bread is very good with cheese
And bugs is twice as big as fleas.

While I was writing, "Uncle Joe", solitary old-man neighbour, shuffled past. He stopped and stared.

"Butiful weather," he said at last to Mrs. Carter.

"Aiy."

Long pause.

"Aiy," said Uncle Joe. Then to Revvy, after another long pause, "What, be looking at your spring cabbages?"

"What?" said Revvy, removing his pipe from his mouth as he straightened up. Uncle Joe repeated his question.

"Aiy."

"Hullo, baby!" cackled Uncle Joe, wagging finger at the baby. The baby smiled. Mrs. R. hugged it. Pause. Slowly Uncle Joe shuffled back to his dingy cottage; slowly returned with dingy photograph of family group. "Yurr!" he said mysteriously. "Did I ever show you me boys?"

"Lots of times," replied Mrs. Revvy, cheekily.

"Me boys," said Uncle Joe, proudly, unaffected, showing me. He clumped along to show me.

"Fine," I said, as I had several times before.

"Aiy," said Uncle Joe, complacently. "Me boys." Nine young men, with big moustaches and fixed eyes, some sitting, some standing and clasping photographer's chair-backs, stared out of photograph. Uncle Joe, and obedient wife, sat in their midst. "Aiy," said Uncle Joe, preparing to return, "I fancied you'd like vor see me boys." He shuffled back, contentedly sucking his foul pipe.

Later, Revvy was eating his supper of bacon and potatoes, using an old knife and his fingers. Ernie and Madge sat at the table; Biell in the best chair, wagging tail, awaiting scraps; cat on floor, uneasy and hopeful. Ernie sat in his own chair, its old broken back mended by enamel plate SUNLIGHT SOAP. His curly head lay on his empty plate. "Poor li'l boy, he'm tired," said Revvy. The fire glowed. The sun went down: it was so still, chilly. The stream was loud in the night, lit by stars and yellow windows. Revvy sang to his children.

After supper, Revvy belched and said, "The Lord be praised, my stummick be aised."

"If you sing at table, you'll die in the Grubber," said Mrs. Revvy to me, looking round my open door, where I was eating bacon and eggs. The Grubber was the Workhouse, or Union.

5

The cottage where club-footed Willy Carter lived with his sister and his London-born wife was divided from the drang, or passage-way, by a high wall built to shield its garden and front-door from the gaze and noise of children playing in the drang. A dairy window with a sliding wooden grill looked on to the drang. In the shadowed coolth of the dairy a pale thin woman with a woeful face was sometimes to be seen, moving against a dimmer background of rows of jugs and glass basins, a lime-ash floor as clean as the gravelly bed of an Exmoor rill, a coal-stove very shining and black set with half a dozen clome, or earthenware, bowls three-quarters filled with milk. The gradual heat made the cream rise to the top, and form a pale yellow crust which, when carefully scooped off, was the most delicious scald-cream in the parish.

Bessie Carter was Revvy's cousin, the sister of Thunderbolt Willy. I never saw Revvy or his wife or children in Cousin Willy's house. Revvy, whose nickname was given when he worked for his reverence in the rectory years before he married, often had bitter words for Cousin Willy. "They wouldn't give naught away, not if a man was dying in a ditch." Revvy probably knew that his bitterness was unreasonable: had not he, when young, spent the few pence he might have saved each week in the Higher and Lower Houses? On the contrary, Cousin Willy had always been thrifty: he saved every rusty nail and broken slate; every dried chicken-foot for the "furnace"

MY NEIGHBOUR "REVVY"

firing-heap of the weekly washing by his sister Bessie. It was said in the village that he had found his wife through an advertisement in *The Matrimonial Times*.

In the Higher or Lower House he would wait to borrow a lighted match with which to light his pipe. It was on record, however, that on Armistice Day he stood a stranger a pint of beer, and not in mere return for a former pint. Shyness and deafness and club-feet were handicaps; he had worked steadfastly and methodically, until at the age of sixty-five, when he looked no older than fifty, he was able to retire from his seven-acre farm, sell his field and his cows, and invest the money in the very safest way, which was to put it on deposit in the bank at $2\frac{1}{2}\%$. When Farmer Willy sold his seven-acre field to Farmer Billy Goldsworthy, the two sat up by candle-light, half the night, counting and checking the purchase price, nearly three hundred pounds, in silver, most of them sixpenny and shilling pieces. Revvy often told the story with feelings between laughter and accusatory scorn; the settling of the payment was that of a "proper miser".

When he had worked as a farm-labourer before the War, Revvy had earned eleven shillings a week, and lived with his mother and father in the cottage opposite the Lower House, which adjoined the Dead House, as the small lean-to shed with sloping slate roof was called. Revvy's father, whom a later generation knew as Granfer Jimmy, had been one of the best wrestlers in his early manhood: the blue scars of the kicking were thick on his shins. He had been a quick and skilful kicker, as the son knew. In those days it was usual for a boy to be thrashed frequently. "He used to serve me proper bad," said Revvy, one summer evening, as he sat at table having his supper with his family. "But I was a young heller, sometimes, I expect. He's been a good vather to me, I reckon."

The scene in the cottage was one I had known scores of times before. Revvy had been home from work for an hour: it was half-past six o'clock on a June evening. The sun was still high in the west, throwing an oblique shadow from Uncle

19

Joe's cottage over a third of his garden. The door was open, and the window; not many days in the year when they were open together.

Although it was one of the hottest days of young summer, a bright fire was burning in the bodley, the kitchen range called after Mr. Bodley, an ironmonger whose name was on the "new invention" fitted into many of the open hearths about the time when Revvy was a boy. Before this, he told me, the weekly baking of bread was done in two ovens, one on either side of the hearth, each domed and hollow. A fire of dry sticks—furze if possible—was made in the ovens, until the clome lining was hot; the ashes and embers were raked out, and the level bottom wiped out with a malkin, a bundle of wet rags tied to a stick. The dough was then put in, and the door closed. "Butiful plumm bread 'twas, too," declared Revvy, stretching his legs and scratching his head, belching a little discreetly, happy and easy after his supper. As usual, my dog Biell was curled in the best chair, the grey cat on the floor facing the light. "They don't bake bread to-day as they did in they days, noomye!"

Nowadays the baker called every afternoon in a motor van. The baker was a tall young man, calling no man "sir". When first I had known Revvy the baker came twice a week with a cart, a small man accompanied by a little boy. Now the small boy was twice the size of his father; his father, after two attempts to drive the new car, stayed at home.

Ernie was eating bread and jam for his supper, with a cup of milk. The remains of a cabbage stalk lay on his plate. Ernie was five years old, Madge was three, and Megan was one. Their father earned one pound eleven shillings and sixpence a week. His rent was five pounds a year, just raised from four pounds. Recently the landlord had built a small brick house on to the back of the cottages, a building of two compartments, each with a water-flush pan, instead of the old earth pails. Revvy considered this "rise in the rent" another example of landlords' tyranny.

To be sure, the building of the new lavatories had not been

due entirely to a desire to help raise the standard of English rural hygiene, but because the sanitary inspector had reported many times that the adjoining cottage, then occupied by myself, had no convenience worked either by earth or water, since it had collapsed a year previously, fortunately while unoccupied. The cob wall, which had stood during five centuries, had become wet owing to neglect to repair the roof. For a year the landlord, on being accosted by me, had been muttering that he would see about it sometime: time after time, in response to letters suggesting that he should see about it, the landlord had come to stare at the ruins, and, before departing, had asked me again what I wanted. Upon being told once again, he muttered he would see about it, and so the months had passed.

After three visits of the sanitary inspector, the little brick house, a benefit to the two cottages, arose with the rent. I said to Ernie, grinning beside the dog Biell, "Ernie, when in years to come Varmer turns this place into a museum and charges a penny a head to see the rickety table, etc., you must shout out, 'Yurr, maister, what about the time when the famous author was drove to walk about the fields at night.' " Ernie smiled, and said nothing; Ernie always smiled. "Dear li'l boy, he be," Revvy said, at least a hundred times a month. Ernie had fair hair and brown eyes; he was gentle with smaller children, sweet-voiced, and when a very small child, was always to be seen playing in the water. Was water anciently a symbol of new spirit because the prophets, when children, were sweet-voiced and gentle, playing with bright water?

Probably neither Revvy nor I realized in those days that the brick lean-to cost the farmer-landlord a year's rent of the two cottages; and it is possible that the landlord did not entirely realize the responsibilities of owning property.

So many of the words used between men in the village, in the time of which I write—the interval between the two purgative European wars—were without meaning; the experience of having promises made, broken, made again, broken again, jobs of work put off, held up, neglected, was irritating to my sharper consciousness until I came to accept such a behaviour as natural, formed by the rain falling on a hundred centuries of village life, mud clogging sled-runners and hoofs and boots and ploughs, the soft speech, the lazy relaxation after heavy work.

The winter rains came through Revvy's thatch, and stained a patch on the bedroom ceiling: the landlord would see about it. A flake of plaster as big as a large cabbage fell from above Revvy's door: the landlord would see about it. The sanitary inspector said that Revvy's larder, a dark cupboard in the wall of the kitchen or living-room, must have a window joining it to the light and air of outdoors: the landlord would see about it.

Sometimes I did odd jobs in the cottages, such as the cementing of the cat-run from Revvy's coal-house to my living-room; and then the invariable comment of the village was, "What be you about, improving other people's property? I shouldn't do it if it was me, noomye!" Farmer George from Hole Farm opposite, Revvy from next door, Thunderbolt Willy and old Uncle Joe, Clib the postman and gravedigger, Charlie Tucker the rate-collector and builder, and many others, all said the same thing. "I shouldn't do that if I was you, noomye!" "Stroyle" George, leaving the yard of Hole Farm opposite, particularly came out of his way to advise me not to be foolish, while his cows lingered and pulled mouthfuls of my currants over the wall. Stroyle is *agrostis*, a grass creeping tenaciously underground, with strong white runners which can pierce a potato in their vital thrust; a poor or garrulous farmer's fields are sometimes full of it. Behind his back, he was called "Stroyle" George.

All tenants grumbled in the village against landlords, of which every third man was one. When the stream flooded Revvy's floor, Revvy cursed the landlord. There was a drain running from his wash-house, under the dividing wall, and across the gardens; often I heard water, or liquid, gurgling under the stone by my threshold, where there was a grill. There was also a grill by Revvy's back-door, but this was usually taken up, to save the bother of clearing it, and Mrs. Revvy's potato peelings, washing-up water and soapsuds went down direct, with the result that the grill under my threshold was often choked. During a rainstorm this would cause the water to well up, and form a wide pool in the passage-way outside. Muttering rapid curses against landlord, while drops from the thatch pattered on his back, Revvy would pull up the stone by my door and heave out the grill, bellowing like a gorilla when it was suggested to him that it should be put back after being cleared.

So the unwanted relics of the Revvy household accumulated in the pipes under the garden, and during the next rainstorm all the tugging and poking and muttering and cursing availed nothing. Revvy, sack on shoulders, had to dig up the pipes, while I tried to explain. in the intervals of relieving him at the long-handled shovel, that a grill was put in a convenient place in order that the stoppage might occur in a convenient place. "They bliddy landlords, they ought to be shot," shouted Revvy. "They'm ready enough vor take th' rent, ban't em tho, but they'm bliddy well out of the way, biding on their arses by th' fireside, while us volks stands yurr in th' rain catching a death of cold."

"H'm! what's this? Chicken's foot. Wonder how that got down, past your grill, too. And here's the head of a doll. Eggshells. Potato peelings. Chicken's head. Good idea, to put them down the drain. I've got some old boots, and those worn tyres of my motor cycle, I'll put them down."

But satire was lost on Revvy; the mental attitude of a lifetime was not easily penetrated.

"Proper pigs' houses, these cottages," snorted Revvy. "And Farmer have rised the rent five shillin' every quarter! Wull, let'n turn me out, I won't pay it, noomye!"

But when next quarter day came round, Revvy paid his twenty-five shillings without protest. Good luck had come to his household. A "gennulman" called Admiral Bamfylde had bought "the big house" at Pidickswell, and Revvy worked in the garden, while his wife worked at the wash-tub. The good quality of the articles hanging on the line in the garden was observed and approved by many village women. On rainy days

Revvy left his cottage with a waterproof coat covering him, gift of the gennulman. The sounds of occasional strife lessened behind the dividing wall, and as the weeks went on, they ceased.

6

The grey cat slipped in less frequently through the cat-hole in my door, and when it did come, was even permitted to sit on my lap before the fire. It was less lean and hungry-looking, and arched itself against the spaniel in greeting.

There were two people in my cottage now; and in the early spring there would be three. Feeling that we would now need more room, I moved to a larger cottage fifty yards away. Revvy helped me to move my furniture.

The Carter children shouted and played with old pram wheels, tins, bottles, and motor tyres; except when, once a week, they would walk up the village street dressed in their best, with faces, hands, and knees very clean, and hair brushed or ribbon'd, on their way to the mild entertainment known as Sunday School. The young maids and matrons who took the classes—very young ones behind, graduating to the big children in front—did their best with the not very interesting material which had been used immemorially in the village for the instruction and interrogation of children on these occasions—fragments of military history, family and tribal intrigue, heroism, stupidity, and treachery, supernatural rewards and punishments dealt to an uneasy and ancient people which claimed for itself special celestial preference; whose descendants were slowly getting a financial hold on the entire human world. The parson, in his long black skirted robe and foreign-looking hat, was in charge of the Sunday School.

"Vivian Carter, look to your front! Now, Ernie Carter, to whom did God send the ravens in the wilderness? Elijah, quite right. What did God send in the raven's beak, Madge Carter? Do not answer out of your turn, Tikey Gammon! Besides, 'fruit' is not the correct answer. Grapes, quite right, Madge Carter.

MY NEIGHBOUR "REVVY"

There are wild vines growing in the Holy Land, you see, children, and no doubt the birds fed on them, when they were ripe, just as they feed on our English berries in the autumn. They would be currants, if dried, you know. Now, Daisy Gammon, to whom did God appear in the burning bush? Moses, quite right. Tikey Gammon, turn round in the pew. You also, Vivian Carter. Look to your front, children."

It used to distress me, to think how the opportunity truly to awaken the children to the world of creative imagination was being lost. The teaching was unreal to them. Heads were soon moving, with grins and smiles in my direction. I often played with them, scaring, chasing, and exciting them. After Sunday School there was to be a christening of my own baby. Ernie, Madge, and Megan felt more excited about this than the others, for they knew me very well, and also Old Biell the dog.

While his children were hearing about the Burning Bush and the currants, Revvy the labourer was in his cottage, coat and boots off, lying on his bed with his wife, the li'l tackers out of the way for a bit (but he'd be seeing them again at teatime, the li'l dears), and Sunday dinner of potatoes, cabbage, and beef making him comfortable and drowsy. The rooks cawed in the elms outside the small window, and his first-early tetties were showing green and good, if only the frost didn't come and cut them down black as your hat. To my eyes, the frost, when it spoiled the early potatoes, appeared to singe the delicate ear-like leaves, withering them greyish-brown; but "black as your hat" was the village expression.

Revvy and his wife came to the christening, and the sight of him sitting so still in the pew, his hat on his knees, made me think of his goodness and kindness, his patience, his fidelity to his family: and to wonder whether it was better to be like Revvy, or to be like myself, sharp and critical, at odds with so much in the human life about me, dreading and thinking that the complaisance and acceptance of things about me, which most people accepted, would culminate once more in a terrible world war, in which the children I knew, and even perhaps the little baby boy now being christened, would die in mental agony and body misery. It was a problem that I could never clearly resolve. While I was thinking, I had not noticed that the parson was looking steadily at me. The parson held a printed card in his hand. He called me by name, and required me to stand by the font, with the godparents. I had recently published a book which, having taken many years to write, had been condemned by *The Church Times*, which declared that it were better if such a blasphemous work had not been written. It was a book about an ex-soldier, which I had written with my heart and soul. The Rector thought it was a deplorable book.

William Carter, the man with the sack over his shoulders in wet weather, the man who addressed as "sir" or "zur" any man who did not wear a sack, never went to church, except for services of burial or christening—marriages he regarded from his garden, standing on the rummage heap and looking over the wall, and perhaps, at a very special wedding, standing outside the lych-gate.

The baby slept in the Rector's arms. The children turned round in the pews, some smiling; the bold, bad Tikey grinning. Tikey was bidden to look to the front. Discipline was good for the young. The church was not the place in which to wriggle about, even if the seats were hard, or smile out of the social instinct.

"You have not answered my question!" said the Rector, sternly.

With a start I realized he was looking directly at me.

Revvy glanced round, as though timidly, and turned his head again quickly. Mrs. Willy Carter and Cousin Bessie sat still and upright, looking towards the mural painting of an idealized, or sanctified, or unreal, Anthony with birds, which a local artist had painted on the wall.

"If you do not answer my question, the service will not be continued. I will read the question again."

Yes, I hastily renounced the Devil and all his Works, on behalf of the child. The service concluded. The Rector said, as the names of the sleeping innocent were being transcribed into the parish register, "I hope that you will not parody this service in your next book."

The names of the infant were written down. Afterwards, in an attempt to lighten the situation, I said jokingly that I had felt some doubt about renouncing the Devil and all his Works, after *The Church Times* review, which I knew the Rector had read, as it had occurred to me that my books might be part of the more comprehensive Works.

"Self-renunciation is a lesson that all men must learn."

The Rector, his superhuman duty done, became human. With a sudden smile he complimented the mother on having a son so serene and good. "He takes after his mother," he said, twinkling his eyes. "But everyone is good when they are harmonious," he said, giving me a friendly glance. "Great responsibility, being a father, isn't it?"

Revvy came out of the porch, modestly, quietly, fingering his hat, and saying good afternoon to each in turn, half raising his finger to his head, while his left hand held his cap by his side.

"I was glad vor see the christening to-day, midear," said Revvy, outside the lych-gate. "I minds how you used to play with young Ernie; 'tes a nice li'l boy you'm got now for yourself, and he couldn't have a better feyther, if you'll excuse me saying so, zur."

7

Maurice Hewlett, whose books of the West Country I buy and read and keep whenever I can find them, once wrote, *The West Country labourer is a gentleman.* It is perhaps not mere bigotry which prompts the thought of how much of Revvy's courtesy was due to the very economic system by which he was condemned to go to work in the wet with only a sack over his shoulders. In his boyhood there was the squire "up to big house", the large landowner, a Tory; there were the farmers, some of them yeomen whose farms had been family-owned for generations, most of whom were Liberals, and therefore set against the large Tory landowner. It was as in a stream running into a pool: the largest trout had the best position whence he could watch the food coming down; the lesser trout were either behind him, or in lesser runs, the next largest ready to take his place as soon as he quitted it. The labourer, who raised his cot of cob and wattle on any odd bit of land unclaimed and unwanted, was like the loach, a little squat fish of the gravel and stones, on which the big trout lived. Was his reputation for courtesy based on his habit of always addressing his superiors as "zur", and doing what he was told to do with the obedience of the lowly loach crouching for its very life against the gravel?

The "big house", of course, did not gobble up the cottages, but often looked after them in sickness, and sent them its old coats and shirts, and gave them pensions in old age, long before the State assumed its responsibility to worn-out working men and women; but always the William Carters went forth into the winter mornings, with a mug of warm beer, or, after the War, a cup of hot tea, with a bit of bread and cheese inside them.

And when the squire's farms were sold, one by one, and at last "the big house" became a hotel, or a country club, or a school after the Great War, or was even demolished for its slates, oak flooring and doors, fireplaces and stone of the walls, the William Carters still touched their hats to a gennulman, who might be any man not labourer, mason, carpenter or gravedigger; but they walked slower, their backs were rounder, and they still wore potato sacks against the slant and lash of the rain.

During the decade following the Great War, I watched the motor car, from being a rare sight, become commonplace, even a nuisance, in the village. The ancient stagnation of the parish was stirred by the coming of wire wheels in place of the wooden wheel. The baker's horse-drawn cart calling twice a week at the cottages changed into a Ford van arriving thrice a week, then into an American six-cylinder, thirty-hundredweight van delivering bread to Revvy's threshold every afternoon. The schoolboys, sons of labourers, became masons and mechanics earning nearly thrice their fathers' wages. They owned motor cycles, and bought their own cottages. "Times be changed, zur," said Revvy, stooping to pluck weeds of lamb's-tail and groundsel from his row of peas; but for him it was only the sack that was changed, and the pains in his arm increasing to pains in his back and legs. "Aiy, they be, zur," while the motor cycle raised the red dust to settle on the lime-washed cottage walls, and the happy riders, young men of freedom and savings increasing in the bank, no longer touched their hats or added the "zur" of immemorial custom, no longer absorbed into their youthful blood-streams the poisons which in middle-age would settle painful acid-crystals into their joints and muscles. Their bungalow cottages had double walls to keep out the damp, and asbestos roofs, sometimes of an unpleasing pink; but these were all they could afford.

I left the village after ten years, and when I went back, I felt myself to be half a stranger. Where one summer visitor used to walk along the lanes, now there were a hundred; and nine hundred more passing through on wheels. I was not sure of myself when I saw Ernie, Babe, Tikey, and the others, standing by the ditched wall at the top of Church Street, after their day's work. The Ernie I knew was no longer a little boy, playing with the water; and the Tikey I used to see fitted into a rubber motor tyre, bounding and wobbling down the street into the stream, was a pert youth. As for Madge and Megan, I did not know what to say to them, nor to the other girls who had grown up, and wore clothes like film-stars and even sometimes bathed in the sea about August Bank Holiday time.

Old Revvy was still about. He had moved to another cottage, drier, lighter, with more room in it. One day I went to see him, hearing he was ill, and there he was, lying on the bed, unable to move, unable to speak, perhaps unable to hear. Revvy had had a stroke; it was his turn to die. I did not know what to say. The stones of every cottage wall cry out their history, of the hands that shaped and placed them, of the lives they sheltered: the very stones cry out, in the silence of the heart.

Chapter Two

BIRDS OF SKIRR COTTAGE

I

It was always a comfort, when I was lying in bed in that time soon after the war, to hear the owls moving about over my head: their secret and mysterious life was the medium by which I could live and have my being in the world of truth.

Sometimes there was drama. One night I was sitting before the fire, my feet to the blaze of the fire, to the brass and lilac flames biting the hissing elm branches, reading Arnold Bennett's *Books and Persons*, when quite suddenly a frail scream was in the whitewashed room—an old room, built by field-workers before men smoked tobacco: a room of tunnelled walls, wherein at night feet scamper and unseen things squeak.

My spaniel looked at me excitedly. The cat left her one kitten, and stood with waving tail, intent, like a little lion, on the lime-ash floor. Her eyes were green. I rose quietly and opened the door, and the scream seemed to be coming from the stars. I walked down the drang, or stone-set passage, and the noise followed me, always remote and ghostly.

Outside in the night, a throaty, bubbling cry tore the darkness—*skirr-rr-r!* Signal of the parent owl's coming. A white bird, moth-like, with wings stretching a yard, floated through the elms. I went back into the living-room. The noise through the ceiling increased. Thump! Something was running about on the ceiling upstairs. Sounds of struggle, squeals, flump-flumping. *Skirr-rr-r*, as the old bird floated away to the cornfields, leaving the fledging owlet with a rat, which was alive.

You should have been with me in my dark room under the glimmering uneven ceiling, to hear the screeching, the screaking, the screaming, the angry squealing, the raging of rat and owlet, the wrestling of fur and feather above my ceiling! They seemed to be wearing clogs. I could hear the owlet slogging with his long beak on the rat's skull. The mix-up went on, while my cat fumed and paced the floor-boards and growled, and the spaniel whined his immense excitement and leapt up at me. Then it was over, and the rat dashed over the ceiling, too big and strong for the owlet, and rustled away down the thick tunnelled wall, full of life and fight.

I returned to my wood-fire, and my book. The dog sighed and slept; the cat settled still on my knee. I heard a rustle in the corner by the unused beehive and saddle. There sat the rat, washing a bloody face. Skirr-rr-r, the rat gibbered, flicked round, and vanished.

2

The owls entered by an angle-shaped opening where the wall did not fill the apex. The opening was large enough for a man to scramble through, with the aid of a ladder.

During my first year in Skirr Cottage, I often used to watch the owls at night. It was a time of great drought, and possibly an increase of mice.

On April 17th, the first egg was laid. Another appeared on the 18th, and a third on the 19th. There was no nest. The eggs rested on the lath-and-plaster of the ceiling, among ancient mice bones and fragments of owl-pellets—the owl swallowed its prey whole and afterwards cast up from the crop the undigested portion.

During the second week in May the three eggs were hatched, and two more were laid. The owlets were blind, partially naked, and made a shrill, lisping noise for food.

By midsummer there were three fully-fledged owlets over my ceiling; two snow-white bundles with long hooked beaks and immense claws; two tiny lisping parcels of skin and blindness; and two fresh eggs.

A month later there were five grown owls, four adolescents, two babies, and one addled egg.

I climbed up, crept warily over the sagging ceiling amid bones, fur, feathers, and beetle-skins, and examined my owlery. The grown owls shrieked at me and flapped into the far gloom, the adolescents rushed away, and the babies blinked.

What astonished me was the number of dead rodents lying near the nest. I counted twenty-seven mice, nineteen young rats, two sparrows, and forty-two field voles.

The time was ten o'clock in the morning. At seven o'clock in the evening I climbed up and nothing remained of them. Ninety animals eaten by eleven young owls in nine hours! And this, moreover, during the time of rest and sleep.

Lying on the grassy slope of the garden wall in the summer dimmit-light, I watched the parent birds at work.

At sunset they emerged like unfolded white blooms against the reddish-purple-grey tower of the church, and floated east-wards over the tombstones to the glebe field.

At intervals of from three to six minutes either the cock or the hen would return with a mouse, or mice, held in beak or dropped foot. Their children hissed frantically, the prey was cast among them, and the bird sailed away, pursued by scream-ing swifts.

Throughout the summer nights the toiling owls brought food for their young. When they fed themselves I know not. They worked for about an hour and a half after dawn.

For themselves and their family the barn owls caught a hun-dred and fifty mice every night. From April to the end of August I reckoned that nearly ten thousand mice and small rats were brought to the owlery in the roof of Skirr Cottage.

3

There were other birds nesting in my thatch. I loved to think of them living there so close to my life. The other birds were small, black, and the thin sharp wings made a noise like *frer-r-r* as the birds dived whistling past my head as I stood in the door-way. They were swifts. The hen had a nest on the lath-and-plaster near the white owls.

BIRDS OF SKIRR COTTAGE

The white owl had her eggs and downy fledgelings in a corner, by the brittle beam which was bored and rebored by the death-watch beetles. The chalky eggs and dough-like owlets lay amid bones and beetle-shards and the dust of fur and crumbled rats' tails. A yard away the swift brooded her two frail eggs in the saucer-shaped nest made of straws and cobwebs gummed together with her own spittle.

At dimmit-light, or dimsey as they said in the village, the owls left the loft, and floated through the elms of the church-yard to the meadows and cornfields beyond. At this hour the swifts were usually ringing in packs near the church-tower, and espying the owls, they dashed down and screamed around them. The owls flew on, unheeding. They separated and went their ways to the sunset mice-runs.

Dusk settled over field and lane. The male swift began to scream in a different way, and he harried his mate so closely that often I heard the clatter of wings striking wings. Almost fiercely he pursued her until suddenly she swerved, fluttered at her nest-ing hole, and crept down the brittle straw-tunnel to her long, narrow, pointed eggs.

Having hustled her inside, the male bird circled above the tower, calling other swifts. Venus had been visible over the sea an hour since, and the gulls were roosting on the ledges of the headland. The male swifts cried ceaselessly as they gathered above the bats. The pack screamed over the dim cottages, where the small bedroom windows gleamed with candle-light and oil-dip. The screams came down fainter to where I was lying on the grassy garden wall under the dark still mass of the elms. The birds climbed towards the stars. The cries ceased, and the night was quiet with the murmur of the stream and the gentle flutter of moths.

Where did the swifts fly? The owls floated through the elms, skirring as they glided away pale in the midsummer sky still glowing with sea-quenched sunset. The swifts were far away, wheeling where Aldebaran and Vega shone without quiver in the unearthly air. Did they sleep as they glided? did they

B   33

dream themselves into spirits of star-solitude as they plied their wings in alternate thrust? did they play in the thin airs of their ranging, hurtling in pursuit of one another far above the glimmering Atlantic, falling down to the warmer earth as the stars paled before the beams of sunrise? *Frer-r-r* went the wings by my open door; and the wild faint screaming drew my heart into the sky.

Chapter Three
THE SAWYERS

The Church Council had decided that the churchyard elms were dangerous, and must be topped. There were fifteen trees, the largest four feet thick at the base, and for more than three centuries their roots had been pushing into the darkness of graves. Nine stood at the western end of the churchyard, shutting out the beams of the morning sun from my cottage and garden immediately under them. Rooks had nested in their tops since the childhood of "Uncle Joe", my next-but-one neighbour, an old white-bearded and pensioned railway porter who lived alone.

One morning in March three sawyers came to do the job. They began while I was frying breakfast bacon in my cottage. Afterwards I took out my chair, set it on the path of cinders dividing my garden from my neighbour Revvy's, and watched them at work. It was the first warm day of the new year. Tiny leaves of nettles were growing out of the cracks of the low stone-and-earth wall, where snails were gummed still in sleep. The sky was a pale blue, and hurt the eye when looking up. Above my head came the sound of steady sawing. A man, looking small, stood in a fork, just under the black nests. Below, in the road, two young men were waiting at the end of a fifty-foot rope tied to the branch being sawn. The sexton joined them.

Steadily the sound of sawing came down. The rooks were away somewhere.

On the chimney tun of Hole farmhouse over the road a starling was throwing its head from side to side and clapping its wings as it sang. The song was a wheezy rattling and cluttering of other birds' notes and cries; the mew of a buzzard—the wistful call of a kestrel—the upward scraping cry, ending in a liquid trill, of the flighting curlew. Often in the past I had watched the rooks look up when the starling threw out the kestrel cry; they had never seemed to realize where it came from. They drove kestrels away from the rookery whenever the little brown-winged hawks glided over. Every morning for a week the bird had been singing on the square smoke-blackened stone chimney beside the dead ivy, but this morning its song was continuously audible, for no cawing overlaid it.

The starling flew away when the saw clattered through branches to the earth. The branch was sawn through about three-quarters, and the pulling on the rope would bring it to the ground, clear of my garden wall, it was hoped. Two of the trees had been topped already, and their blunt trunks and shortened limbs were black against the sky and the other doomed row at the top end of the churchyard. My neighbour Revvy had already gathered a store of sticks for fuel—even the heaviest branches are called sticks—and had stored them in his empty pig's-house, and gone to his work.

The gilt weathercock swung to the east in the flowing wind, shining on the grey stone tower. Bees went past in the sunlit air, a cock crowed in the farmyard over the road, chaffinches were singing—I counted seven. The spaniel slept stretched on his side, pressing down the green leaves of a dock. The sharp chirp of a sparrow came from the thatch of my cottage, which was loose and rotten, and covered with green-greyish lichens. Rain dripping from the trees had rotted it before its "allotted span" of a score of years.

On the cleft rungs of the tall ladder the boots of the descending man tapped musically. Sawyers and sexton seized the rope

and tugged, the branches swayed and creaked; the two rooks'
nests clawed the sky. Down it swayed, up it swayed, down it
swayed; it grunted for nearly a minute, then *crack!* a shout, a
hissing of twigs rushing through the air and the thud of the half-
ton sappy bough on the grass and the celandines. The gravestones
directly under the inner branches of the trees, and a solitary jam-
jar on the weed-grown mound of a suicide in the unconsecrated
ground at the edge, were already removed by the sexton. A shower
of dry twigs and lichens floated and trickled through branches to
the ground. I could hear the voices of children, released for the
eleven o'clock "break", loud and shrill in the playground at the
western end of the village.

A young man with an axe lopped off the lesser branches. With
one swinging blow he cut through a six-inch limb. He was an
Exmoor man, heavy, red-faced, with big hands. He was dressed
in corduroys, without a collar, but his shirt was fastened with
a stud. He would have felt untidy without a stud.

The stick, bounding off a lower branch, had fallen wide and
broken a gravestone. The top-sawyer took from his coat a cloth
folded around a small mason's trowel, and a tin box of cement.
Water was taken from the jam-jar, sullied and smeared by snails,
leaning in the long couch grass—once it had held flowers, but
long ago they had withered and been forgotten. I have a memory
of the poor old fellow tramping in his heavy khaki uniform one
summer's day, returning from leave, with his bundle—he was
in the Labour Corps, salvaging on the Somme battlefields. He
had killed himself, and had been laid there, without a parson's
blessing. I think, when my turn comes, I would like to be laid
beside him.

The broken top of the stone, with its cracked angel, was
stuck on again, while the sexton, who was also the postman,
scratched his red nervous head and stammered that Lady Maude
would not like to hear of it. Lady Maude was the churchwarden,
a benevolent woman, who organized some of the children to
tidy the graves and issued small shears to them, so that the grass
might always be short, and the weeds and wild flowers dis-

couraged. "Her Ladyship won't like to zee it, her won't like to zee it," he kept repeating.

"Who be 'er?" asked the top-sawyer.

"Proper lady, her Ladyship. Wonnerful lot o' money her's got, her Ladyship. Wonnerful lot o' money. Her Ladyship."

"Well, then, let'n pay for a new stone."

A young girl of fifteen came into the churchyard while they were setting the stone. She was awaiting work as servant in one of the new boarding-houses being built in the lower village by the sea. Her name was Marty Gammon, and the cottage women said she was "one for the men". She had been maturely conscious of men for perhaps three years. The sawyer who had cut the bough aloft, a short, quick dark man, with powerful biceps and thighs, began to cheek her at once. He wanted some cement, he said, and knowing that her father was a mason, he suggested she should bring some with her after dinner and meet him at two o'clock up the lane.

This man, whose name was Robert Chugg, preached on Sunday afternoons at various chapels. One evening, just before the Fair, I had passed him at dusk near a roadside barn, with a pot of paste and a roll of papers. He was affixing to the stone wall a poster on which was printed, in large brown letters,

REPENT YE!
FOR THE KINGDOM
OF HEAVEN
IS AT HAND.

Robert Chugg was a married man, thirty-five years old, and the father of several children. He preached fervently against those sins which disturbed his conscience.

The other men, younger than Chugg, stopped working while he cheeked Marty, and grinned at each other. They were warm from labour and enlivened by their thoughts. Chugg, who was not so tall as Marty, stared at her while he asked her questions; he stared not exactly with a leer, but he used his eyes to say boldly what his words played around. Marty would say neither "Yes" nor "No" to his request for cement.

Marty Gammon was dark, strong, and graceful, with hair cut after the fashion of women in towns. She had red lips and merry brown eyes. She was chewing a toffee. With a smile that showed her white and regular teeth she held out a paper bag.

"Who wants a sweet?" She gave all the men a toffee, and laughed at the small hatchet with which I was hacking off lesser branches of the great bough.

The Exmoor youth was enjoying himself hugely, staring at Marty, but saying nothing, for he had nothing to say. He admired and envied the fluency of Chugg. He grinned at the notches in my hatchet—he called them natches, changing the vowel, so usual in West Country speech. His own axe-head, bigger than my hand, was sharp as a knife. In a pocket of his waistcoat he carried a slip of stone, and every fifty strokes or so the edge was rubbed with it. His dog, lying in the road and waiting for interesting smells, had a greyish scar in the pupil of one eye and he said it had been pracked by a brimble. The sun shining in his eyes, shaded by an old earth-red felt hat, was called the zin.

Soon after noon three little boys from the church school came through the lych-gate. They lived in the village down the valley and did not go home for dinner. They ate bread-and-jam and cake, playing with the spaniel and feeding him. The youngest spoke to the dog in a soft, sweet voice,

"Dear doggie, dear Billy doggie, O Billy, take cake from me, Billy dear," while the scrounging dog wagged his tail-stump and made friends with them, rolling on the warm turf with the children, always wagging a curly stump and looking from food to face, from face to food.

A flight of herring gulls passed over, white birds in the pale-blue sky, slowly moving their anchor-shaped wings, which were tipped with black. They swung over the trees, and, lying on my back, it seemed as though the sky were a pool with a chalk bed, and the gulls were elbowing their slow and placid way through it, on narrow wings edged with shining where the sunlight touched them. Their cries, to human ears, sounded hard and derisive. After them came the rooks, silently wheeling high over the trees. It was before the time of egg-laying. When they had flown away an old man shuffled along the drang, as the sett-stoned way between cottage and garden wall is called, and stared up at the nests and said, in a slow voice,

"So you be goin' to cut down they craw's nesties."

The burly young Exmoor man answered him:

"Aiy, granfer. You won't be plagued by they no longer."

"Wull, I reckon they be turrible destructive things, they craws."

Pause.

"Aiy."

Pause.

"I've just been looking at my zeedling tetties. Wonnerful weather for tilling tetties."

Pause.

"Aiy."

Pause and spit.

"Aiy, wonnerful weather."

He repeated his thoughts about the weather and his seedling potatoes, but the lopper of sticks was too busy to listen. I listened, and wrote in my notebook.

It was lovely in the sunlight. All troubles are disentangled from the spirit in the warm sunny air. Children were playing near me, climbing the branches, and pretending to be monkeys. The young sister of Marty was among them, a child about five years old, with the same red lips and dark eyes; but the eyes were lit by a gentler inner light. They called her Daisy, and her smaller brother, a round-headed child with eyes that always looked a little startled, was saying to her in a hoarse voice,

"Biell woan't titch 'ee, wull 'er? Thiccy spannul woan't 'urt 'ee, wull 'er?"

"Don't be frightened, Boykins," I assured the three-year-old. "Bill's a good dog, and won't bite anyone."

Boykins stretched out a stiff arm and hurriedly drew the tips of fingers down the spaniel's head, muttering hoarsely, "Nao, Biell's a gude dog. Er woan't titch 'ee, wull 'er? Noa, Biell woan't hurt 'ee, wull er?"

Dog yawned, and Boykins hurried behind a tombstone.

Goldfinches fluttered among the graves, piping to each other. Soon, O, soon, the apple-blossom!

Children began to gather twigs for firing; but the sexton hurried them away lest they be injured by falling boughs. The great limbs were sappy, with brown centres of the cross-cut sections. Some had black circles around the brown, for they were decaying. I longed to swing the long-handled axe, to feel the glinting head cut deep into the live wood, to swing again and send the cracked chip flying.

One heavy bough, growing over the road, had to be roped to a higher bough before it was sawn, for if it fell straight it would crush the front of a cottage. Like a two-legged spider the top-sawyer ran about the tree, sliding down the rope when made fast above, and whipping the saw from its sling, commenced to cut through the lower end of the limb, which was eighteen inches thick. He stood in the fork, forty feet from the ground, not holding, but leaning at an angle of forty-five degrees against the roped branch he was sawing. When he had cut through two-thirds of the branch he began to climb down to the top of the ladder fifteen feet below. Suddenly the branch creaked and cracked and plunged down hissing, to be held by the rope, and to crash against the trunk where he was holding. It hit the trunk two seconds after it had creaked; but in that time the sawyer had run like a spider round the other side of the tree, using his hands only and holding to thin, bristle-like twigs. He laughed gleefully, looking down at the horrified face of Marty below, her hand to her mouth. He would laugh like that when he met her in the lane at two o'clock; whatever she said or did he would laugh. He knew she would be there.

A blue-grey gossamer floated past me, cast into the warm breeze by a woken spider. It gleamed red and blue as it drifted, as though from the sun. One o'clock struck in the tower. The sawyers went to their dinners in the sexton's cottage, where they were lodging. The old tiller of potatoes, a widower, whom no one visits, placed against the hasp of his lower window an earth-stained postcard. On it was written: *Up in me garden.* The brown faded ink of the lettering was very old, and the card was spotted with innumerable tiny freckles—black of flies and yellow-white of spiders, all that was left of many summers' window tenants.

The old man's boots scraped on the irregular stones of the drang; they ceased; and after some moments of waiting his stringy voice said,

"Be 'ee there?"

I spoke.

"I wasn't sure," he said. "My eyes ban't so strong as they were."

He gazed at me amiably, and pointed a crooked arm and finger in the direction of the lopped elms.

"Us won't be bothered by they craws no more, wull us? Now, ye know, 'tis a funny thing, but I fancy they craws used to take my tetties early mornings. Aiy."

He lowered his arm and paused.

"Aiy," he said, slowly and heavily.

A quarter of a minute later: "Else 'twas they rats."

He cleared his throat and spat.

"Aiy, p'raps 'twas they rats."

He reflected, then he said:

"They rats be masterpieces for stealing. Aiy."

Then looking at me earnestly with his ruined eyes, he said in a low voice:

"Yurr! If 'ee can spare a moment."

I went to him. He glanced round, and to the other side, and whispered:

"Do 'ee think his Reverence would mind if I were to gather up a few of they broken sticks for me bodley?"

A kitchen range is called a bodley in the hamlet, from the maker's name which appeared on the earliest cast-iron stoves to be mortar'd into the wide open hearths of cottages.

I told Uncle Joe that the Rector had said that anyone could have the wood, which was not worth the cost of hauling to the sawmills. This appeared to amaze him. He said in the same low, confidential voice, after glancing round to see if we were alone.

"They do say that they chaps be getting a pound a day for cutting they trees. 'Tis a turrible lot o' money, don't 'ee think?"

I told him that the contractors were to be paid thirty pounds for the job, which would take three days.

"Three days, did 'ee say? Well, I never!"

When he had worked out three times three, making it nine, and subtracted nine from thirty, he told me that twenty-one pounds was left for they contractor chaps. Aiy. 'Twas remarkable what some folks did get, when you came to think about it. Aiy.

Meanwhile, I helped Uncle Joe to gather sticks. With thickened fingers he pulled at a rook's nest, muttering that it would "yett proper", that is, heat proper, meaning the bodley.

It was no easy task to remove the nests from the branches. Now I knew why they had stayed in the treetops during the south-west gales of winter. They were fixed in the supporting branches like the crooked fingers of a hand upheld, and the birds cleaning their beaks on the branches had cut the bark, causing them to swell, to become knotty, to grow distorted, and so to clutch the sticks.

Uncle Joe took the nests to his backhouse, once the dark, damp abode of successive pigs, where he kept coal, garden tools, and all sorts of old rummage—parings of horse-hoofs, rope, string, odd nails and screws rusted and useless, ancient boots and broken pails and books, and on the wall three tattered corsets; and in shallow boxes on the worm-eaten beams above, his beloved "zeedling tetties". To-morrow would be Friday, and he would draw his Old Age Pension at the post-office, and while he was away the post-card would be in his window, showing the reverse side, not so fly-marked:

Gone up to Shop.

Friday was the most eventful day of the week for him, and in the afternoon he would stand in the doorway, smoking and waiting, quiet and happy, for the butcher's van to bring his weekly piece of beef.

"Aiy, they craws' nesties wull burn fine," he called, as he scraped back to his cottage, where before eating he would wash his hands in the water that had lain for more than a week in his only enamel bowl. Some thought him a dirty old man, but the well where he dipped his pitcher was more than a hundred steps away from his threshold—past Revvy's cottage, then mine, then round past the backhouses—and the bending of rheumaticy knees and back and neck was very painful.

It was quiet again in the sunshine. The song-birds were resting; men to their dinners. A solitary rook flew over the broken trees, with moss in its beak. It wheeled, cawing its misery to the empty sky, and flew away.

Chapter Four

FIRST DAY OF SPRING

I

Hot sunlight flooding the red lane below my garden wall had made the inch-high nettles a deeper green since the morning, and warmed the stones and mortar chinks between them. For days the lane had been cold and wet, the sky over the village a ragged grey travelling ever north-east. This morning gleams showed in the Atlantic clouds, and soon a golden tide was pouring over the hills; grass, hens and pigs in the glebe field, tiles of barns, lichens and leaves of pennywort on the walls and chimney tuns, budding daffodils in the gardens and orchards, all were luminous with hope. And into the bright heat by my garden wall a little numb creature came, sliding on its coils out of the crack where it had lain all the winter. It took

43

the heat of the March sun, which laid a glisten on its skin, and drew from it the torpor of cold earth. It felt joy along its length, and moved, but grew tired; and lay like a grey S in the grooved wheel-track of the lane.

As I set out for the headland, drawn by the sudden rush of the sun, my shoe nearly crushed the snake-like innocent lying there. I picked it up between finger and thumb—a slow-worm, called longcripple's mate by country people. A longcripple is a viper, whose hollow fangs hold poison. The name longcripple's mate is certainly ironic, although bestowed in ignorance, for the slow-worm is without venom, bringing death only to flies, which it lances with a little black forked tongue. Its only connexion with longcripple is that sometimes the viper eats it.

The slow-worm writhed slowly between the skin of my thumb and finger, its tiny eyes, shrunken and sleepy, holding the remote fear of death. As I walked with it to my cottage, to show my two-year-old son, a woman appeared from behind Billy Goldsworthy's barn, and seeing me, gave a concerned cry. She held in both hands a tangle of bright green leaves, which she was about to cast on the heap under the wall of the barn.

"Nasty stuff, this shamrock," she said. "It gets under the walls, and makes the whole house damp. Oh, what is that you've got there? A snake? Yes, as I was saying; this shamrock grows everywhere, there's no stopping it when it starts. All over the stones of our path, it used to spread, until Will had concrete laid down. Will hates it. Oh, how can you hold that dreadful thing like that? Horrid, it looks. What is it, a snake? Isn't it dangerous? I wonder you are not afraid to handle it. I wouldn't hold it if I were you. What do you think about this new Revised Prayer Book?"

She was an elderly London woman, a little different from the rest of the village. Tom Gammon's proud description of one of his daughters can be applied to her, within the local meaning of the phrase—"a grammatical speaker". After working some years as a dressmaker in the neighbouring village of Cryde, she had married William Carter, a club-footed dairy farmer with a variety of names—Vanderbilt, Rumbling Willy, Cousin Billy, Thunderbolt—this last being a derivative of Vanderbilt, owing to his supposed wealth. He lived in the cottage behind the barn with his wife and his sister, a tall, pale, thin woman, who seldom went more than a dozen yards from her iron garden gate, except on Sundays when going to church. Their cottage adjoined that of Revvy Carter, who was their cousin, another William Carter. Cousin Billy and his grammatical-speaking wife, and the spinster sister, did not approve of the untidy ways of their poor relations, who let the shamrock grow, with its vivid yellow flowers opening only in the sunlight. Shamrock and relations had received many glances of displeasure during the years I had been neighbours with them all.

"Will! Will! Do come and see what Mr. Williamson has got," she cried out, as heavy slow boot-falls sounded on the concrete path behind the angle of the barn. "Come along, Will! Isn't the sun nice? My cold is so much better. Have you had the influenza? We've all had it. Will was so strange, we knew there was something wrong when he wouldn't eat his dinner." Her voice rose, for her husband had closed the iron gate behind him, and was clumping towards us.

She shouted in his ear, "Look what Mr. Williamson's found. Nasty, I call it. Don't you, Will?"

"Hey?" cried her husband, hand to ear, out of which grew long reddish hairs.

"A snake, Will!"

"Oo! Ah!" ejaculated the retired seven-acre farmer. "Fancy that, now. 'Tis one of they longcripple's mates, surenuff."

"Are you sure it won't hurt you, Will? Don't get too near it. One can't be too careful with strange things, that's what I always say. Ugh!"

I explained to her that it was not a snake, but a lizard, and entirely harmless.

"Mr. Williamson thinks it won't hurt you. What do you think, Will? Isn't it probably poisonous?"

"Hey?"

"I said, it might be probably poisonous."

"Aw, no, it won't rain, I vancy."

"Will's hard of hearing. A pity, isn't it! Is it pois-onous? Poison-ous?"

"Oo, I can't say for sure," mumbled Farmer Bill. "'Tis a znake of sorts, surenuff. I've seen scores of'n up to Booayes—scores."

"I don't like the look of it. I was saying before you came that it had better be killed."

She was a childless woman. On her big head was a bigger hat, consisting of various bits of cloth and fabric sewn around a bought wire frame. It was meant for decoration, and she had got pleasure from using up odd bits so neatly. It was a hat conceived and made behind closed windows, with the curtains drawn to shut out the sun.

"I wonder if it thinks we had better be killed?" I asked. "I don't suppose it likes the looks of us."

"I meant that it looked dangerous," she explained.

"It isn't dangerous," I said. "And it is an outrage under heaven that I should be holding it tight between my finger and thumb. All the time it is writhing and straining to escape. It is in agony. Its tail might drop off with fright, and so I am going to put it in the sun by the barn, away from the wheels in the road."

She gave me one of her quick sidelong glances. Four years previously I had heard her saying to her sister-in-law Bessie, whose voice in the cool dark dairy—spotlessly clean with its lime-ash floor and clome scalding pans on the bodley, seen through the wicket window where Bessie's thin arm used to pass the milk-jugs—often used to arise in shrill condemnation of her, "Doesn't he say peculiar things. Some say he isn't all there—a little mazed. Firing off guns in the middle of the night, and having dogs sleeping in the same room with him. Crawling about at all hours after those dirty owls in the roof; I wish the landlord would stop up the hole under the thatch, I can't sleep at night for the noise they make. I wish they would fly in his

46

windows one night, they're open winter and summer, just the same in all weathers. He never goes to church either, and they say he doesn't believe in it; and he talks about the Germans as though they had never behaved like they did all through the war. And we might all be burnt up in our beds one night, there's no telling. Hullo, Mr. Williamson, have you come for your milk? I was just telling Bessie here about your burning those old motor tyres and that mattress in your garden last night. Will woke up and thought the thatch was on fire. He was ever so scared."

It was the same tale whenever I made a fire of weeds or manuscripts in the garden. I had never heeded her much; for me she was a symbol of frustrated Europa.

To-day I was impatient to be off on my walk, to see the tide heaving and ripping over the reef called Bag Leap, and how far built was the raven's nest, and if the peregrine falcons were over their eyrie, and if— "Now this little putty snake will be out of danger here," I said, "and now I'm going round the headland."

"Oh!" she said, "are you going all that way in this cold wind? Well, I suppose you must like going, or you wouldn't be going, would you? I can't say that I would like to be going with you. What do you think, Will?"

"Hey?" he boomed.

"Mr. Williamson says he's going round the headland, in all this cold wind. I was just saying that I wouldn't care to be going where he's going. Nor would you, either, eh?"

"Aw, don't 'ee till tetties yet!" he replied, shaking his head. "Aw no, the ground ban't in temper—it's no use mucketting."

"Poor Will, he gets deafer and deafer," explained his wife. "Although sometimes he pretends he can't hear when he can. He's had his ears syringed out, too, but it was a waste of money. What a blessing it is to have all one's faculties, isn't it? I should kill that snake if I were you. With so many children about, there might be an accident. What a pretty little boy yours is, isn't he? Just fancy now if that snake bit him. You'd never forgive yourself, would you? You can't be too careful, you know."

The slow-worm, feeling the sun, moved slightly on the warm earthenware shard under the wall of the barn.

"Dad," cried a voice, as I walked back to the cottage. "Dad, will 'ee, will 'ee come back to have tea with me to-day?"

"I'll be back in three hours' time," I promised my two-year-old son; and the wind rushed against my face.

2

There was more air and light outside the village, from which I strode with head clearing of indoor contacts. Past the three cottages of Rock Park, whose garden walls bristled with old snapt stalks of red valerian—called "drunkards" in the village —among which new green leaves were showing; past the Church School, now shut because of the influenza epidemic, with its tiny windows; past the worn steps leading in to the bare playground; past the schoolmaster's house adjoining, and the old square garden once tilled by the children—but now sold by the owner, a wealthy childless farmer, for a bungalow site.

By the new square bungalow, with its asbestos roof, the banks rose above the lane. Brambles hung out of the thorns a-top them, stripped and made ragged by the shoulders of passing carters. There was a gateway just beyond the bungalow, opening on a wide green pasture called Netherhams, sloping gently to the blue northern sky—a fine field for mushrooms every third or fourth summer. Its lane frontage was for sale as sites for bunga-lows, at many times the price paid for the land five years before.

The ruddle pools were shrinking in the lane; already the rutted mud was plastic, taking a fine clean print of my nailed shoes. By the wayside such large celandines were facing the sun! One, a veritable Sirius, was two inches wide, with thirteen petals. A hemisphere of starry petals was shining there; constella-tion after constellation had broken into light since the morning, for yesterday, when I passed here in the rain, I saw only the shovel-shaped leaves. The flower leaps out of the plant, the essence of its being; for days and weeks and months it prepares for the fullest moments of its existence, the risen beauty of its flowers. Ecstasy shines in the yellow-glistered celandines, sudden and lusty as the March sunlight.

The lane began to sink deeper between the fields; a ragged shadow of the hedge-top divided it. Where the wheels of carts and motor cars had worn the red iron-stone metalling the shale bedrock showed grey, smoothed by the runners of sleds in use along this way before the coming of the wheel. Shale is soft and easily worn; when used for building, it slowly crumbles into dust. Lichens eat it at their ease. The iron-stone beds lay a few hundred yards to the north; the rock for the road metalling was carted from the quarry half-way up the hill to Ox's Cross, and tipped out in the bays cut in the hedge banks. There the stone-crackers, wearing gauze spectacles and sitting on the ground, tapped with their blunt double-headed hammers until the rugged piles were graded into neat rectangular heaps, when their faces, clothes, and hands would be stained a browny red by the dust and the sweat.

Half a mile from the village I passed one such bay, where the lane, which had been rising gently and steadily, flattened on the ridge before descending again. Brambles leant over the red heap of stones, seeking to put down roots between them and find a hold in the earth. Always the overhanging feelers had been stripped or broken when the horse-butts had come to the stone dump, yet the sun in the sky ever renewed their blossom-thoughts, and the long brambles crept forth again. Their claims are ceaseless, and if Man were to leave this lane, the brambles would very soon hide it with their entanglements.

3

Between the hedges I could see the Atlantic's white upflung bursts of waves a mile away and below. Above my left shoulder the bare grey ash saplings of the hedge, with their dark brown cloven buds, rattled and swished in the south west wind which was blowing half a gale. Gulls drifted overhead, rocking and crooking their wings. The fields of plough and pasture, the trees and thatched roofs of the farm buildings below, the flock of yellow-hammers alighting and flitting along the ruddy twigs of dogwood and the young leaves of honeysuckle, the plants of foxglove, the lichens on the stone—all took light from the sky, and freed the thought-cumbered spirit. Air and sun and wind, these are the inspiration of life, the ancient source of renewal, whose inherited essence is the beauty in Man's mind. A lark was singing, and another lark, many larks: and it seemed to me, in the beauty of that moment, that the inspiration of walls and pavements was false, bringing upon men the things of darkness.

The wind and the sun vibrate the tissues charged and impressed in ancient days: I am one with the sunlight, and the lark is my brother. These feet must not break the flapping arrow-shaped leaves of the wild arum, as I clamber over a dog-gap in the hedge to the open fields, for its hopes are my hopes under the wide sky.

The wind smote me, filling my sleeves and hollowing my coat, pulling out my tie and flacking it on my cheek. Its fragile roar rushed against my ears. The grass was not yet tall enough to be flattened and disspread, the old tussocks were sodden, hard-cored, and unresponsive; soon the green of the new blades would be pushing through. In June this field would be a haunt of meadow pipits, fluttering from their nests in the tussocks when my feet were one stride distant: poor little things, feigning a broken wing, in anguish, but not for themselves. Then the thistles would hold the field, rank upon rank, so that to walk through them would be to make a crooked course like a rabbit along its run. Now the roots were preparing summer's down as they crept underground. The stems, just before flowering, would be cut with a scythe, for they were "noxious weeds", and condemned by law, which also condemned the yellow ragwort, with its wind-borne seeds, and the dock; but the stems would arise again, and in August the sun-dried cardoons would break, and free their glistening aery wheels into the warm air, as in every year I have known them float away.

FIRST DAY OF SPRING

So many times have I crossed the field, climbing through the gap worn by the feet of every dog that passes, that I could draw from memory almost all the rabbit runs which, numerous as the boughs and branches of an oak tree, were trodden everywhere through the grass. Every year from September to March iron gins were tilled in some of the banks, and many of the rabbits used to lie out in the open, squatting in layers, or sheltered places in the tussocks. Then the trapper brought his wires of twisted brass, made into nooses with slip-knots, and fastened to wooden pegs. The pegs were driven in beside the runs, a hazel twig with a cleft top holding the noose as high as the head of a rabbit travelling to its feeding ground; and the rest was not silence, but screams that were throttled, and a dance that wore the grass away, with periods of rest and the agony of half-breathing until . . . but I must not feel beyond myself, for this is the first day of Spring.

4

The lower part of the field sloped into the coombe bottom, and a bank had to be climbed before the brook was reached. This bank was guarded by a single strand of barbed wire, stretched between short posts, parallel with the ground, to keep cattle from breaking the hedge. There was a magpie in the next field; the wind had prevented it from hearing my footfalls. It had not seen my head appearing, and while crouching on the bank I was able to watch its work of opening the skull of a dead rat. Probably the rat had been caught in a gin the evening before, discovered this morning when the trapper went down the hedge, knocked on the head, and flung a couple of yards from the bank.

Blow after blow of its beak the magpie, standing on the rat's shoulders, delivered between the ear and the eye socket. Six daps it gave, then looked around, before bending its neck and striking again with all its strength. The wind lifted the small black feathers of its back, which gleamed with green and purple.

FIRST DAY OF SPRING

The magpie hammered the skull about a dozen times and made two rapid surveys, in about eight seconds. When it raised its head for the third survey, it saw me, gave a short sharp cry, and flew away. I jumped down, and turning the rat over with my stick, noticed that both its eyes had been picked out. Magpies, with the relative crows and daws, have the eyes first, probably because they are the easiest to take.

I ran down to the brook, for a leap across the turf of its low banks broken and holed by bullocks. The stream at this place is normally eighteen inches wide, flowing clear and fast, but the marshy ground is eight feet in width. Trout live in the water, the biggest about eight inches long. A heron comes regularly to stalk them. Furze was in bloom on the bank just above the cattle drinking-place, and kneeling down, with my face near the reflected sky, I found the first water-cress of the year.

It grew among the multitudinous leaves of another water plant, which is poisonous, but whose name I do not know. A common plant, but I have never sought for it in my Sowerby—a beautiful book, with illustrations faithfully coloured by hand: a book dearer to me because Richard Jefferies could never afford to buy it. Easy to pluck a leaf and take it home and lay it beside its likeness in Sowerby; but no. In how many other waters have I seen it since the first leaf was plucked in the brook we used to dam with turves in a far-off country, where once a voice (very young still) cried anxiously, "P'ay don't eat it! P'ay don't eat it! Very pois'nous, nasty dirty plant!" as I pretended to munch the leaves, secretly pleased at the show of care for me. Ten years ago, this very month, I saw it in the waters of the Ancre, flowing cold and swift on its chalk bed under Beaumont Hamel; and a ghost, not long of the thin air, rose up beside me among the charred poplar stumps of the dreadful swamp. The waters of this fair Devon brook move under and over the leaves of the mock water-cress plants: let them be of the far-off country, nameless for ever.

FIRST DAY OF SPRING

5

Beyond the brook the pointed leaves of the yellow iris had pricked through the grass, and were two inches high, in patches of twisted points, each with its shadow. At the end of the month they would be as tall as a bullock's dew-claw, green and straight; for cattle do not eat them. A good farmer would cut them with a scythe when they were tall in May, to exhaust the knotted bulbous roots which increase by pushing through the ground. The farmer who tills the ground can have few aerial brothers.

By one of the iris patches lay a path, nine inches wide, in the grass. It was of beaten earth, rough and dark. Nothing ever grew on it. Morning and afternoon the cows followed along the path, one behind the other, never varying the pace of their slow and swinging walk. The horn of their hooves kept the path trimmed and everywhere exact in width. The path wandered like water, but without the reason of water, which must ever be falling. All the lanes probably were begun as casually as this cow-path, which would remain there for as long as the leading cow lived in the field, to amble to the open gate, knowing by its almost instinctive sense of time, and also by the weight of its udders, when the milking hours of morning and evening were nigh. One cow is usually the leader, for animals are more creatures of habit than are men; and the way is regularly trodden in the lives of all the cows which graze together in a field.

The moles were busy mining under the grass, throwing up their heaps at the pit-heads, as they cleared the galleries for the hungry hunt every four hours. White splashes on the bank marked where a buzzard had waited while watching for a heap to heave—when it would jump off the bank and grab with its yellow feet. One mole run was made almost the length of the cattle path; a mole will always tunnel under such a track when it finds it. Perhaps the worms on which it feeds find more food there, and also the absence of grass roots makes easier the work of digging.

I passed through the gateway in the corner of the field, where an elm tree grew almost parallel with the bank which it covered with its branches. Under it the ground was pitted and broken by bullocks sheltering there during the storms which had helped to make the tree's shape. All the trees along the banks of this high open ground grew one-sided, and without much height, for only those boughs growing north-east, away from the south-westerly gales, had not beaten against one another and broken their bark, lost the leaves by which they breathe, died down-wards, become brittle and damp and the holding-place of fungus, and fallen rotten. Most of them must have more roots in the ground than limbs in the air. Lichens grew on the living branches, like little withered trees, like wisps of hair on the heads of corpses bleached by chlorine gas in the Salient. The dry, greyish-green lichens love the rain and the wind, and do not appear to thrive so well in sheltered places out of the salt blasts of winter.

Through another field I followed the cattle-path, over ground beginning its steep decline to the wide wet sands and the white heaving waste of the sea below. The wind came direct from the waves; I could lean against it, and with arms out-held imagine the effortless beauty of flight. I glided over the field, tenuous as wind; and out of the grass sprung the blue-rayed flowers of the chicory, and the brilliant hawkbits of summer, and the yellow claws of the bird's-foot trefoil. In that moment the spirit was free in the wind rushing from out the vast spaces of the sky, and unbounded in creation with the sun.

6

Yet the body cannot fly over the gate by Vention Lane. The gate?—there were two gates: a new gate of ash-wood, with new white concrete posts. It stood six feet back from where the old lichened gate, with its loose rattling top-bar, swung from the engboo of pitch pine, timber from a wreck, with iron trenail pins thin-flaked with rust. An engboo is the post on which the gate hangs, probably a corruption of hang-bough. Hereabouts the engboo is usually either a bit of wrecking, or an old rutted trunk of an apple tree, or an upright slab of shale rock, or a living tree. All the engboos in Vention Lane, and its continuation called Stentaway Lane, are doomed; the wood will vanish with them, and very soon there will be only ferro-concrete posts. A notice-board stands by the gate, proclaiming the site of the proposed new motor road to be cut along the side of the downs and to merge into Vention and Stentaway Lanes, which it will devour, hedges, engboos, and all, on its way to Cryde and Town. Here will come the many-coloured motor coaches from the northern Exmoor coast in summer, above the loveliest bay in the West Country. There will be houses and hotels and many people, and perhaps laws about bathing made by old men with minds deadened by paving stones, who never reveal their bodies to the sun.

From the beginning of time, which man invented, this place has been to the soaring hawks and the gulls gliding over from the inland fields, to the fox lying in the furze, the rabbits, the wild partridges, and the stonechats. Here was the solitude of the sea and the sky. In the days when first I saw it the Immortals dwelled in these hills; the still bright noons shimmered with mystery, ships in the Severn Sea were sailing in the sky, the sun setting under the far world's sea-line took the heart into vast and unutterable spaces. That last day of May, 1914, when the boy walked over thirty miles in the hot sun, taking a last look at trees and lanes and cliffs and streams, taking farewell of enchantment, and saying on the lonely headland while the heart ached with all longing, *Good-bye, I shall return, but it will never be the same.*

The crumbling and brownish-red stump of the old engboo has been heaved out of the earth, and the bank levelled. That corner of the field, now rutted with butt-wheel tracks between the wire road-fences, used to be the home of a colony of teasel plants, with their curious green water-holding leaves, prickly like the teeth of fish. One day, coming down the field, I saw a goldfinch sipping water on a teasel stalk; a lovely sight, with the crimson of its face and the yellow and black of its wings, beside the bristly head crowning the plant's life, hung with pollen almost the colour of the grey-purple shale rock. Now the engboo is fallen, my teasels will not bloom in that corner again, and soon the wheels of civilisation will be grinding their seeds with the dust; but to-day a little of the rare and precious illusion of boyhood has returned, and the sun is shining for me in heaven.

7

Opposite the new gateway stood a telegraph pole, rising out of brown loops of old barbed brambles. Under them grew the low leaves of the new year's nettles, each with a minute hole gnawn in its centre. What tiny teeth, or sets of rasps, had been at work there? The small black slug, that lays a glistening track from its home under the damp rotten stalks of the old nettles, and returns before sunrise? The yellow-banded snail, not yet eager after its trance on the underside of a stone in the bank? It could hardly be any new-hatched caterpillars of the red admiral butterflies, which lay their eggs on the nettles, for they are still asleep in the dry chinks of the hollow ash-trees of Combas Lane, in the crevices of cob walls, and under the thatched roofs. While I was peering among the nettles for a sight of the leaf-eater, I heard a shout, and looking up the field, I saw a farmer on a horse, two hundred yards away. The eyes of a dog were also upon me, as his master's mingled protests and insults were roared into the wind. After his rabbits, was I, and breaking down his banks? I was to get out of it quick, or he would pitch me out quicker than I liked. He didn't want no bliddy German on his land. Waving my hand in acknowledgment of this tremendous insult, I jumped down into the lane again, where I squatted under the wind, and considered the problem.

It was the tenth anniversary of the great German attack on the Somme; nearly a decade since the War had ended, but still the effect of what this farmer had read in newspapers, or heard from pulpits, platforms, and inns, lingered as verities in his mind. Like many another young and healthy farmer, during that War he had remained on his farm, tilling his land and making much money from his crops, especially potatoes, and from his cream and butter. Cream at five shillings a pound soon increases a bank-balance and consequent self-estimation. Ten years since the face of Truth was spat upon more than usual— Truth, which has been demonstrated, at least once during our known human history, to be magnanimity. Every man has his vision of Truth: what was the vision of that man on the skyline, that farmer with his heavy hands pulling back the mouth of the cob which usually he cantered on the hard surface of the lane, that man whose voice I had heard so often bawling at inoffensive animals? Would anything ever bring him to see plainly, to unlearn all that he had read and heard until the old world was ended for him . . . the old world which was made of men's thought?

I told myself that his anger was reasonable, for were not many of his gaps unstopped and widened by summer visitors, and new gaps broken in his hedges? Why then all this cogitation ten years after the War, which some said was a natural solution of the problem of surplus population: as it might be said, crucifixions were good for the timber trade.

The telegraph pole went on humming to itself, heedless of my ironic contemplation. Surely it was one of the things a "healthy-minded man" should laugh at, this German business; but I could not laugh. For me the sunshine lost some of its pleasure: now it was like the Somme sun, which was never like the sun in England. Ah well, perhaps in some other field, in wind that blew under the same sky, a farmer was shouting at another man who walked about and peered at birds, while others had to work hard for a living; and perhaps the farmer was calling him an Englishman. That Englishman in German fields, and this German in an English field, both released parts of grievous and ghastly things—manifestation of innumerable money-thoughts, formed out of ideas alien to the human spirit, cohered by virtues suborned and exploited—smile at each other across the land and the sea, as we smiled at each other in No-man's-land on Christmas Day, in the year of the prophetic fare-well to these very trees and lanes and streams and cliffs.

The lark is our brother; the sun shines in beauty again.

8

Having given the farmer time to depart, as I hoped, I got up and looked over the hedge. There he was, sturdy and statuesque on his horse, beside the new notice-board which had been erected when the manor house, with a few fields, had been sold over the unsuspecting head of the old tenant, an artist. The new board, bearing white letters on a black background, barred the way to the headland path. It was not a right-of-way, but until recently travellers were allowed to pass over the rough grazing land to the paths along North Side. In the lane, on hot summer days, man is but mortal, enduring dust and glare with the vision of cool, green, hollow waves toppling on head and back; but when he has passed through the gate the world suddenly falls away, and the wind finds him, the everlasting and immortal wind, with its secret gifts of heaven.

Beyond the gate is the green top of the world; far below are the sea and the sands. Your companions are the clouds above the dim far coastline of Wales. Children shout when they run on the sward after the dusty lane; dogs prance and course in circles, barking with delight, and rolling with ecstasy. The shoulders feel broader, the toes strive to pass through encumbering leather and press into sward.

A branch of the path led down over the fields and the low scrub-grown cliffs to the shore. I remembered a stile between the two fields in 1914, and again in 1916, and for some years after the War. Now the stile was altered, and another notice-board at the foot of the cliffs confronted the summer walkers from Woolcombe:

NO PATH

NORTH SIDE ESTATE.

FIRST DAY OF SPRING

The way to the headland being closed, I set off down Vention Lane, meaning to climb the Naps cliffs from the sands. Vention Lane was sunken under banks, and little more than the width of a horse-butt. The naked rock showed worn in the wheel-ruts where the winter rains, rushing down the steep hill, had scoured the stones and earth of its rough surface.

It led down to the old round lime-kiln by the seashore, and the two lime-burners' cottages. It is said in the village that the name Vention was derived from those two cottages, which were called the Cottages of the New Invention—since they had been built with chimneys, which were, apparently, the new invention.

Old Muggy told me that, in his "kid days", barges were beached on the sands at half-tide in calm weather, and chalk from the French coast carried away in horse-butts up the lane and the grassy sloping track to the rim of the kiln, and tipped on to the firing of "sticks" below. But tonnage prices rose, lime-burning ceased.

The two cottages stood empty, and brambles explored the round kiln, dropping down their green grappling lines into the shadowy damp hollow. Seeds of ferns and briars, scurvey-grass, pennywort, polypody fern, were blown into the kiln, or dropped there by birds. In time lichens like molten silver anciently splashed on the stones and corroded by sea-salts, loosened away the surfaces on which they were spread. Rain unsettled the mortar, and mosses filled the crevices. A pair of wagtails—who love ruins—built in one or another of the spaces made by fallen stones, year after year. Lizards and longcripples stole out of the chinks when the summer sun had made hot the upper stones.

After the War masons came down Vention Lane, and the cottages were made into one building, with a new roof in place of the former slate roof sunken like the hide of a stranded and dead whale. The kiln was covered with corrugated-iron sheets, with wooden steps leading up to what, I was informed, was a bathroom. An extra wing with lean-to roof was added to the cottage on the kiln side, and a garage erected in the field above, with a threatening notice-board. Sometimes in the days of summer when passing the Cottages of the New Invention on my way to swim I had a glimpse of a figure in a black-tailed coat and stiff shirt-front sitting in the new wing, polishing tumblers, and keeping discreetly out of the sunlight. Soon afterwards the shadowy figure vanished, with the voices it used to await, and after awhile others came; and near the sward of the kiln, once so bright with hawkbits and bird's-foot trefoil, a grey heap of stuff began to increase and slide down towards the sea—as though it were the roosting place of a gigantic pterodactyl that had not heard of the extinction of its species. For months I wondered idly what this grey mass might be, visible from the sea at low tide a quarter of a mile away, until one day an old woman gathering sticks told me. "Oh, 'tis wonnerful what they do be inventing nowadays. If tidden one thing, 'tis another. They say 'tis water on a bit of old stuff like chips of stone doth make a light in ivry room to wance. Oh, 'tis wonnerful what they be inventing nowadays."

9

As I walked on the wet sand under the Naps I heard the notes of a blackbird, and looking up the cliffs, I saw my old friend on his usual perch—an elderberry tree which, growing crippled away from the sea winds, put forth a few poor twigs and leaves every spring among the bleached bones of its dead branches. To what age does a blackbird live unless it dies violently? I had known that blackbird six years before; I recognized him every spring by the quality of his notes. He sang more quietly and slowly than most other blackbirds; the song seemed to come from beyond the bird; and at intervals he repeated a refrain which was a perfect cadence. One year I asked a friend to write it down, and he was amazed by its perfection of time and tune.

I remembered that a white wren had appeared in the village some years before, to be shot immediately, and eventually to be much admired, in a tiny glass case, for its pink feet and eyes, and the perfection of its plumage; and as I walked away I thought it was fortunate we were not musical in the village of Ham.

10

At the bottom of the cliffs was a clitter of great rocks fallen in past ages from the sea-worn edge of the land. Seaweeds and shell-fish grew on the lower rocks, making them slippery, but it was easy to climb and scramble from point to point and so to reach the base of the cliff, where the waves never broke and the grass began. The way up the cliff was steep, but not dangerous. There were many footholds on the embedded pieces of fallen rock, half hidden by grass and ivy. At the top of the cliff the land broke vertically, and there it was needful to tread warily. The sands beneath, with their pools and watery ribbed hollows, and the jumbled heap of dark, sharp edged rocks now appeared immediately beneath my feet: to miss a hold by hand or foot would mean a series of bounding rolls down the steep green slope and a final crash on the rocks. I clung with taloned hands to the tufts of grass, stiff and inactive, until in hot desperation I clawed my way to safety. "Mind-forged manacles", I dragged them over the edge with me, and sat down, wishing I had the courage to climb down again, and so to conquer my fear. I started, and drew back; I would be shackled until I died, having no courage to submit myself to the spirit's anvil, quailing before the raised hammer of the will.

There was rest for the defeated in the long grass. Jackdaws were flying against the white-broken blue of the sea; some pitched on the ivied crags farther west, and watched me. For months they had passed and repassed this place without a cry or a check in their steady wing-beats, or flown with the rooks in the fields, each for itself; but one morning, when the rooks had flown to the Pidickswell trees, each pair to claim a nesting site and to caw satisfaction to the sky and the colony, the daws held aerial tourney high over the fields and the sea. They twirled and dived, they hurled themselves upon each other, they imitated the flight of other birds when chasing each other, they croaked deeply like ravens. Pair by pair they fell out of the revel. The place became precious in the glow of ancestral memory; the cliffs grew bright with detail. The fire of spring was kindled, and lit their pale blue eyes. Every gull was an intruder, every passing of the delicate-winged kestrel a menace to their dreams.

Primroses were blooming among the wet tussocks of withering coarse grass; the leaves of the bluebell plants were sprouted thickly on the slopes. Suddenly, as I sat there, all the daws flew out with a rush of wings that conquered the noise of the wind, with cries of *Jank-jank! Quank!* The gulls, farther along the cliff, broke into a white wailing swirl over the sea. Looking around, I saw two herons flying below me, their broad grey wings easily visible against the brownish-yellow sands. One followed the other. The leading bird, I thought, was probably the heron I had seen many times, flying from the pond fed by the brook I had crossed; he had a regular round of fishing stances. From the pond he flew to another brook where it began to wind its deep way through the sandhills behind Cryde Bay. Now, with his mate following him from stance to stance, the dull routine was gone from his life—until the young in the tree-top nest across the estuary began to grow, when it would return again—and his world glowed with the fire of spring.

After leaving the pond, the wind had carried him off his course, and, with his mate, he had probably taken the easy way, a glide down the land until he came under the wind below North Side. And gliding nearer the sands, and the long un-rolling white of the shallow sea, he had swung round, remembering the rushes and the water of his stance in the sandhills. His mate swung round after him, and the long beat upwind began.

The big hollow wings beat steadily, lifting into the wind the narrow bodies with the long legs held stiffly straight behind. They rose higher and higher, above the reddish line of the Wool-

combe houses three miles away, above the black houses under
the hill-line, and into the blue sky over the Morte; but they
grew no larger in my sight. Many gulls and daws, blown errati-
cally by the gale, swirled about them like grey and black ashes of
paper above invisible flames. One minute, two minutes, three
minutes—my head was tilted more and more, but they made no
forward progress. Other gulls joined the pestering flock, some
of them following the herons, until at last the grey birds turned
downwind and glided towards the cottages of Vention. I
watched them trying to cross the base of the headland, by Stentaway Lane, where the ground was lower; but when they met the
wind again their wing-beats only lifted them higher. After
awhile, they turned and glided down to the sands, where they
pitched, and rested side by side.

I I

My way lay westwards along one of the many cattle-paths
which the cloven feet had beaten in the grassy slope, where
plants of primroses, and bluebell bulbs, turned purple by the
light, were broken out of the dark brown soil.

The path I followed led through a brake of trees with trunks of
a thickness between a child's wrist and a bullock's body, but of
the same height; a wood of wind-dwarfs, interworn by cattle-
paths, each tree the shape of a blown candle-flame. The biggest
tree was an elm on which one could almost spread a cloak and
recline. Tufts of reddish cow-hairs were on many stumps of
trees which had failed.

Under branches spread parallel with the slope of the ground
the celandines were flat and starved, the small-leaved primrose
plants were without flowers, dwarf bluebell leaves were either
cropped or crushed.

Farther on were thorns, both black and white, their only
branches bent away from the salt sea; the ingrowing twigs were
thick like hair. Shaggy mosses and lichens made them look very
ancient. So thickly were their twigs ingrown that, although it

was possible to look down at them from a few feet away up the slope, I could not tell if their small tops held magpies' nests or not. Here was a thorn six feet tall, crowned by an elongated ball of spiky twigs the size of a magpie's nest: but surely it was a magpie's nest? The magpie tops her nest with thorns, entering by a hole at the side: I peered at the black mass, a rolled-up hedgehog of a bush-top; yes, there was a twig of elderberry, cunningly worked like a joist through the mass. It was an old nest; last spring's twigs had matted its roof, so that it must have been almost draught-proof. While I was gingerly feeling for the opening I heard a chatter below, and saw the black-and-white flickering of a magpie before it vanished in the brake lower down.

Like the spirits of men, the trees are the shape of their suffering. The everlasting talons of the wind pierce them; the salt spray blights their buds as they break, corrupts the edges of the opening leaves, ruins the tender stems before they are set in their strength. They grow close and bent, with roots interwoven, their few branches rubbing brown sores under and against one another. The blast shakes them, and they cry out with the sharp and brittle cry of the mouse pierced by the talons of the brown wind-falcon. Do trees feel pain like men, do they despair? We know that they die.

The spirit of the tree endures, like the spirit of man, to renew hope with the sun in the sky. Here among the black and savage thorns break the blossoms of its happy morning, the all of its endurance. Nothing so innocent as the opening buds of the blackthorn; the white petal beauty is of the air, wan-travelling starlight. Delicate and coral are the stamens within the white buds of the thorn; coral the lips of the bride, virginal, sad with all loveliness and ancient sunlight.

12

It was quiet in the brake on the cliff, for the wind had lessened and swung to the south: the shadows of trees did not move: the burring of the first humblebee was loud in the grove of the bullocks. Now I would have to climb again, or get my new stockings torn by brambles. The quickest and easiest way to the ravens' nest was to climb to the top of the slope of bracken, furze, and bramble, and walk on the landsherds at the edge of the fields. Cattle-paths were liable to end suddenly: they were treacherous with hidden rabbit buries, which filled the shoes with earth; and if not recently used, were overgrown with clawing loops of bramble. There were several tracks lying on and near the edge of the cliffs, but to follow them was arduous and prickly work, with much clambering up tussocks where the way rose steeply around broken hollow precipices.

By following the easy top path on the landsherds of the stony fields, where thin and wind-scythed oats grew with the charlock in summer, the mind could be given to the sea and the sky; the least attention to the way in front was needed. So strongly was the yellow charlock settled in these fields that, walking there in the late summer, it was necessary to sit down every few yards and empty the seeds, round and hard like shot, out of my shoes. The flowers held much honey, and the bees loved them; the farmer has long since ceased to curse at his yellow fields, and accepts them as he does the scything of the wind.

The mated gulls cried out below as I passed above their nesting ledges; they floated out white in the sunshine, and joined the birds already yelping and weaving in flight against the cliff-shadows in the sea. A kestrel—the little brown falcon that luffs into the wind and watches for mice and finches in the bracken—made her dainty swoop out of the cliff, followed by her mate, who chased her through the wailing throng, flickering easily from the petulant and clumsy swoop of the gulls. High over the fields a buzzard soared in the wind, watching on still crooked wings above its eyrie in the middle bay of the Ramson Cliffs, by the big clump of bladder campion—a lodgment of sticks on which both birds recently had been standing several times a day, and preening each other's neck feathers.

I watched for the ravens along the uneven cliff-line as I stood between two fields, upon a stone-ditched wall repaired with pieces of old iron bedsteads, but I could not see them. Had they lost heart at last, and forsaken their old ledge? For the ravens of Bloodhill Cliff—I was standing on the boundary wall between Ramsons and Bloodhill—have been unhappy in their nesting for many seasons. Year after year the same things have happened. About mid-February the first new stick of the year was added. A month later, when the sandmartins appeared, the nest was rebuilt and relined, two feet high, and in the third week the first egg was laid. The nest held five—called a clutch by the human collector—at the beginning of the fourth week. And on Easter Sunday afternoon the nest was usually empty.

The ledge was in the cliff-bay directly below the end of the rabbit-tunnelled bank dividing the two fields of Bloodhill. Just over the wall, as I jumped down, there was a landsherd—lanchett, lychett, is apparently the same thing, a sherd or fragment of land—a grassy bank too steep to plow, an island cut to the shape of a mussel-shell by the ploughshare. I scrambled down the slope beside the bank, and reached the long withered grasses entangling the scanty bushes of ling at the edge of the cliffs. Holding to the tussocks with taloned fingers, and making sure of footholds, I slowly raised myself and gradually, very gradually, looked over the edge.

I saw the sea and the rocks a long way down, and my nervous control stiffened and became brittle like isinglass. I sat down again gradually, and even then was not at ease. I told myself that this was foolish and unreasonable; that I could not fall; and rising again, I craned over, and looked into the ravens' nest on the ledge at the bottom of a smooth grey face of rock.

The grey rock faced the west, and slanted inwards, so that its top overhung the nest, which was made of sticks of a light colour; and peering through my glass I saw, after a dilating moment when I felt I might be swaying outwards without realising how far, that they were sticks either of dead furze or elderberry. It was lined with sheep's-wool, grasses, and the brown fibre inside the bark of dead blackthorns; and four eggs

lay in the centre of the hollow. They were very small: the nest
was lower than I had thought. When empty, it looked about
ten feet under the cliff edge, but the nest must have been at least
thirty feet down.

The scaur at the end of the grey rock was whitened, where the
old birds had perched. That point was the look-out; it com-
manded a view along the cliffs on both sides. The raven is a cunning and most cautious bird, almost a timid bird when he sees a
man; but he is not always wise. He will choose several look-out
places, a minor perch near the nest, and a major perch or perches
on the top of the cliffs—one of them was on the bed-rail stuck in
the boundary bank above—where he cannot be overlooked by
man, his only enemy. Nevertheless, year after year he will
return to the same ledge, although year after year either the eggs
or the young birds are stolen.

Usually on Good Friday two or three youths came out from
Cryde village, with ropes and an iron bar which they drove into
the earth above the grey sloping rock. Then they tied one rope
round the chest of the climber, and hitched the other round the
base of the bar. Sometimes there was one rope and one bar, and
the climber descended hand under hand; the distance was so
slight that he did not need to be hauled up on the second rope.
The eggs of the raven did not appear to be worth anything,
unless it happened that a visiting "gennulman" had said that he
would like to buy a clutch. Once I saw a boy holding two in his
hand, which he had blown with a thorn; and asking him where
he had got them, he replied that "several Cryde chaps" had got
them that morning.

13

The younger "Cryde chaps" were not superstitious about the
ravens, as were the Kift brothers—John and "Tiger" among
them, men more than sixty years old. John Kift explained to
me that one Sunday, when they were young men living at Southside Farm, they went ferreting on the Northside slopes; and sud-

denly flushed the two ravens off the nest, where they appeared to have been dozing together. They must have been very young birds, he said. They shot them, and saw them splash into the sea.

Returning some time later they saw a raven flying away from the ledge, a raven with a white pinion-feather which they recognised as the hen-bird of the Southside nest. She had been taking food to the helpless young in the nest below them. The men stared at each other. They remembered the story of Elijah; and now the Lord had sent the spicketty bird to feed the orphan birds. "And I'd never shoot a raven, not if you was to offer me a hundred pounds for to do'n!" declared John Kift to me, when telling me this story.

As I passed Cox's Cliff, a few minutes after leaving the raven's nest, I remembered a similar story, which old Muggy Smith of Cryde once told me. Below Cox's Cliff is a flat rock, about half as big again as a farm butt, showing only at low tide. It is balanced on other rocks at the landward end of a narrow channel lying north and south. At low spring tides fishermen can stand on the rock, which gives a good grip to nailed boots owing to the small shell-fish encrusting it, and cast their conger-lines in the direction of the Morte Church, whose square grey tower stands in the hills across the bay. If truly cast, the lines, weighted with bits of old iron, splash into the channel where among the heavy ribbons of the thong weed conger eels pass in their grey, cold-eyed roving.

One Good Friday, the wind being favourable, a north-easter that made no waves, two men were fishing from the flat rock. One felt the snatch and tugs of a conger bite, and hauled in rapidly, but the tugs increased so considerably that the fisherman's mate grasped him round the middle as he pulled in the line. Slowly the end was drawn to the rock, and they saw, to their amazement, a conger eel with two heads—a monstrous eel as thick as a man's thigh. After cutting the line they removed their hats, remembering that it was Good Friday. Never again would they go fishing on Sunday or Good Friday, they declared fervently in the inn on their return. "A master gr't conger swallowing a smaller conger after it had been hooked?" suggested Muggy. Even so, the men were convinced of their wrongdoing; and in due course two regular chapel members, in white clothes, obtained salvation by being immersed in the tank under the chapel floor.

I recalled another case of salvation, of which there are so many variants in the human species; a case vouched for by no less an authority than the wife of a parson. A remark of mine about the late War being sanctified by various high ecclesiastical authorities in Europe, following upon an "unsolicited" reading in a certain drawing room, where I had invited myself in a hopeful moment, so disturbed her that she told me, with a genuine emotion which ended the argument in silence, the story of a very dear friend whose husband was taken during the War because she, the wife, had loved her husband more than God. They were free-thinkers, like myself, and had not gone to church; but now, to the widow in her loneliness, her error had been revealed; and there was no one among the parishioners who attended church more regularly than she. Not that God hadn't taken His time, for He had: He had waited patiently while she had dabbled in spiritualism.

John Kift, one of the brothers who shot the ravens, was one of the "saved", as they call the metamorphosis in the village. He confided to me in the Higher House one morning how it had been brought about. I wrote down his words immediately after he had told me. "I don't go neither to Church or Chapel, I don't: they'm a lot of bliddy rogues, and no better than you nor me; they go zinging psalms a Sunday, and the next day they'm just as likely to be staling from ye. But I believe in God's Houses, mind; I love God's Houses. And I'll tell 'ee for why." He lowered his thin-nostrilled nose, with its sharp point, together with his voice, sharp usually with assertiveness. "I'll tell 'ee for why. One Saturday, I says to myself, in a bit of a temper, 'I'll finish that job, I will, I'll go right ahead and finish'n.' And I did. And on Monday morning, I was cut down bad." Shyly, in a quiet voice, but with assertiveness returning, "I reckon Jesus Christ cut me down. And I never worked no more on a Sunday, nor never will, not if you was to pay me a hundred pounds. Noo-mye!"

"How do you mean, 'cut down'?" I enquired.

"Why, I had this yurr bloomin' influenza," he replied.

When I told this story to the parson's wife, on the occasion of my hopeful reading of *The Nobodies*, she laughed, calling it nonsense; but suddenly her face became grave, and she said, "If the dear old man has faith, does it matter so much as all that? Wasn't it possible to be too materialistic? If he believed, wasn't that all that mattered? Such simple faith should not be laughed at (I had not laughed), and, after all, who were we to say what might have been the Hidden Purpose in the affair? Did not God move in a Mysterious Way, His Own Way, which was not man's way?

Then I told her the story of the mysterious movement of the simple old man's donkey, which, after many years of simple work, had disappeared: and on the day following its disappearance a farmer was busy, two miles away, in the valley of Annes-well, with hauling tackle in position over one of the hillside shafts of the disused iron mines; for one of his men, happening to pass by in the bracken, had heard groans, and it was thought that a bullock had fallen down the shaft. A flaming furze bush was thrown over the edge, and the light went out; another was thrown, and that too went out. The air at the bottom of the shaft was foul, and it was not wise for a man to descend. As they were listening to the groans someone saw greyish hair on the outjutting rocks of the ragged edge of the shaft; and, examining it, they thought it was not the hair of a bullock. In the evening, the farmer called at Mr. Kift's cottage, and asked Mrs. Kift where the donkey was; and Mrs. Kift said, "My husband shute'n, and buried'n to the bottom of the garden." The farmer (who told me this story) then told her how he had been working with the hauling tackle in Anneswell, after a bullock that was supposed to have fallen in over, and to be lying at the bottom of a mine-shaft; but it wasn't bullock's hair they found, but donkey's. Mrs. Kift went upstairs to tell her husband, and returned saying, "I told'n what you said, and he jumped out of bed twice as quick as a' got into'n."

When I had recounted this story to the parson's wife, she said that he ought to have been thrown down a shaft himself, just to see how he liked it. But why? I asked her: the simple old man does not know what he is doing. The Raven, the Influenza, the destruction of the donkey too old to work, and otherwise unmarketable—surely all these things were the same thing: why then does one please as an act of simple faith, and another induce a wish for a repetition of the pain of dying slowly after being pushed over the edge of a mine-shaft?

14

One of the South Side ravens watched me from a jut of rock as I lay on the lip of the precipice, breathing the wild thyme of the sward. While I lay there in the sun two peregrines flew swiftly over the cliffs, stooping upon each other in play. I could hear the buffets of their wings as they touched in the air, crying the shrill spring chatter of joy, falling as though with wings wrapped round one another. The female was a third as big as the tiercel, or male. I hoped to see them fall upon one of the gulls, but they ignored them. Sometimes a gull left the floating, wailing throng and pursued a falcon: the sharp black wings flickered, and the gull was easily outdistanced.

The stoop, or dive, of the falcon is magnificent. He shuts his wings and dives head first at so steep an angle that it appears to be a perpendicular drop. It is not a swooping down, but a drop of a bundle of sinew, muscle, bone, and feathers compressed between the barb of wings, directed by fearless power concentrated in one terrible thing—the intentness of the eyes.

The shags on the rock below, holding out their umbrella-segment wings to dry, watched them with anxious jerks of their thin black heads.

FIRST DAY OF SPRING

After their play the falcons rose on the wind until they were six hundred feet above me, "waiting on their pitches", in the term of falconry. They remained still in the wind. The wings were bent back, sharp and dark, the head blunt, the tail thick, short, and stocky. Whereas the windhover, or kestrel, can remain still in a favourable wind by constant delicate shiftings in its leaning, the peregrine appeared to cut its hover, as it were, by suppressed force.

A little finch or pipit came fluttering in from the sea, a frail-looking thing of flight, fluttering to reach the land after its rough journey in the wind. Had it come from Lundy, or Ireland? One of the falcons tipped up, flickered blackly, *swished* down, and curved up again as though it controlled the force of gravity. The small bird struggled on, and the larger falcon stooped. She too missed. Her speed carried her, like the tiercel, almost into the waves; she swooped up without a wing-beat, and within a few seconds two black stars were motionless on their pitches again, six hundred feet above my head. I waited in dread for the struggling pipit, but after the first colossal dives they ignored it, and it fluttered to the cliff-face, and crouched on a green hummock of sea-thrift near me, its beak open as it panted.

The wind blew up the cliff, shaking old heads of sea-thrift; the pipit began to preen its wing feathers; the black stars, with never a flicker, turned down the wind and slid across the sky and out of sight along the North Side. The shags on their white rock below seemed easier; a general preening of neck-feathers began, shaking of tails, and flapping of wings. A bird squatting on a higher pinnacle, apart from the others, continued to cock an anxious eye at the sky. The raven sat still and huddled on his scaur; the lower part of his body was hidden by rock, but his eye saw all that moved. One of the shags jumped off into the wind, swung round, and beat its big black wings steadily over the sea, just above the troughs of the waves. Another launched itself into the wind, flying towards Cryde Bay, followed by a third and a fourth, while a strange cormorant appeared flying down the wind to the rock; it slowed into the wind, alighted on a perch just quitted, and opened its wings. Its head seemed rather large, and looking through my glass I saw that it had caught a flatfish, which it could not swallow. It opened its wings and gulped, half ejected the fish, and gulped again; then settled down with the tail sticking out, waiting until there was more space in its crop.

On the sward lie many small white feathers of gulls; and, among the broken hummocks of the sea-thrift, which cover the headland with pink, wind-trembling flowers in May, are fragments of blue shells, crab-claws bleached white, fish bones, and sometimes a rabbit bone, thrown out of the crops of the gulls which rest here when no human figures move into the sky above their green slopes.

15

While I sat there on the grass and the thyme which I shall love forever because I learnt to know it first in the *Story* of my dear Jefferies, an animal was lying near me. It had, for some reason possibly not known even to itself, made almost the same journey as I had made since leaving the village. Half the time it had been digging in a hole in the ground, tearing at grass and thrift roots with its teeth, throwing out earth between its hind legs, which often were the only portion of it visible; the other half it had been lying, panting, shaggy with earth, twenty paces away, watching me with its yellow eyes.

For years it had been walking where I had walked, usually uninvited; for years it had been living in my house, and sleeping in my chairs when it did not choose to sleep in another chair in another cottage which for a night or two had taken its fancy.

It spent most of its days lying outside the cottage, usually in the middle of the road, curled up in cold weather and lying on its side in hot weather, now in the ditch to cool, and now in the sun to get warm again—a dozen changes each sunlit hour. Motor cars came down the lane; their brakes suddenly squealed, and I would hear them pulling up; I knew then that the animal was comfortable, if not asleep. Often the car passed over the brown hairy circle, which might then raise a weary head and stare bemusedly at the rear number plate, before settling on paws again, having decided that the exhaust note was unfamiliar, and so no chance of a free ride was probable.

When the numerous dinner-smells moved about the village airs it would get up and trot away; but before the church clock struck twice it would be back again in the road, awaiting the rattle of the loose lock on the front door. Hearing that noise, its head would lift alertly; and if it saw a figure or figures, the animal was liable to stretch and yawn, especially if it saw a stick; and if certain that the figure was going out for a walk, and not merely to the shop or the pub, it would jump on its hind legs and flack its tongue with the excitation of its thoughts.

It had been behaving like this for eight years now, ever since it followed me, after thirty shillings had changed pockets, from the blacksmith's steps in Cryde village to my cottage in Ham. Although only eight weeks old at the time, it was "lousy as a cuckoo", as my neighbour Revvy observed on its arrival; now it was eight years old almost to the day, and still lousy as a cuckoo. Periodically it was deloused, a process which made it whine and shiver; and periodically Mother Nature, "ever providing for her own", alloused it again. To observant visitors, arriving during one of the provident periods, it would be explained that it "picks up insects from the sheep in the fields".

Every year I had paid 7s. 6d. so that this animal might continue to sleep in my chairs, to eat the bones that fell from my table, to bark at cats and unfamiliar figures, to act as a pony to my son and other village children, to provide a mattress for the cat and her kittens on cold winter nights, to be a half-wit companion for myself during my walks. I had been told that when I left the village the animal waited and watched in the lanes until I should return, although the period of waiting and watching might be several months. This always seemed to me to be an extraordinary service in return for a few bones and biscuits, a chair which it could, and did, get elsewhere, an original deposit of thirty shillings, a leather collar with brass studs, and occasional motor rides on the floor under someone's feet.

As I sat there on the edge of the precipice, watching the bright flicker of waves on far sky-meeting sea, I marvelled that this animal should be, to many men and women and children, but to one in particular, so single-minded, so jovial, so selfless in its devotion: and when I considered that often I was careless and unkind, in my moodiness and irritability; that if I spoke harshly to it the brightness went from its eyes, and the straightness from its back; and yet at a releasing word, no matter how incomprehensible the harshness, its whole being would light up and dance with gratitude; and when I consider, moreover, that I have an immortal soul according to the Church, and this animal has none . . .

But enough of idle thoughts! It is time to move on.

16

The wailing of gulls increased as my dog and I moved up the sloping grass. By which way should I return? The regular South Side path, cut in the slope above the break of the cliffs, led to Cryde Bay; but I remembered that dogs were forbidden on the path. It would be more pleasant on the higher path, beside the stone wall at the top of the down, guarding the fields from the winds and furze and brambles of the waste land.

Like most of the walls built on high places, this wall was beautiful with lichens. Where it met the full force of the Atlantic wind its base was fortified by clusters of sea-thrift, in clumps of green strength or brown ruin according to age. The southwest wind had driven the seeds of the thrift into the crevices between the stones, from which the earth originally binding them had long since been scoured, and there they had sprouted, to explore the inner earth with their long tentacle roots. Rabbits dig tunnels in the wall, but their holes are not numerous in the length built above the Point: this is the home of the thrift roots, and, on the higher stones, of the grey-green lichens which flourish best in the salty driven spume.

Along the wall, where it turned inland, beside the green path in the furze, the grey lichens changed to orange-yellow disks spreading flat on the grey stone; the clumps of sea-thrift were seen only occasionally. Foxglove plants grow in the southern ditch, their dry summer stalks leaning out of leaves dark green and eager with new life. The wall was topped with slabs of stone which were bonded and kept in place by a layer of soil; and on this soil lived the poorest plants, which all their lives must struggle to be themselves in the place where their seeds were lodged by wind or birds. Here was a sow-thistle which, had the wind rolled the seed over the wall, might have grown as high and straight as my little boy; but it was lodged in a crevice between two stones, and there it must live, there it must make its seeds, and there it must die. Every wind scoured more earth from the crack, every rain washed more rootlets bare, but it hung on, although the gusts shook it and wore away its minute leaves. The tap-root that held it was fibrous like string; the leaves, no larger than the wings of a wasp, had turned purple, the colour of last hope, to absorb more of the vital sun-rays. A rabbit had eaten half the "milky dashel" in one bite. Milky dashel, milky thistle, is the name given it by village boys, who seek the sow-thistle in the hedges for their tame rabbits; its sap is white. There the poor milky dashel endured, one of the hopelessly unfit of the dashel or thistle tribe, waiting to put forth its yellow bloom in the spring.

Seeing its human equivalent, what would be our thoughts? Of the poor thistle, I know this: there was no destitution in the seed when it was lodged there.

17

Over the wall was a goyal, or valley, with a gaunt farmhouse standing near the sky. By striking across the fields I should come to Cryde by the sunken lanes, and so avoid the boarding-houses of the bay, with their names like Lorna Doone and Belle Vue.

I climbed over the wall, and crossed the valley. After climbing several gates, and passing along hedges, I came to the first lane, called Middlesborough. It was the width of a horse-butt, and its stony bottom was also the bed of a brook, which ran fast and shallow and very clear. A fine walk to bring a beloved, whose feet must be kept dry. The water fills the lane for two hundred paces, four hundred if burdened, and, farther on, it is very wild and lovely with rushes and brooklime. There it joins its brother of the Middlehill, also secret and sunken between high mixed hedges of ash, elm, thorn, and oak. Thence it slopes gently down for a mile, wandering crookedly, making a three-way junction with Ramson and Broadhill Lanes.

At the join the base of the lane was deep under the hedges; and at the beginning of Ramson Lane, which leads uphill to the Ramson fields I had passed on my outward journey, a carter standing in a butt could scarcely touch the overarching branches above with his whip.

The lane was sunken deep between the fields. It was dark even on the brightest summer day. The tracks of sled runners and butt wheels were worn a hand-span deep in the soft yellow rock, and the iron shoe-tips of horses had grooved a rugged trough between them. Water ran in both wheel and foot tracks, smoothing and abrading them with its everlasting patience. Walking up the green tunnel I could see in the sides of the lane no mark of pick or blasting bar; the stratum was of shale shillets, and the walls so straight that it was hard to believe that sled and wheel and water alone had cut so deeply into the rock.

Beyond the tunnel the sun was hot on my face, and the rock was warm. I sat down, and leaned on my elbow, letting the earth bear me as it would, letting all thought float away as the gossamers gleaming in the gentle ambient air. The thorns matted on the blue sky were still as the dry bleached grasses entangling their exposed roots: so silent and quiet the sunlit air that the cough and whistle of a bird flying over the lane two fields away

told quicker than sight that the bird was a wild rock pigeon.
Here the primroses were large and warm—always they were big
in this lane—and I saw in my mind a thin wizened little man,
with a bunch of primroses in his hand, a little man with grey
hair and small face, with the sharp nose and eyes of a poet; a
poet ruined by some inner drought. He used to be seen about
the village, talking rapidly to whomsoever would listen to him,
wearing a short black cape over his thin shoulders, with a small
close-fitting tweed cap of a previous century on his small head.
Several times we met in the village, and after a few brief words
I made to pass on, but he seemed eager to talk; I stayed, although
I did not want to listen to him: no grain in his words, only
chaff.

One day—it was soon after the War, during the great
drought—he met me coming down Ramson Lane. I frowned
to see him in the lane here, waiting for me, as I came down from
the headland. He was a bore; he broke into your reverie with a
vehement declaration about whatsoever he was, not very
coherently, thinking at the moment. He enquired, with gesticu-
lations, and many jerky pointings of his ebony stick, my opinion
on the origin of the sunken lane. Was it not most curious? He
had been much puzzled by it: no one in the village seemed to
know anything about their own country. Why so deep at the
junction? Had I considered that problem? Had I? Had the idea
of smuggling presented itself to me? What? Cover from the spy-
glasses of revenue men on Middlesborough Hill, what? Wasn't
it feasible? Would I care to use the idea in a novel of adventure?
He would present me with the idea: my imagination must do
the rest. Well, all my imagination did was to want to avoid him:
I was not pleased to see him, and he must have known it from
my face. I hurried away from him, leaving him staring after me.
I remember that the primroses were wilting in his grasp.

He did not find anyone with whom he could talk and ease his
mind of its scorched and congested thoughts; a little queer in
the head, it was said, and so he was avoided. Once he invited me
to tea, and I made the excuse of work. No one called to see him

in his cottage near the sea, he was shabby and insignificant; and when he died of a nervous malady soon afterwards, no one in the village went to his funeral. For some years now he had been forgotten: I did not know why he had risen in my mind to-day, when the air was so warm and still, and the living water glistened on the rock, and the sun shone on grass and tree and flower and all happy living things. Little sharp-nosed man, lonely hedge-peerer, I thought, come you out of the darkness, and I will listen to you.

18

I left the village of Cryde by the bend in the road where stood its newest boarding-house, until last year the water-mill which had ground corn during four hundred years; past Fig Tree Farm, a whitewashed building beside the road, before which grew a fig-tree with two grey trunks bound and held together by linked iron bands, a Samson of a tree, contorted with the struggle for freedom, which had sunk the rusty iron into its limbs, while with its roots it strove to heave up the walls and stone floors of the house; past the Baptist Chapel where the two men fishing for eels on Good Friday had found salvation; past the strange apparition of the jawbone of an ox hanging in the hedge, supported by intertwining vines of honeysuckle and bearded with moss about its yellow teeth; past the cottage of the parish nurse, brightened with blue paint; past the hollow interior of the pump-shed, papered with bills announcing auctions, circuses, and political meetings; past the row of cottages which formed the hamlet of Cross—but I had to stop in the middle of the row, and speak to Grannie Parsons. She was peeping out of the door of her cottage like a jenny wren out of its nest. The cottage was in the middle of the row; it was the smallest cottage in the parish. It began at the door above three steps, then came a tiny window beside the door; and that was all. It was scarcely so long as a horse-butt. It had one room downstairs, and one "up auver"; and a raised garden under the window of the living-room, about one yard square, enclosed by stone ditching. No garden so neat as Grannie Parsons' garden, which had been dug to-day, by the look of it: one wallflower, one sweet-william, one pink, a border of saxi-frage, and, in the midsummer heat, seven great scarlet poppies —that was her garden. Nodding and smiling, with the shyness of a young maid, Grannie Parsons, in her soft voice, tells me "tes proper weather, midear, tes butiful weather, and the li'l grass-bird be back by the stream".

So Grannie Parsons, whose children have long since grown up and flown away, heard it this morning—the little grass-bird —the chiff-chaff, the celandine among birds, whose plain-song is so precious as it comes hopefully over the border of winter; and Grannie Parsons called me midear, a usual term of greeting, but truly a thing of sweetness and light when spoken, scarcely more than whispered, from the small brown face, with the bright eyes, and smiling withered lips. All the beauty I had known that day: of wandering air and bright water, the white innocence of thorns, the scent of wild thyme on the headland, the happy burr of the honey bee, the sunward lark-song, the glistening, flowery constellations and red plastic mud of windy spring: all the beauty of the day was fused and made one for me.

It seemed that I came home to my village very swiftly.

19

As I walked round the corner of Church Street, I heard sing-ing. The Lower House stood at the corner; and on the threshold I saw the landlord, leaning against the wall, smoking, an amused expression on his face. He was watching a group of people down by Hole Farm. "Something going on," he observed laconically, and spat beside his dog, the badger-digging terrier, known as the Mad Mullah.

Thunderbolt Willie, the retired dairy farmer, was there, standing by the stream, leaning one elbow on the wall of a cottage garden: his wife stood outside her gate, talking to a neighbour: the white face of Bessie, her sister-in-law, peered round the gateway. Several children stood in the road, watching the singing stranger.

"Some tramp, I reckon," said John Kift, coming round the corner. "He came zinging outside my place, but I told'n to get out. Some tale about starving, but us'v all heard that yarn before, I reckon. You've got to look out for yourself these days, or you'd soon be nowhere at all. Noomye!"

I walked down. A bell tinkled behind me, and a man passed on a bicycle. I had passed the same man by the blacksmith's shop, holding a book and pencil in his hand, and speaking earnestly to the blacksmith.

As I went by the doleful singing, I saw, in a quick covert glance, a man in a worn grey suit too large for him, with a muffler round his unshaven chin. His boots were too long, and of a light pattern known as dress-boots, with buttons, and cracked across the toe-cap. The heels had dropped off. The man was singing a hymn, or the first verse of a hymn; but as I went by he stopped, muttered to himself, and turned away.

Beggars rarely come to the village of Ham.

Mrs. Vanderbilt Willy moved towards me, half confidentially. "Who is he, d'you know?" she whispered. "Do you think he is all right? What a voice! Like a crow's, isn't it? My word, he's hoarse. I shouldn't think he gets very much, should you? Of course one can never tell whether they are genuine or not, can you? There are so many strange characters going about to-day. And whoever can that be, talking to Bessie?"

The man with the notebook and pencil had leant his bicycle against the wall, and was speaking to her sister-in-law. Bessie turned her ear to hear, and I heard her mumble doubtfully, as her pale face moved in negation, "Oh, I can't say for sure. No, I don't think so, not to-day, thank you."

"But, do you realize, madam, that if this monstrous new text is passed through Parliament it is definitely a step towards Rome?"

The last words, poured out earnestly, were cut off by the angle of the barn. I entered my cottage, and sat down to tea with my

wife and son; I was raising my teacup, with a sigh of contentment, when I saw the tramp pause outside in the lane. He
looked at the cottage doubtfully, then up the lane; walked away
a few slow steps, then returned, and began to sing again. The
same hymn:

Onward, Christian Soldiers, marching as to war.

"What a rokken ol' noise," said my little boy.

"Rotten it is," I agreed.

"Wha' for is it a rokken noise, Dad?"

"Ah, the causes are beyond your understanding."

"Wha' for?"

"Oh, shut up."

"Who, me up-up?"

"Yes."

"Wha' for?"

"John Kift, his belly full of cabbage and rabbit, said the man
had told him he was starving," I told my wife. "And that he had
heard that tale before."

"Wha' for the man 'e tol' Jan Kift starvin', Mum?"

"He's probably had no dinner and no tea, dear," said my
wife, smoothing the little boy's hair.

"Wha' for 'at man 'e 'ad no tea?"

A bicycle wheel moved across the open gateway, and stopped.
The singing also stopped. The cyclist in the dark suit walked
quickly up the path, and knocked at the door.

"Good afternoon," he said, looking at me through his
rimless glasses. Past his head, I saw the hymn-singer moving
away.

"Don't go away," I shouted. "Half a minute!"

The shabby figure hesitated. "Wait a minute!" I called again,
and looked at the dark-suited man before me.

He wore a clipped brown moustache, and his face was thin;
his brown eyes, small and inscrutable, were fixed on mine.

"Would you please add your name to my list, protesting
against the introduction of the New Prayer Book?" he said.

"Every one is of vital importance if we want to retain the authentic and authorised version of our Prayer Book."

"I really do not know much about the controversy," I said, "and so my name, if I wrote it in your book, would have no real spiritual value."

After hesitation, the shabby figure in the lane was moving on again.

"Ah, but surely you cannot regard with complacency the changes which are threatened, which, in effect, are the most insidious—"

I replied, feeling suddenly tired, "Why not two Prayer Books? It will give a little variety to children who, forced to go to church, are like dogs awaiting their masters in the street, *always* on the look-out for something interesting to happen. Just think—"

"It is hardly a subject for cynicism," he replied. "It is very real, if only you knew. Do you realize, sir, that this New Prayer Book is definitely a step—"

"Towards Rome? Yes, I heard you. And really, you must forgive me repeating it, but I don't care what happens to the Prayer Book. Oh, damn—he's gone away, and I wanted to give him some tea. Would you like some tea?"

He put the book back into his pocket. "No, thank you," he said coldly, and turned away.

"You see, I'm not a churchman," I explained, as he lifted his bicycle around. "I quite understand how you feel about it, and am sorry if I am unsympathetic, but—well—I believe that the letter killeth. Come in and have some tea, won't you."

"It is to Another you must make your explanations. Good afternoon," he replied, and mounting his bicycle, he pedalled away.

A small figure, wearing bib and holding biscuit, appeared by my side. "'At poor man with bikkerkull, 'e wouldn't 'ave no tea, where be'n tu (to), Dad?" enquired my son.

"I'm afraid I hurt his feelings," I replied. "So you see I am no good really."

"Wha' for no gude, Dad?"

"I want to find the singing man."

"That poor singin' man, where be'n tu (to), Dad? Can 'e have my bikky, 'at poor man 'e didn't have no dinner and no tea, Dad? Where be'n tu?"

"Gone."

"Wha' for?"

"Fed up."

"Oh."

I listened. I heard the curt, rather loud tones of Mr. Bullcornworthy, the policeman.

"Dad, wull 'e come and play trains and tar ingines with me?"

"No."

"Wha' for? Where be ee guin, Dad?"

Walking round the corner by Hole Farm, I saw the village policeman speaking to the tramp. Several more children were there now; and John Kift, the man who would not shoot a raven. Vanderbilt Willy still leant against the wall: his wife, having moved to someone else in order to discuss the event, was watching too, her eyes alert with curiosity.

"You get out of it," said the policeman, "and look smart about it, my lad."

The tramp, who had a long-drawn hollow scar in his cheek, said something bitter about the reward of fighting for his country, and the policeman said, in a more threatening voice, "I don't want no answers from you! Just you clear out sharp, while you've got the chance."

Thrusting hands in pockets, the tramp gave us all a scornful glance, and walked away up the hill.

"Too many of they bliddy rogues, who won't work, about the country," exclaimed John Kift, after the silence in which the tramp was watched round the corner. "On the dole, I reckon. Come out from Town to see what they can pick up."

"Well, I mean to say, you never know, do you?" said Mrs. Vanderbilt Willy, half confidentially, moving over to us. "That's the trouble, you can never tell the genuine man looking for work from the man who might be a burglar. I didn't like the look of his eyes: if you noticed—I don't know whether you noticed it, but I did—his eyes never looked you in the face, but kept mostly on the ground. They say you can never trust a man whose eyes won't look at yours, don't they? I think there's something in it, myself. Now that man with the Prayer Book petition, he could look you fair and square in the eyes. Did you sign your name?" she turned to me.

I told her, No, I did not sign my name.

"I did; but Bessie wouldn't: nor would Will." Her voice lowered and became entirely confidential. "Will's very timid about signing his name, you know. They say the Rector and that man had the greatest argument. In fact, they say the Rector shouted at him. 'Get out of here!' he cried. The Rector feels very strongly about having the New Prayer Book, so they say. D'you believe it?"

"No."

"You don't believe it?"

"No."

"What don't you believe then?"

"What you say."

"Dad!" cried a voice from my cottage. "Come on in yurr, and have 'or tea, wull 'ee come?"

As I went back, the low rays of the sinking sun dazed my eyes; and suddenly I remembered the longcripple's mate on the shard of red earthenware under the wall of the barn. Among the old nettle stalks it was lying, battered and broken by stones.

21 March 1928

Chapter Five

"MUGGY"

From the high ground of Ox's Cross many hundreds of fields were to be seen, covering the slopes of the hills like a far-lying patchwork of irregular green and brown pieces stitched together with thick dark wool; some fields bright with sunlight, others dull under distant clouds. Most of these fields, varying in extent from a rood to twenty acres, were enclosed by wide banks of earth and stone, topped with hedges of beech, ash, thorn, elm, furze, and bramble.

In every one of these banks were many holes; they were tunnelled from gate to gate. Few of the tunnels were straight or level. They rose and fell and twisted round inner pieces of rock. Each system had several outlet and inlet holes, with one or more bolt holes used only in panic, hidden by the grass and the plants on the bank.

Sometimes the rabbits which scratched out these systems, called buries, caused the earth and stones of the banks to fall down; when sheep and cattle trod the breaks into gaps, and wandered from their rightful pasture. The rabbits nibbled the roots of turnip, mangle, and rape; they ate the young corn, the clover, the cabbages, the peas; they dug for potatoes, and rasped the bark of fruit trees. They multiplied rapidly—a doe having five or six litters a year, with five or six young to each litter.

Part of the area of these fields, which came by gates to narrow lanes leading past farms and hamlets to the roadways, were traversed from October to February by a Ford van, loaded with rectangular wicker baskets, each bearing two stout hazel-wood bars on which were strung the crossed hindlegs of dead rabbits— a hindleg being thrust between the bone and sinew of the other. The van usually stopped at the cottages of trappers, and other places where rabbits were collected. The collector got down from beside the driver, examined the rabbits, selected what he would take, weighed them on a spring balance, and bought them by weight. The price in a normal season varied from $5\frac{1}{2}d$. to $7d$. a pound, including the skin.

In his round the buyer was regular and punctual, and if he knew he would change his time he sent post-cards to the trappers, who were busy men. The rabbits, which were sent by train to one of the largest Midland factory cities, must be slightly injured—that is, caught by the forepaws only. A rabbit trapped by the hindlegs often strips the flesh in its struggles, and is not marketable. In five months the van carried rabbits to the value of £6,000; that is, between 120,000 and 150,000 rabbits were sent away in the wicker baskets. It is possible that another 40,000 were caught during this period, but buzzards and crows "break abroad" some of them by day, the fox and the badger take them by night. Many were trapped lightly by the forepaw, and escaped. Indeed, one rabbit in five packed in the basket had a forepaw already missing.

In the village there were several trappers. One of them paid for the trapping rights of a farm by giving so many weeks' labour to the farmer in summer. A good trapper visited his gins at daybreak and in the evening, but some went along their banks only three times in a week, having other work to do. During the first hours of its agony of struggling a rabbit fills the night with crying; but terror and pain, long-borne with hunger and perhaps the beating of rain and wind, bring the ease of little-knowing.

Besides the regular trappers, there were farmers who held from seven to ten or twenty acres of land, and kept two or three cows, with a sow and her farrow. Sometimes they brought home a couple of rabbits, taken in their half-dozen rusty gins tilled for rat or rabbit, or shot in the early morning, or caught by the dog at dimmity. The "bad ones" they ate themselves; others might be offered at the doors of one or the other of the bungalows or small modern houses built since the Great War in and around the village. Those unsold rabbits were hung up until an old man called "Muggy Smith of Cryde" knocked with his stick on the door, standing there with a basket.

"Good morning to you, ma'm. Any rabbuts to-day, please? Thank you very much." It may be "Good morning, midear. I hope you'm very well. Will you please to ask your mother if she has any rabbut skins? I'm paying three ha'pence to-day—rabbut skins is come back." Or, "Rabbut skins is gone up—I'm giving tuppence to-day, if you please. That's right, ma'm, thank you very much."

Between the two villages he walked slowly, giving a cheery good day to all he met on the way. Sometimes he had a joke to tell, or a riddle to ask. "Now, sir, let me ask you a question, please. Can you tell me what it is that is longer when cut off at both ends? I am asking you a plain question, if you please. Just listen to what I be asking, if you please. What is it that grows longer when cut off at the ends? That's it, if you can answer me."

The riddle may have been asked before, and Muggy forgotten; but no matter. As with his other riddle ("Why did Gladstone wear yellow braces?" "To keep his trousers up, if you please, sir. That's it!") the answer must not be known.

"'Tis a grave," said Muggy, moving away; and stopping, to explain that "in his kid days" he saw a coffin lowered in Ham churchyard, but coming to rest on the eastern and western edges, so that it had to be dug longer while the mourners waited around the pit. "Yes, sir. That be the explanation. Good day, sir."

He had no remarks or comments to offer on the actions of other people, and was not concerned with your own. "I don't want to know your own business, midear. No, sir. 'Tis no concern of mine what other volks be doing of. I don't want to know their business."

He was born at the inn below the sharp turn of the road, which stood opposite the club-room steps where he used to rest, perched above the stream; but as a young man he sold the inn, and went to America, coming back to end his days in the village. For some years when first I knew him he had a shanty in the corner of a hillside field, which he reached by climbing the "ditched" wall on juts of stone. The shanty was as tall as himself, but not much longer or wider than a coffin. His bed was a shelf, and he cooked on an oil stove covered with soot, as the stones of the ditched wall outside were covered with moss. His larder was a box on a post; the rats raided it regularly, once gnawing a way into the precious food within. Beside the larder was his letter-box. In the shanty he shaved and washed and ate, kept his accounts with the rabbit collector, wrote his occasional letters, stored his rabbit skins; until the local sanitary authorities found and condemned it.

He migrated to the village up the valley, renting in Ham a two-roomed cot for £3 a year. But after a year the landlord "rose the rent" another £1, and Muggy, whose income from rabbits and their skins, telegram tips, water-cress and crabs in summer, could not meet this increase, had to move. He made a room in a cottage opposite, long since disused as a dwelling, wherein sacks of artificial manure, faggots, and garden tools were kept by the landlord of the Higher House.

His journeys between the two villages began to take longer, his jokes and riddles were rarer; but his cheerful courtesy brightened the wayside. Everyone knew Muggy, and was sure of him—no casting of eyes on the road or the hedge, awaiting the unsure and awkward moment of glancing up, and acknowledging that it was a fine day, or what dirty weather we were having, or that it looked like more rain. "Muggy Smith of Cryde" was plain as a field was plain, plough, arrish, or pasture; a rare and simple being, warped to no property, true to himself, and therefore to all men. Shakespeare would have loved him.

Four years after the above was written, my old friend Muggy Smith of Cryde fell down and died as he was going into his cot, at the age of 75 years. During his life he asked me frequently not to omit, when I "put him in the book", the facts that he was "proper wild" as a young man, and a great brandy drinker, which had resulted in the loss of the freehold inn owned by his forefathers, and his wanderings round the world; and that he had "conquered his craving". And I am sure Muggy would have been the first to laugh at the joke of his own funeral in August, 1929, when his coffin could not be lowered into its grave because it was too long.

Chapter Six

ON SCANDAL, GOSSIP, HYPOCRISY OR SELF-DECEPTION, ROGUERY, AND SENESCENCE

I

The tales which passed on the tongues of the village people rarely gained or lost in the telling. The plain narrative was told as it was heard. After twenty minds had taken it in and given it out again, it remained almost the same. There may be several reasons, or a combination of reasons, for this. Lack of imagination, this faculty not having been used for inward self-searching; fear of being found out; or because most of them were naturally factful where their money was not concerned. Much of the gossip was "news", which usually moved in a circular path, returning to the subject of it.

That the tales passed unvarying did not always mean that they were true. Some of the stories might have been started by someone incapable, through the shallowness of personal experience or intuition, of understanding the motives of others. Thus all stories of others are steeped with the quality of the originator; but how infrequently is this recognized! Too often the facts of the story are not strung with the spirit of their origin; the motives of others are not taken into account, causing distress to the sensitive. To an intelligent and impartial listener, a story going around reveals only the quality of mind of the first speaker, just as what a man writes about his neighbours reveals his own quality and nature.

The ordinary villager did not like to express an original opinion unless he or she was certain others would agree. This timidity led to the rows that frequently occurred: when timid natures gave way. But before the row, a man might begin with the words, "They say," and a woman with "You know what they be saying up in the village? 'Tis awful what they do tell about. They be masterpieces for scandal. There's no saying what they'll be saying next. They say that—," and then followed the story.

It does not need much intelligence to see the beam in a neighbour's eye, especially if a beam of similar size and nature inhabits your own. Indeed, having a beam yourself, you are made the more aware, and thereby the more irritated, by the presence of other people's beams. The beam of gossip is a most subtle one to pluck out and hold with the tweezers of truth. Are not all things relative; as many worlds as there are pairs of eyes serving the interiors of skulls? Sometimes, however, the intangible issue of Truth may be escaped by humour. Such a case occurred in the village during the time I lived there.

One Sunday morning the Rector preached a sermon on this very subject of gossip. The subtlety of cause and effect, the influences of remote aversions and complexes, which may have had their share in the original spite, were not touched upon, but only what he termed the "malicious effect of thoughtless scandal". The Rector, I knew, was suffering from some himself, and felt it keenly. Being full of trenchant generalization, it was considered a good sermon, and nearly all those who heard it were confirmed in their righteous dislike of their neighbour's shortcomings. It was talked about all the week, and the next Sunday the congregation awaited with interest another such sermon. It happened to be the Sunday when the local company of the County Territorial regiment held their annual Church Parade.

ON SCANDAL, GOSSIP, HYPOCRISY, ETC.

The Rector had something direct to say about another unpleasant aspect of village life. It appeared that a lady visitor to the village during the past week had told him that never in all her experience of English village life had she seen so much drunkenness as existed in the village of Ham. The Rector said that if "things did not improve, some people might find themselves within the arm of the law".

It made a sensation; the good people knew whom he meant. Albert Hancock, landlord of the Higher House, was a regular churchman in his neat blue serge suit, and after morning service he called upon Mr. Taylor of the Lower House. Mr. Taylor did not go to church; Sunday for him being the day when he could lie up a bit extra. Indeed, after a jovial Saturday night, he had just got out of bed. Together the two publicans, with the village constable, and some of the regular customers of the two inns, led by John Brown of Crowcombe Farm, called on the Rector. John Brown said, with respect, that he represented the considered opinion of those present with him, if his reverence would excuse him saying so. He wished to say, with all respect, that the sermon preached by his reverence the previous Sunday, dealing with malicious gossip and the evil effects of a thoughtless word, had made such an impression on them that he felt he would like to suggest that the observations of a visitor, after staying but three days in the village, might possibly fall within the meaning of the word gossip. He hoped his reverence would excuse him for telling what his reverence probably knew already, that his remarks in church would be in the local paper next Thursday, that many of the Territorials in church, strangers from Combe, Town, and Cross Tree, would carry away a bad impression of the parish; and the constable would be asked by his sergeant why the alleged drunkenness had not been reported. Men had a glass or two sometimes at night, and they sang a song sometimes, but the charge of general drunkenness seemed to him, a rough-and-ready man, without education, to come precisely within the meaning of the term scandal.

The Rector, a man of courage, who was then new to the

parish from a London suburb, apologized during the evening service for what, he said, he then knew to be an unfounded charge; but he had made it in all good faith, and for the good of the village, as he hated trouble, and looked upon them all as good children of God. He did not say (and he may not have known) how the nervous tissue of the complaining spinster lady visitor—another from the suburbs of London—had been wrought upon by her interpretations of what she thought was actuality when, walking down Stony Hill on the Saturday night preceding, silently on rubber soles, she had passed between two lines of men standing with faces to the ditched walls on either side of the lane, where no nettles or other weeds could grow. One of the men—it was Willy Gammon—was singing; others were talking loudly, and sometimes there was a word that had a meaning in a town different from its jovial everyday use in the country. It was a few minutes after ten o'clock, and the men had just come out of the Higher House.

What were natural acts were thought to be "vile and beastly" in the good woman's mind, and out of her reaction and indignation—without thought—she had made her charges against the village. By her words had she revealed her limitations. In the Higher House they understood, and were not angry with her; but it is doubtful if she will ever understand the Higher House.

2

The Rector himself was well-meaning and sincere, and yet his very sincerity seemed at times, like acid, to corrode the silver tongue of tact. There was, for example, the disharmony over the Church School. The Church School was governed by Managers, elected for life by the Church Council: the Rector was the chief Manager or Chairman. The Managers, whose office was honorary, were personally responsible for what was spent, or overspent, out of the School Funds. At a meeting the Rector declared that alterations were needed in the school building: the windows, except for a small area, were fixed, and should be made to open; the sanitation should be improved; drinking water should be laid on, and a dining-room added.

"We agree," said the Managers—including Colonel Ponde, Admiral Bamfylde, and Mr. Furze—"that such work would improve the school, but we cannot at this moment authorize the spending of more than one pound one shilling and twopence, which is the bank balance of the School account."

The Rector said that the Board of Education had written that the work was necessary, and further, both the Diocesan Authorities and the Bishop had urged that the school be improved according to the requirements of the State.

"One fully appreciates the necessity for the work, Rector," said the cool voice of Lady Maude Seeke, the Manager whose horticultural work in the old churchyard was occasionally praised in the Rector's *Monthly Bulletin*. "But surely we should not undertake any work until we have the money to pay for it?"

"It is good of you to infer that your Rector is unaware of the business side of life," replied the parson. He had been anticipating opposition, and this had made him feel unwell; he was a Londoner, with a hard struggle for education and advancement behind him; he was therefore inclined to impatience with those whose ease in life, and grace of manners, came from the possession of inherited wealth; and so his manner was different from the amiable imperturbability he admired in others.

"It is a question of our simple duty as Managers," said Colonel Ponde. "Can we spend money, as Managers, that we do not possess?"

"Very well," replied the Rector, with pursed lips, "I can only say I am sorry you do not appreciate the crying necessity for protecting the little children who are in our care."

The next day the Rector, after solitary prayer before the altar, wrote a letter ordering the work to be done. Hearing of this, the Managers resigned. The Rector called a Churchpeople's meeting in the Schoolroom. As he entered he saw Colonel Ponde sitting there. Immediately he felt weak and unwell. Colonel Ponde and his family had recently forsaken the Church and gone to the Chapel in Cryde, after other disagreements with the Rector.

"Be careful, Captain Ponde!" cried the Rector. "I warn you that anything you say against me may lead to an action for libel."

"I have come here to tell the meeting why the School Managers resigned," replied Colonel Ponde.

Ignoring him, the Rector explained that he had discovered "in an old book" that the period of office for the School Managers was three years, and not for life. Therefore, new Managers were to be elected.

"Now I will tell you the truth why the Managers have resigned," cried Colonel Ponde. "It is because the Rector ignores the Board of Managers; because he is, furthermore, discourteous to the Board, and discourtesy is a form of untruth!" Thereupon Colonel Ponde arose and left the meeting.

The Rector then explained that the Managers were ignoring the teaching of Jesus, who said that little children and their needs must come first in life, before any other questions of money or red tape. The Rector's wife went home arm-in-arm with the Rector after the meeting.

In the next issue of his *Monthly Bulletin* the Rector tried again.

My dear Friends,

I have not felt quite well for some time, and so when this letter reaches you I shall be away in Bonny Scotland to recoup. The Rev. F. Merryweather, like a good friend, has kindly offered to take charge of the parish during my absence, and the Bishop has graciously accepted his kind offer.

On October 16th Health Week commences, and we shall think of the blessings of health and how to preserve them.

In November comes Armistice Day, when we must meet to honour the brave dead, especially those of our own village.

We are a busy folk in this village, loyal, kindly, and neighbourly. True neighbourliness is helped by constant worshipping together, forgetting the things that are not important, and thanking God with contentment for the blessings he showers upon all alike—creation, preservation, redemption, means of grace and hope of glory. The things that matter bring us close together, and make us one in God through Christ.

"O Lord how happy should we be, If we could cast our care on Thee, If we from self could rest."

This expresses a happy thought for the Autumn, and we should be happy. We are, are we not?

The Harvest Gifts in Church were kindly conveyed by Lady Maude Seeke to Barum Infirmary on Monday, September 19th, and the Rector received a p.c. on Tuesday expressing the Matron's most grateful thanks to the people of Ham and Cryde. I hope you have all observed how very beautiful the flowers in the Churchyard are this autumn; we are truly fortunate in Our Lady Bountiful.

The School Managers were very cross and severe with the Rector because he had not consulted them before putting the repairs of the School in the hands of the architects. The Rector submitted to all their harshness because they could not understand him, but he resented the unwarrantable criticism of one of the Managers who is not a Churchman nor at all interested in the Church School. What is the situation? The Rector accepted the command of the State through the Board of Education to carry out the plans for the betterment of the children. The Managers refused to comply, therefore the Rector had to act alone. The Diocesan Authorities and the Bishop pressed the Rector to stand up for the Church and improve the School according to the State's requirements. In loyalty to his Country, his Church, and the welfare of the children, the Rector took full responsibility and gave the order for the work to be done. The Managers at their meeting entered in the minutes that the Rector accepted full financial responsibility, therefore no liability rests upon the Managers. To save the injured feelings of the Managers the Rector undertook not to spend any more on the School than the money raised at our recent Harvest Tea. This means that the children are to wait for the dining-room and the fresh supply of drinking water until the money is in hand. Let us get it and finish the work. If the children are poor, ought they not to have a place to sit down where to eat their food instead of the stuffy class-room where they have been at lessons all the morning? Shall they not have a drink of water at hand instead of rushing down to the pump in all weathers? It is the little ones who need watchful care, the elder children can take care of themselves. It is a disgrace to the village to see the children rushing about regardless of the weather, eating their food like the chickens. They do not act so at home. Many of them catch colds, have to stop at home to be nursed, and so the average attendance is reduced, and poor mother suffers. What for? For the simple reason the School has not safeguarded the children's health by giving them a place to sit and eat comfortably like civilized beings. It is so easy to blame the Parson.

The Managers stated that the masons of the parish are deeply offended because they were not asked to tender for the mason's work in the School improvements. The architect laughed at the Rector when he suggested putting out advertisements for tenders. He said:

"No mason would tender for so small a job as to knock a few holes in the walls for pipes to go through, or to knock down a wall to enlarge a W.C. It will be a waste of money and time to advertise." That is why the plumber who did the work chose his own workman. The Rector is sorry the Managers and the masons are all offended with him, but he puts the children first.

* * * *

The Archdeacon of Exeter has written to the Rector that he will support his application for a grant from the Bishop's Fund, and he has no doubt of success. The Archdeacon will also visit Ham and preach upon Church Schools early in the New Year. The Bishop of Crediton writes to say he will heartily recommend a grant for Ham School.

* * * *

The Harvest Tea was held, as so many of you will remember, in torrents of rain, yet a number of happy, cheery people sat down and thoroughly enjoyed the good things. The farmers' wives kept up their old reputation of generous giving, and delicious cream and butter were abundant. The Social and Dance from 7.30 p.m. to 12 o'clock was a jolly affair with much fun and merriment. The comical community-singing led by the schoolmaster raised the roof. The folk dances, recitations, songs and attempts to dance the Charleston, kept the "pot a biling" until midnight. The results for the School Funds, after paying all expenses, amounted to £7 10s. The Harvest Thanksgiving Service in Church between the Tea and the Dance drew together all the serious-minded people. Prebendary Sutton preached, the Rev. F. Merryweather read the lessons and the Rector said the prayers. The collection for the School amounted to a further £2.

To sum up, your kind efforts, with individual subscriptions, have produced the following:—

School Fund.—Mrs. Hove-Scotch, 10s.; Miss Pines, 10s.; Mrs. Snow, 5s.; Harvest Tea and Dance, £7 10s.; Collection in Church, £2. Grand Total, £9 15s.

3

After the Rector's return from Scotland, an account of which was printed in the next *Monthly Bulletin,* there arose the question of a new People's Warden being elected. Fearing that the ex-Managers were about to arrange the election of Mr. Matthew Hammett, the gardener of Admiral Bamfylde, in order to use him as an agent to oppose him in the Church Council, the Rector said, from the Chancel steps on Sunday,

"I warn you that if you elect a certain individual for your Warden, you and your children will be sorry for it."

It is possible that the Rector, in his essential modesty, or inexperience, or sincerity, did not realize the full effect of rec-torial words from the pulpit. It is certain that his feelings were too strong for him to acquire and practise the art of restraint in using words, which art is more effective than the emphasis prompted by one's nature.

ON SCANDAL, GOSSIP, HYPOCRISY, ETC.

Matthew Hammett, the certain individual obviously referred to, was not in church, and so many hurried to tell him what the parson had said about him.

"He said, 'If you were elected Warden we should be all sorry!'"

The effect on Matthew Hammett of the repetitions was like that of the Chinese torture by water-drops. Matthew Hammett, a peaceful and rather weak-looking man, burst into tears, and could not eat his Sunday dinner of cow-beef, greens, and potatoes, which, in accordance with an old village habit, he had been anticipating since the previous Saturday afternoon.

I felt sure that the Rector's words had been inspired by his vision of happy children eating in a nice new room, instead of competing with the chickens. In that vision he saw them drinking from a nice new tap in that nice new room, instead of venturing through storms to quench their thirst at the old-fashioned pump, to return wan and shivering.

As a fact, the children ran about happily during the dinner hour, often feeding the chickens with scraps; and when it was wet, those who lived far away ate in the schoolroom, happier than any chickens. As for the pump "down to Zeales", it was a joy to a child to run down the steep hill with arms wide like wings and the wind keen on his face. While someone clattered the iron handle, you put the palm of your hand over the leaden spout and then held your mouth open over the hole in the pipe, to suck at the jet of water which spurted up.

The Rector called at my cottage one evening and asked me if I would care to stand for election as a School Manager. "I know your interest in education," he smiled.

Not wishing to hurt his feelings by revealing my reaction of almost the horror of captivity to his suggestion, I replied lamely that I was not really qualified.

"But you are the very type of person we require!" he replied, patting my shoulder. Returning later in the evening, he said, "I fear I may hurt your feelings."

"Of course you won't," I replied.

"Well, there were emphatic objections when I proposed your name. It was even stated that you were immoral, and the worst example to the children. I am so terribly sorry. Now please tell me, for they are using my proposing your name as a handle to attack me—please tell me frankly, is there any basis for their statements?"

It was a difficult question. I reviewed my past life swiftly. Had it been immoral? What man knew when he was being immoral? "I am very sorry I have been the cause of trouble to you, Rector. I don't think I am altogether immoral, but I am sure that I am not fit or qualified to be a School Manager."

"I'll tell them," he replied. "Thank you for your straight answer."

"Oh, Rector, I wonder if you would care to use my services as sub-editor of the *Monthly Bulletin*? I believe that things could be put in such a way that they are unexceptionable. I'm afraid you might think me—er—unqualified, judged by my past writings, or some of them; but I see their faults, and think that it is perhaps possible to make all things clear to all men, by holding a balance—not a compromise—between conflicting points of view. I am afraid this may seem impertinent, but if you would care to try me, I will do my best."

Later the Rector said to me, "I put forward the suggestion that you would like to edit the *Monthly Bulletin*, and I'm afraid it was not received kindly. Lady Maude said that her occasional notes concerning the District Nursing Association did not really need editing, as they were usually bare facts stated as tersely as possible to save printing expenses. Someone else said that as you never went to Church, what could you know about Church matters. So your offer we must decline with many thanks."

Foolishly, I tried to explain that I had meant to put my literary skill, such as it was, at his own service, as an honorary confidential private secretary.

"For example—if you will forgive my direct speaking—I know that the effect of the Rectorial Monthly Letters as printed at present are such as to make Colonel Ponde prod savagely into the mud of his lake with a long pole, when before reading he has been quietly, almost dreamily, moving it about to find eel-holes."

"Oh, I see!" retorted the Rector drily. "That fellow! I made a mistake, calling him Captain Ponde instead of Colonel Ponde, much to his annoyance, I suppose. Oh dear dear. Well, I hope he will stick to his mud, and not come near me again. Now I must say good night—my silly handyman is off on one of his alcoholic rovings, which he blames on the War, or malaria, or on anything except his own weakness—good night, I have to try and start the motor for the electric light—a horrid job!" He disappeared into the dusk, and I disappeared into the Lower House.

There I heard Tom Gammon's peculiar laughter, like a box of shards and tins being emptied into the new parish scavenger's horse-butt. " 'Your poor husband,' saith th' parson. 'Your poor husband is now playin' a golden harp.' "A learned'n quick,' replied Lizzie Badcock, "a couldn't play a bliddy tin whistle when 'a was down yurr,' replieth Lizzie. That be true as I'm sitting yurr!"

The next *Monthly Bulletin* contained the following paragraph:

"I have had a very kind offer from one who in our midst is ever taking notes, to edit the *Bulletin*. I felt what a boon to have this somewhat controversial work done by another, but I found that what he meant was to supervise what I wanted to say, and to cross out all that I need not have said. I thought it might end in a blank, so I am still speaking to you in my own way, regardless of disagreements."

The humour of this ripost added to my regard for the Rector; and my spirits rising, I went to see an acquaintance, Colonel Ponde. He was, as usual, down by his lake, trying to stop a leak with a long pole, or sort of rake. I spoiled his water-dreaming by suggesting that the championing of Matthew Hammett against the Rector was excessive, the more so as the entire agitation had been caused by the gossip of the champions them-

selves. They had aggravated the trouble; and they blamed it all
on the Rector.

"Everyone is so eager to point out the faults of his neighbour: not constructively, but destructively. The massed effect of
this accumulates like mud in a pond, and if it is not washed
away, in time the trout lose their lustre, and die. When the
trout in one's stream of consciousness are dead, then one is
dead. That's what Jesus tried to explain. 'Let the dead bury the
dead'—let the blind-worms get on with their blind dogma, as
it were."

"There's something in what you say," replied the water-
dreamer. "Yes, by Jove, you're right! You ought to hear Mr.
Jaggers preach in our chapel! By Jove, look, see that rise over
there? That's a big trout! Hurray, I thought they'd all gone in
that last flood! Yes, you're right about the mud here. My problem
is to get it away without bursting the banks or losing all the
fish."

Later, when I returned, Mrs. Ponde was waiting to see me.

"What we feel about the matter," she explained, "is that it is
so wrong for one in the Rector's position to hurt a poor man.
When I saw him, Matthew Hammett said, very unhappily, 'I
have to depend on gardening for my living, ma'am; and if I get
a bad name, I might not be employed.' That is why the Rector's
action is so deplorable, as we see it."

"I understand, Mrs. Ponde. By the way, there's a big trout in
the pon—in the lake. But surely, if people had felt less indignation, Matthew would not have felt so unhappy."

"I'm so glad about the trout—Harry is so fond of his fish.
Yes, I see what you mean; but I am afraid I cannot alter my
opinion of the Rector's behaviour."

It seemed a deadlock of patriarchal visions: that of the
Colonel's for poor Hammett out of work, and the Rector's
vision of the children shivering and wet after returning from
among the chickens.

Later, realising that direct interference with the sincerity of
both Rector and Mrs. Ponde was crude behaviour, I felt uneasy

whenever I recalled it to myself, but both houses were so kind and hospitable to me that my uneasiness was annulled. Nevertheless, a feeling that I had outlived myself in the district began to grow in me, and I thought to myself that this would be my last year in the place.

4

I began to see how a man's fixed ideas—his ideas of truth—so often seemed to diminish the simple virtues in him. Also, how often it appeared that while a man was a mystery to himself, he was as an open book to others.

Usually the gulf between a man's ideals—his religious aspirations—and his conduct, was wide. Hypocrite, said the easy village judgment: but I wondered how often hypocrisy was unconscious. I came to the conclusion that all so-called hypocrisy was unconscious; and that self-deception by idealism was more dangerous than simple straightforward roguery.

5

During one week five men in another parish died. The eldest of them was ninety-four, the youngest was seventy-six years old. On the following Sunday the vicar preached a sermon about this, declaring in his solemn and condescending voice that the multiple deaths constituted "a direct warning from God about the shortness of our life here below".

6

The same vicar, unable to bear the sight of men tobogganing and sliding down the snow slopes of the hill behind his vicarage, one Sunday afternoon, during the great frost of January, 1929, left his fireside, and trudged up the hill to address the laughing, shouting, merry group. Controlling his agitation, he suggested that "Our Lord made the seventh day as a Day of Rest". One man replied, "Us be working men, zur, and don't get much time on week-days." The parson pursed his lips, waited, and declared, "Very well, men, I warn you that you are heading straight for destruction." At which an old man with a beard, who had been sliding down on a rusty tea-tray with his grandson, replied quite seriously, "'Tes all right, zur, thanking 'ee kindly, but the hill ban't so steep as it looks, and us can easily slow up at the bottom. I've just been down myself, zur, and 'tes quite safe, zur. Thanking you all the same, zur."

7

The wife of a well-to-do farmer, a devout member of the Wesleyan Chapel, who, probably through shyness becoming a bad habit, coupled with the superiority of her fixed ideas, spoke seldom to others in the village, and whose lips moved with the least movement in returning a good morning, found that her sugar jar was empty one Sunday afternoon. She went down to the grocer's shop, and asked the grocer's wife if she minded serving her on the Sabbath.

"Of course I won't pay now, as it is the Sabbath."

"No, I don't object, ma'am," replied the grocer's wife, as she unlocked the back door of the shop. "Us don't make a practice of Sunday selling, but to oblige anyone, do them a good turn if they'm caught on the hop like, then us don't mind. How much sugar would you be wanting, please?"

When it was weighed, packed up, and handed over the religious woman said, to satisfy her conscience, "Well, the Lord will pay, as it is the Sabbath, Mrs. Brooking." She added, "But even so, the scales have been used on the Day of Rest, Mrs. Brooking." She stared intently at the blue packet in her hands. "It would be better to seek divine forgiveness, Mrs. Brooking." As she went out of the side entrance, "Yes, when I get home, Mrs. Brooking, I will offer up a prayer—for you, Mrs. Brooking."

8

I heard it said when I came first to the village that there was a ghost on the sands of the wide bay west of the village the ghost of Cap'n 'Arry, who rode headless on a white horse when the south-west gale swept the dry top sand in long skeins aslant the seaweed-ribbon of the shore. Old Muggy told me that "in his kid days" men would come into his father's inn at Cryde, wide-eyed and out of breath, having run most of the way from the dreaded apparition.

Cap'n 'Arry, he told me, was the skipper of a bark wrecked on the Morte Stone, lured there in the darkness by a lanthorn tied to the horn of a cow tethered on the grassy slopes of the Morte, to give false hope of safe anchorage. The skipper was the only man to survive the pound of the breakers on Woolcombe sands. Seeing the dumb movements of the sailor's lips as the sea washed back from his sodden body, the farmer's wife—the barton, or farm, was the only building standing above the sand-hills in those days—held his head under water between the prongs of a dung-fork; and in due course those pieces of the ship's furniture which had not been smashed on the rocks were added to the collection in the farmhouse.

The skipper's wife travelled down from Scotland by coach, and there was a fuss-up over the furniture, which ended in a curse.

"Yes, sir, the curse came true as I'm sitting here," declared Muggy, in his corner seat under the clock in the Higher House. "Bad days came to the farmer. The farmer died. Yes, sir. The wife moved to Cryde, and became mazed wandering." Muggy went on to declare, on the authority of his grandfather, who owned the inn at Cryde in they days, that whenever boys threw a handful of sand into her cottage kitchen through the open door, she would turn head over heels. The same thing happened when she went into the pub for a glass of beer, and trod on the sanded floor. He was a kid in they days, and saw her turn upsidown. Yes, sir. During one of those falls she died, and in the chapel there were thunderous words from the pulpit about the vengeance of the Lord.

Listening to that story, I could imagine how the poignancy of a fixed idea, multi-barbed by every glance and word of religious neighbours and the incessant jeers of children, destroyed the woman's brain.

9

An acquaintance of mine, a doctor, told me about a white witch in his village who could cure warts. "It's an absolute fact," he said. "General Dashel sent his daughter to me to be cured; but the warts kept recurring. At last she went to Jimmy Chugg, the white witch, a harmless old fellow who lived alone in his cottage. 'Don't think naught more about it, midear,' said Jimmy Chugg. 'In three weeks you won't be bothered no more. Figseye! Figseye! Figseye!!!' And in three weeks the warts were gone. It's a fact."

"How does he do it?" I asked.

The doctor did not know; nor did he know the origin of the incantation, unless it was a corruption of *pig's-eye*.

I got a copy of the white witch's incantations, with the authentic spelling, handed down during how many centuries.

For White Swelling.

As our Blessed Lord can cure all manar of deseases, of a white ill thing, a red ill thing, a black ill thing, a rotted ill thing, an haking ill thing, a cold clapping ill thing, a hot preaking (ill thing), a bizzing ill thing, a sticking ill thing, let all drop from thy face, thy head, they fleash unto the earth in the Name of the Father, Son, and Holy Ghost, Amen.

Blessing for Hurden Hill.

Good Lord, keep this cow from evil, for thine is the Kingdom, the Power, and the Glory, for ever and ever, Amen.

ON SCANDAL, GOSSIP, HYPOCRISY, ETC.

I discovered that Hurden Hill meant Udder Ill: a more modern cure for which used to be advertised every week in the local paper, with the photograph of the rear of a cow, with four arrows pointing at an overplussed milk supply and the words "Something like a Bag!" This photograph, repeated week after week, always produced a feeling of humiliation in me.

For Sprain.

Christ Himself rode over a bridge. The horse spronge. He onlight his joints. He wrestled His sinney to sinney, vain to vain. Pray God to deliver thee out of this pain. In the name of the Father, Son, and Holy Ghost, Amen.

For a Blackthorn.

Our loving Christ's blood was sprinkled among thorns. If the Lord please, the thorn may not fuster nor prick nor rot, but that it may be whole again. If the Lord please. Amen.

For a Kenning (probably a boil or stye on eyelid).

If this shall be a Kenning or perl. If it be white, read, or black, if the Lord be pleased to ease the pain and save the sight of A. B. In the name of the Father, Son, and Holy Ghost, Amen.

For Longcripple Ting (Viper's "sting", or bite).

Our Blessd Virgin Mary Sot and Soad
her Blessd babe sot and Plead their
Came a Ting worm out of eldern wood
He ting our Blessd Savour by the foot his
Blader Blew and never bruk (broke) so shall
A. B. (name)
Break—A. B.—Tong Ting and Ring Ting in
In the name of the Father
Expel thy Ting.

Blessing for Strain.

As Christ was riding over Crosby bridge A. B. (the person sick) his leg he took and blessed it, and said these words, bones to bones and sincues to sincues, in the name of the Father, Son, and Holy Ghost, Amen.

Stenten Blood (?Staunching).

As our Blessed Lord and Saviour went down into the river Jordan to be baptised and the water was vile and hard, our Lord Jesus was mild and good he laid his hand and it stood so, and so shall thy Issue of thy blood A. B. In the name of the Father, Son, and Holy Ghost, Amen.

The white witch was a man of serene temperament, going about his day's work quietly. He invited the doctor and myself to be present with himself at a pig-killing, when, he said, he would staunch the blood, after the stabbing, without going near the animal. "No one can kill a pig unless I say so," he smiled. I intended to go and see him do it; but the months and years went by and we three did not happen to come together at a pig-killing. Then the white witch died, and so the doubt remains.

In Ham village I had a slight acquaintance with a curer of warts. He was a seventh son; a small, quiet little man with a black patch over one eye, living with his wife in a detached cottage behind Rock Hill, at the curve of a lesser lane. As unobtrusively as an owl in a hollow tree he lived there; regularly he went down to the sands to collect sticks for firing. Somebody told me he could cure warts. "He cuts a twig out of the hedge when no one be looking, and speaks to the twig." I asked him if he could cure warts, and he said, Yes, he could. "Will you tell me how you do it?" He was sorry, he was not allowed to tell: but he could cure warts, and took no money for it. Then he passed on quietly down the lane.

10

One midsummer morning, as I walked to the post office, I heard the loud ringing *spink-spink-spink* of a blackbird in the hedge. For a stoat or weasel the alarm cry of the blackbird seems to be stifled as though its heart were faint; for an owl it is deliberate and insistent. This angry *spink-spink* was the cry of a cock blackbird against a cat; and sure enough, just in front of me a large tabby cat jumped out of the hedge to the lane, followed by the bird. The cat ran along with tail low and ears depressed; the blackbird hopped after it, close behind the cat all down the village street, his tail spread and his wings quarter-opened— black-barbed strength, a spiritual power possessed the bird. The onlookers felt it; they were silent, as if awed. One of them, with the patch over an eye, the white witch, said to me, "The cat be shame-faced; he've no right up there after they young nestlings, and he knows it."

At the time I *knew* the power in the bird; but afterwards I wondered how it would have fared against a stoat. Shrieks, feathers scattered, carried away with wings cruciform?

II

The white witches were good people; the black were bad. A butcher in Crosstree village told me about a woman called Witchy Mock, once living in Town. Her landlord, being apparently uneasy about her powers, gave her notice one Michaelmas quarter-day, to quit at the following Christmas quarter. She ill-wished him. He would not live to see the New Year, declared Witchy Mock.

Towards Christmas the man fell ill. "I told him he would," said Witchy Mock. "But he won't die until New Year's Eve." The man grew worse. The doctor was called in. On New Year's Eve the man's wife and family were whispering and sobbing round his bed. Just after midnight, when the bells of Pilton and St. Mary's were echoing down the street and over the mists of the river, Witchy Mock came out of her house and said to a group of people at the street corner, "I've forgive him now." She went back into her unlighted house, and soon afterwards they heard that the man had died when he had heard the bells announcing the New Year.

A farmer who used to spend money in jovial hours in the inns gradually became less outspoken, and sallow about the eyes. He took to drinking whiskey where before he had taken only beer. His hens wouldn't lay, his cattle broke down his neighbours' banks, his sheep had foot-rot, his well ran dry (when many others also ran dry: but no, his well had run dry for another reason). One stormy night his chimney fell down (ferns had been growing between the cracks in the mortar for years). He was a yeoman farmer, owning one hundred acres, with first and second mortgages on them. His farmhouse stood behind a neglected orchard at the edge of a swamp. The plaster was fallen in patches, and the outside walls had not been lime-washed for many years. He was always behind with his work; sometimes his fields were left unsown owing to the tardy ploughing. A cow slipped in the lane, broke its leg, and had to be destroyed. Along one of his banks mulleins used to grow, tall plants of summer with towers of yellow blooms like primroses. They grew too sparsely to be called weeds, a sort of distinctive wild hollyhock. One day I saw the farmer walking idly down the hedge, leaving the brambles which had grown out and rooted in the field, and striking at the tall stalks of the mulleins. He talked with me for more than an hour, and his talk was all of his ill-luck and bad fortune, until finally he told me what was the trouble. He had been overlooked. "There was no way of getting away from facts—I be overlooked."

The farm, where his forebears had worked hard for two hundred years, was sold. When I saw him last he was outside the office of the Ministry of Labour, waiting to get a job; but he would not get one. He was thin, shabby, sallow. Until he died I knew he·would believe that his ill-luck was due to his having been witched.

Many of the older and middle-aged people in the village believed in the power of witches. In two cases I had opportunities of penetrating to the origin of at least one woman's belief. She said she had a sister who was witched by a gipsy, who tried to sell her a broom and was rebuffed. The gipsies had a permanent colony near the moor, and spent their lives going from village to village trying to sell mats, brushes, and such things, at a price greater than need be paid in the town shops. They walked slowly from house to house, and were persistent in a sort of wheedling persuasion, once they had been allowed to get a foot on the opened threshold. Their faces were a golden brown, and some of the young women were beautiful and strong, with yellow hair in thick coiled plaits like ears of wheat about their ears. Their dress was distinctive. The men wore dark suits of thick material with the high lapels of last century's fashions to their coats, buttoning them against the driven rain of the high moor, and trousers with bell-bottoms. The women wore high brown boots, high bosom'd corsets, and high hats with black and purple colours prevailing. One of these gipsy women tried to sell a broom to Mrs. Brooking's sister, and was told to go away. The gipsy became angry, and cursed her. "At sunset you will find rue from me, as you go in this very door, and you won't move a finger until dark," said the gipsy. Mrs. Brooking told me, "At sunset, sure enough, my sister came in from the garden: and over the threshold she seemed to stiffen, and she gasped out, 'I can't move, Mary. The gipsy!' and sure enough, she had to be laid on a bed, and 'a didden move a finger until the night sky was as black as your hat."

I had no hat in those days: however, the simile was usual in the village, though normally for frost on early potatoes.

Mrs. Brooking was truthful, or rather, she said what she believed and had heard. After she had told me the above, she said, "And I tell you who else was ill-wished, too. And that is Farmer 'Stroyle' George's son. He was ill-wished from birth, poor chiel. And ever since he's been a cripple, just sitting by the fire all day, and can't even feed himself. And I'll tell you who ill-wished'n. 'Twas the maid Farmer Riddaway courted before he courted another, who became his wife. Us all knawed it yurr in the parish."

Having heard, from an idle member of the middle class who was loafing away his life in the village, another reason given for the crippled state of the farmer's son—the "sins of the fathers"— I went to the farmer, not without a certain reluctance, and asked why his son was a cripple. "Yes, I'll tell 'ee," he said. "You'm a father, and you'll understand. My wife was taken in labour on the 28th of March, and her wasn't delivered until the 2nd of April. And 'a wouldn't let the doctor use th' instruments, for 'a knowed it would have killed the chiel. The baby was the wrong way up, you see. And from the 28th of March to the 2nd of April—five days—the mother was in agonies of pain down-about. You'm a married man and a father, else I wouldn't be telling 'ee this. And when at last the poor little chiel was born, why, 'twas almost no life in it at all. That's why my li'l boy be a cripple, and can't tend for himself: but he's got all his faculties, you know! Some say otherwise, but tidden true, midear, tidden true!"

Then I asked him if he knew anything about the sister of Mrs. Brooking; and he replied, "Yes, her's had fits since her was a little maid. Some used to say her was ill-wished by a gipsy, but tidden no truth in it: her was like it before, and her's been like it since."

12

Children coughing, retching, and spitting in front of my gate, looking at the little boy learning to walk, May 1927.

I suggested, in my paternal anxiety, that they should go away, as they have the whooping cough.

"Us ban't got whoopin' cough," said Madge Carter, with an edge of hostility in her voice. I saw her mother looking out of her little white face.

"Anyhow," declared Mrs. Willy Gammon, hurrying on her way back to her numerous small family, after her morning's work in the boarding-house up the road, "it's the best time to have it, in the May month," and she hastened on without pausing, scornful of the young parents who were so concerned about their one baby. All that fuss about window-opening at night, and letting the child walk about in the sun without any clothes! Let them have fourteen like she'd had to put up with, then they'd soon learn not to fuss so.

William Gammon, her husband, was fifty years old, and for more than thirty five years he had worked as a mason. In the years following the Great War he earned 1s. 5½d. an hour, working forty-seven hours a week. Some people, including John Gammon, his father, a splendid physical specimen of a man, hale and active at seventy-five years of age—indeed, he proposed marriage to a young girl of eighteen at that age, and nearly got her, too—thought of him as a poor stupid fellow; for William passed most of his evening hours in the village inns, and spent half of his money there.

On Saturday night—he was paid at noon on that day—washed and shaved and clean-shirted, and wearing a pair of brown shoes given him by one of his dozen sons, William Gammon drank bottled stout, sixpenny ale, and a drop or two of whiskey to finish up on. On Sunday before dinner (which he would eat after closing time at two o'clock) it would be sixpenny; on Sunday evening, sixpenny again and perhaps one drop of whiskey. Sunday nights were always quiet in the inns: best suits, boots, and hats; no cards, no table-skittles, no wall-quoits. Sometimes one or another of William's younger sons came in for a mineral —lemonade or ginger beer—boldly smoking their first grown-up fags, caps pushed well back over masses of curly black hair, peaks pointing upwards. The Rector thought they had Spanish blood in their veins—a pleasant fancy about all the dark-haired families in the western seaboard villages, arising out of third-rate works of fiction inspired by visions of the glorious Armada. All the guide books, being hack-works paid for at cheap rates, repeated the legend.

Monday it would be sixpenny, perhaps six or seven pints. Father William was slowing up a bit, for the midweek drought. Tuesday would begin with sixpenny, and change to fivepenny after nine o'clock; the glass rattled on ten o'clock for a pint of sixpenny "to finish up on". Wednesday would be all fivepenny, a quiet evening. Thursday might be cider, if it was not too early in the year—cider at fourpence a pint, "zinging stuff", making a man swing round in his walk after very little. Four pints would do it, but it depended on the cider. Some barrels were better than others, especially if they had had an iron chain or a few pounds of beef steak or pigs' ears dropped through the bung-hole. The acid would eat iron and flesh away, and give a body to the apple-wine.

Friday he might go to the inn to play whist for a pint; if he lost, he would pay the landlord the next evening. Or he might not go up at all, but spend the evening in his garden, if spring or summer weather; or sit at home on the settle (the old brown wood of which was papered with squares out of a wallpaper sample book) and nurse the baby. There was always a baby in the William Gammon cottage during the first twenty years of his married life, a baby lying with white face in the cradle of half a tub near the settle. His wife had had a hard life, bringing up so many children, in a cottage with one dark living-room, and one bedroom divided into two by a thin wall of lath-and-plaster. She had managed somehow, bringing up the children on what money had not gone into the Higher and Lower Houses; leaving the eldest child not in school to mind the younger children, while she hurried away along the lane to some work or other in the village. Everyone in the William Gammon household may have appeared to a visitor to be "crossing" someone else, children yelling and tumbling on the floor, mother yelling at the children to keep quiet, the cat flying from grubby arms that would nurse it upsidown, the hen stalking by the threshold, her chickens running about her, the eldest girl subject to fits when the moon was full—often striking her mother just before they came on. Yet they thrived somehow. Clothes went from one child to another downwards. They were a sturdy lot of children, with the exception of "that poor eldest maid", as William described her to me in his placid voice, in his beautiful voice, so quiet when he was away from the inn. "'Tis an expense, but us don't grudge that: her's been to a Home, but wasn't any better afterwards. Her wull bide along wi' us now until the Lord takes her, but 'tis an expense."

(In fact, the eldest girl did not die: she got married, and had half a dozen sturdy children, and no more fits.)

William's children were never without boots or warm clothing. His wife was strong, and she did not fret. The sun got hold of her babies as soon as they could crawl over the threshold, and made their limbs and faces brown and sturdy. Her husband was kind and gentle, and very fond of the childer; of course he shouted at them sometimes, and trimmed them up with hand or stick—always in anger, as was natural, and never very hard. The more bad beer was poured into William Gammon, the more good nature seemed to come from him, and keep the family going with humour. So had he been born, inheriting his mother's nature, which nothing seemed to corrode. They laughed with him when their quick tears of rage had dried.

Some of the children grew up to be parents themselves. (Heaven knows how many grandchildren and great-grandchildren old and handsome John Gammon had in the district; over a hundred, it was said. They were all vital, quick, passionate beings.) One of William's sons served his seven years with the Colours, and returned to the village with a wife from Malta, and had two children. He too was a mason, riding to and from work on a bicycle. He took the living interest that all the men took in their gardens, telling his toddling son not to pull up his cabbage plants, as once his father had had to tell him. He did not go to the inn. Later on he might go and sit there for an hour or two in the evening, until it became a habit, the interrupting of which would make him unsettled. If he went it would be for talk, for company. The beer was a secondary thing, as I discovered one summer when I bought a nine-gallon cask of the best Bass, dark brown barley-wine, and I asked both William and Tom his brother to come down and drink it with me. They came down, had a pint each, stared at the floor, and after awhile took their departure. I followed them up to the Higher House, having no wife and family in those days. They never came again, and the beer went bad.

13

A sudden loud braying outside the cottage, a light rapid clicking of small iron shoes cantering on the road, a glimpse of a tall and sturdy man running down the wet muddy lane, holding a bowler hat on his head with one hand, and the other clinging to a rope fastened round a donkey's neck—we ran into the sunshine, my son and I, to see the donkey drawing its master round the village.

There was laughter outside the gate, repeated braying, and grey thin legs being kicked into the air.

"Jgee-jgee," lisped the baby on my shoulder.

"Don-key," I said.

"Jgee-jgee!" he repeated.

"Don-*kee*," I said again, pointing. He stared at it, then pointed, gurgled, hesitated, and "Jgee-jgee!" he declared.

"Baby Wee can't say it," a tacker of five years informed me. In Ham small boys were called "tackers".

"Mind the donkey doesn't kick you."

"Gitoom!" he scoffed. "I ban't afraid of that li'l old donkey!"

"Jgee-jgee," lisped Baby Wee. The village children called him Baby Wee. Nor was my real name "Daddy Wee"; but there, in genial moments I acknowledged it.

How old was this riotous donkey enjoying the sunshine? To me, it seemed ageless. Long after it was dead, if it ever died, the donkey would be remembered; already its memorials were on the walls of half the cottages in the village. Master was a builder, and many thousands of the donkey's hairs had gone into the mixing of the mortar. You could always tell when master was going to build or repair, by the hair he pulled out of his donkey.

If that little aged grey beast, being exercised after a week or more in the dark shed that was its winter stable, could but speak!

ON SCANDAL, GOSSIP, HYPOCRISY, ETC.

it would have told of night journeys for loads of hay from stacks in this and that field (not master's): of bundles of bean sticks cut from the wood in the distant valley (not master's): of building stones taken from this or that quarry (not master's): of gravel from the heaps by this or that house being built (not master's): of master's advice to his sons that "Good work on cottages (not master's) is the decay of labour": of slates being broken as they were nailed to the rafter battens (not master's): of eggs being taken from hen-houses (not master's): of old people being turned out of cottages they had lived in all their lives—cottages bought by master to be rebuilt with the £260 subsidy money after the War, and to be let for £40 a year: of master's well-known record of once charging sixteen people for sixteen quarter-days of work in one day.

And best of all, the donkey would have told the story of master's fortune, which was, literally, founded on bones. Young master was building a glass-house for a gennulman, and half a ton of bones were to be buried under it as nourishment for the vines. The donkey drew the bones there in the worm-eaten cart, from the town eight miles away, and master buried them in the light of day, and received his price; and master dug up the bones again in the darkness of night, and hid them, and sold them to someone else. That was some time during the nineteenth century.

John Gammon turned his handsome old face, with its strong jaw, firm upper lip, and John Bull side-whiskers, and spoke amiably to the baby. "Be 'ee going to put th'old donkey in that village book they tell about?" he asked me. I told him I was revising what I had been writing about village life, and that if it was to last, my book must be as true as I could make and think it.

"Jgee-jgee," said my son, staring raptly at the donkey—his idea of truth.

"Ah, there be only one Book that matters," replied the old man. "That's the only Truth that lasts, midear!"

"There are so many interpretations of even that one Book,"

I murmured, unable to look him in the eyes. "Which man's is the right one?" And it seemed to me that the donkey would say, if only from force of habit, "Not master's."

14

Another local "character" was called "Figgy" Tucker; he was younger than the patriarchal John Gammon, being only seventy years old. He was very thin, with a goatee beard, long nose, long loose legs, and long flat feet. He wore a gamekeeper's cord coat, with flap pockets, narrow crumpled trousers, and a big black shapeless billycock hat. He always walked with long stick, and lived in a ruined mill near Crosstree village. He was said to eat rats.

Words were but part of the low cunning that ruled his life. He had a sort of rat mind. One night he was caught shaking apples from a young tree, scarcely taller than himself, and on being indignantly asked what he was doing, replied, "Wull, I lost me turkey, and I be just poking up this yurr tree vor see if my turkey be roosting there."

Another time he was hired to help thresh corn, and afterwards he begged a sheaf of straw "for his pig". As he was walking out of the farmyard the farmer called him back, saying, "What have you got in the straw?" Then he looked, and saw one of his young turkeys hidden there; but before the farmer could say anything Figgy was threatening to sue him because the turkey was "robbing his corn".

One evening in the Plough Inn he heard of a fowl that had died being buried by its owner; so he went at night, dug it up, plucked and washed it, and sold it in Barum market for 2s.

He would buy a cow, and on payment being demanded, he would say that his son had bought the cow. Meanwhile, Figgy had sold it.

Once someone saw Figgy digging in a nettle patch just outside his garden, and being curious, the watcher kept still. He heard the old man say, in an urgent whisper, "Be 'ee there?"

A frying-pan arose over the hedge, and he took it. He knelt down, and was busy for some moments. Getting to his feet again, he said, "Whip on the pan, missis!" as he handed it back. The watcher saw him cleaning a knife on his trousers. Then he shovelled back the earth he had dug into the pit beside the nettles.

When the old man was gone into his cottage, the watcher went and dug up the earth, discovering the remains of a pig, which, he realized, was the animal belonging to a farmer who had lost it nearly a month before. The observer did not like the farmer; but he could hardly contain his desire to inform him; yet he was timorous of incurring Figgy's wrath, and also of appearing as a possible witness in the police-court. Thus the facts were known by all in the parish, including the farmer and the thief; and yet nothing was said openly, no accusations made, for fear of the law.

Figgy was a great beer-drinker in his younger days. He could swallow a quart of beer at a draught, without pausing. One night in the Railway Inn, when he had gone outside for a moment, the landlord dropped a dead mouse in the pint he was drawing in the pink china pot.

"You drain thaccy at a draught, and I'll give 'ee another pint for nothing," said the landlord.

The pot was emptied.

"Do you know you swallowed a mouse in your beer?" asked the landlord.

"Aiy, I felt something," replied Figgy. "I thought it was a 'op going down."

Figgy was rageful when drunk. One night the moonlight annoyed him or he pretended it did. "I'll have the booger down out of it!" he roared, and seizing his gun from the ceiling beam, he fired at the moon—through the window. "I've changed the booger's shape, anyway," he said, regarding the ragged hole in the glittering glass.

He would come home drunk, and want his boots changed. His wife would fetch his other pair. "These aren't my boots!" Through the window they went, into the stream.

ON SCANDAL, GOSSIP, HYPOCRISY, ETC.

One day she had a brace of partridges for his tea. "Bliddy small things, no food for a man," he shouted, and out of the window they went into the stream. Half an hour later, "Where be they birds to? I want my supper!" The crash of plates and cups followed.

Once his wife prepared a special meal for him. When he came home, she had on her cape and bonnet. "Where be you going?"

"Your dinner be hot on the hearth," she replied. "My cooking don't please you, so I be going for a week's holiday, and you'll be able to please yourself by what you cooks for yourself. Good-bye, you miserable old booger, you!"

When Figgy stuck his knife into the pie, the edge grated. Opening the crust, he saw that it covered the shards of many plates he had broken recently. He laughed, and told the story against himself in the inn; but the week went slowly, his wife stayed away two extra days, and when she returned his good humour, and his good resolutions, if any, were gone.

A discussion arose in the inn one evening about baptism. Figgy had been baptized, he declared. He showed his vaccination marks.

He was a great eater. Someone bet him that he could not eat eight ducks at a sitting. He managed to finish six, then turning to a man beside him in the inn, sighed, "Dalled if I can eat t'other two, midear."

"What did he say?" asked the other man who had bet.

"I said, 'Tell 'n to go and cook eight more,' " shouted Figgy.

"Greedy devil! Here, give me the two ducks back, and I'll pay you the five shillin'."

Soon after this his wife made Figgy a giblet pie.

"What's this, missis?"

"Giblet soup—from they ducks you won the bet by."

He chucked it out of the door. "Let the ducks eat up their own bliddy giblets."

Figgy had a friend, called "Shiner" Pugsley, who killed pigs during the day and went poaching at night. Shiner was caught only once, when a new keeper set a trap for him—a pheasant in a rabbit gin under a hedge, or stone ditched bank. Shiner, going down the hedge at dawn, saw the bird caught by its legs, took it out, twisted its neck, and put it in his pocket. The keeper and his assistant jumped over the hedge, and "Shiner" got 7 days in prison, and was fined 10*s.* as well.

When he came out he went poaching again, and after awhile another trap was set for him, almost in the same place—a hare in a gin. Seeing it there, Shiner exclaimed, "Ah ha, there you are, Mr. Booger, are you? Well, before you'm cooked, you'm basted first!"

He knew the keeper and his assistant would be watching and listening behind the hedge. He took down his trousers, and messed over the hare. Then he went away, laughing; and hid, and watched them depart, leaving the hare in the trap as a useless thing, now that it was soiled. When they had gone, Shiner went back, took the hare out of the gin and killed it, cleaned it and washed it, and sold it in the market for 2*s.* 6*d.*

This story was told as a rare joke among the older men of several villages; the wit of Shiner's act appealed to them; a later generation did not think it so funny. "Shiner" Pugsley had a nimble mind, though he lacked the sensibility of a Revvy. Shiner was a hard case. An old sick man in the village, meditating fearfully on the approach of death, was addressed thus by Shiner, who came in to cheer him up:

" It ban't so bad, dying, Charlie: the only trouble is you'm so bliddy stiff the next day."

But the "masterpiece", as it was called, of the Shiner legend occurred one Sunday afternoon in Crosstree village. Shiner walked past the old elm standing at the cross of four ways where many men stood and lounged and talked, Mr. Bullcornworthy the constable among them. Shiner's pockets were bulging. Feathers showed under the flaps of the pockets.

"What have 'ee got in your pockets?" asked Mr. Bullcornworthy.

"My own property."

"Where did 'ee get it from?"

"Picked it up on the road just now."

"Oh, you did, did you? It wasn't walking or running, I suppose, and your dog there didn't pick nothing up?"

"I told 'ee, 'tes my own property."

"Turn it out, wull 'ee?"

"You can't order me to! 'Tes my own property, I tell 'ee."

Mr. Bullcornworthy's voice grew harsher as his face reddened before the onlookers. "Once more I'll tull 'ee, wull 'ee turn out what you'm got in your pockets?"

"'Tes my own property, I told 'ee."

"Then I'll do it for 'ee."

"You'm no right to do so without a search warrant! I'm warning 'ee! 'Tes my own property, I tell 'ee!"

Mr. Bullcornworthy put his hand in Shiner's pocket, and pulled out a few feathers on some fresh horse-dung. This he dropped immediately on the road.

"Now you pick it up," said Shiner, "or I'll summons 'ee for throwing my property about. I be going to put in my cabbages with that."

And with delight they tell you how Mr. Bullcornworthy had to pick up the dung again, and put it back in Shiner's pocket.

15

Granfer Billy Bale had three teeth left in his jaws, two being sound, the third being rotten. It annoyed him so much that he went upstairs with a length of twisted brass rabbit-wire, one end of which he fastened to the leg of his bed, the other to his tooth. Then he fell backwards on the bed, shouting with pain when the tooth did not shift. He tried this several times.

The tooth continued to ache. Will'um Bale went into Town on Friday on the bus and went to see the Cash Dentist who hired a room near the Slaughter House every Friday. Mr. Bale was told it would cost him 2s. 6d. The tooth was lifted out so easily that the old man complained that it wasn't worth the money. The argument went on until the dentist said that, of course, if he had pulled out other teeth there would have been a reduction. His fee was one tooth half a crown; two teeth three shillings and ninepence; three teeth five shillings.

Granfer Bale said he would give him three shillings if he pulled out another tooth. This was done, and he went home satisfied.

One night in the Higher House old Farmer Counebere, hitherto silent in the discussion—very long-paused and very one-sided, almost a monologue conducted by myself—on the subject of English Literature.

"There be only one I've read, and that be the Bible." Pause while he put down half a pint. "Aiy. I read 'n drough once." He put down the lower half, and rattled the glass for more. "'Twas when I were in prison: shouldn't 'v read 'n else."

Laughter: Farmer Counebere and myself silent for another half an hour.

[The name Coneybeare, Counebere, Connebere, Connbear, was derived from *Coney*, a rabbit, and *bere* or *beare*, a wood.]

Chapter Seven

VILLAGE INNS:

THE LOWER HOUSE

The village of Ham had two inns. Labourers called them the Higher House and the Lower House. Both were built on grey rock. The Lower House, which stood at the top of Church Street, where it met the village street, had a stable yard, which the Higher House had not. Under the sign a tall yellow stalk, taller than a man, had grown since the War, with a white globous head bearing the word *Petrol*. Rarely was a pony seen tethered to the wall-ring of the Lower House; but the sight was frequent outside the Higher House.

The Lower House was not "tied" like the Higher House, that is, the property of a brewery company; it was a free house, which meant that the landlord could buy any beer that he liked. Mr. Hancock, born and bred in the parish, kept the Higher House; Mr. Taylor kept the Lower House, his own property, purchased out of savings made in the licensed victualling trade during the War in the holiday town of Combe eight miles away. Mr. Hancock was quiet by nature, and thrifty; Mr. Taylor, who did no other work during the day, was more ready for good company at any hour of the day and night. He spent his money easily.

Both drank the beer out of their own barrels every night, and on Saturday nights the glasses were filled more often. Then Mr. Hancock was wont to become quietly philosophical, and poetic in his soft thickening whispered confidences about his love for fields and trees and sunlight in the early morning, and how he read *Tit-Bits* to increase his knowledge, and how every moment of living was a grand moment for him; while Mr. Taylor usually drank whiskey after nine o'clock, and was singing a song at ten o'clock, in a high false voice, the only words of which I have heard being *My own true love*. Singing and joviality out of which anger and rage were liable to burst.

Mr. Hancock of the Higher House seldom drank whiskey; he drank his owner-brewer's beer, which did not always agree with him, especially after the heavy meal he took at six o'clock when he returned from work in the fields. He was never quarrelsome. He never "took a drop too much", in the police-court sense, but often I saw him tapping his paunch with his fist, to rid himself of wind. He was a short little man, with a round and honest face; answering to the name of Albert. Some time or other during the evening he would call every one of his customers "sir". Most of them he had known since days together at the village school, and outside the inn they were Billy, Tom, or Farmer Jack. Everyone in the village liked Albert.

VILLAGE INNS

Mr. Taylor bought the freehold and goodwill of the Lower House at public auction for four hundred and fifty pounds, two years after the Armistice, in 1920. The owner put up for sale by auction the place and its effects; the old tenant, coming home demobilized from the Army, had to clear out. Cottages were not to be had in the village, but he found lodgings in another village, and set up as a cobbler. He had a wife, two grown daughters, and a son; a rather shiftless family, saving nothing, indeed, having little to save. They were rarely harmonious; and their sufferings caused harsh speaking. He had little work to do, cobbling or botching boots. One morning he cut his throat with a razor. Afterwards his widow used to walk the three miles to the inn, and was to be seen at night, sitting in the corner, one with the shadow cast by the smitching yellow flame of the oil lamp. She used to say that he was a good man; and then she would weep, and moan that she had treated him bad, and take a sip of the glass of beer given her in sympathy by the new land-lord.

In spring nettles and celandines grew on his grave in uncon-secrated ground under the elms of the churchyard, where withered flowers and broken pots were heaped by the sexton. The Lower House, when he kept it, was always gloomy, and the Higher House was warm and noisy. A small dislustred gold-fish in a bowl on the mahogany-varnished counter passed the years in rounds of weak-finned and aimless nosing of dirty glass. One day I saw it lying in the road, flat, dusty, insignificant; but released.

The new owner of the Lower House had the roof repaired, the corner stone and lower borders tarred and the walls lime-washed. The martins' nests under the eaves were poked down, and their young died on the sett-stones under. The gutters were cleared, the window frames and the doors and the sign were repainted. The word *Garage* was painted on the yard doors. The new landlord brought with him a small bagatelle table, and a row of coloured liqueur bottles. Occasionally in summer a couple of London visitors, hatless and in flannels, would call for one of the minute drinks from the bottles. The beer sales were scanty, too. The Higher House had nearly all the custom, except for the two Gammon brothers, Tom and William, who walked—but never together—from Higher House to Lower House, and up to Higher House again, every night at the beginning of each week, for variety.

To get custom, and also to have a merry evening, the landlord of the Lower House gave a Rabbit Supper, to which all were invited by means of printed bills advertising the time and the day, the name of the Chairman, the free beer, and songs afterwards. It was held in the bar room, which was filled with chairs and tables. For some reason the Chairman, John Brown of Crowcombe, did not turn up; nor did one half of the number expected. The landlord was disappointed, and as the supper was liable to be zamzawed, i.e. dried up, if kept longer in the oven, it was decided to begin under another Chairman.

Would I take the chair? I would. It was a jolly party, beer unlimited; but no one got drunk. Someone said that the supper was too early—half-past six o'clock: that the men had not had their tea, or time to tidy up a bit. Yet at six o'clock about half a dozen men were standing in the usual meeting place by the ditched wall under the glebe field outside the inn. They had to be persuaded to come in. Free food and beer! "Times was changed since my kid days; in they days the whole of Ham would have been yurr to opening time, gathering to the rattle o' the pig bucket." This the serious comment of old Muggy.

The Church and Chapel people, who did not as a rule "go to pub", did not come, nor were they expected. Those in whom the social, or friendly, spirit was more widely open, were there already. Also the regular drinkers—William and Tom Gammon; Jack the blacksmith; "Sailor" Zeale pensioned from the Navy, who worked in the quarries when his monthly pension was spent in Higher and Lower House; Jack Brimblecombe the trapper, another pensioner; John Tucker the mason, who served through the War as a sapper, and had repaired the roof of the Lower House; "Thunderbolt" Will Carter, the retired seven-acre farmer with club-feet; Arty Brooking the grocer and butcher, whose elder brother Clib was too scared to be seen in any pub, since he dug the graves and cut the grass in the church-yard and "you never know what they'll be telling 'bout 'ee, do 'ee?"; John Kift the ferreter, and his handsome unmarried son; and eight others. More were expected to come along later. Well, they didn't come, and Mr. Taylor said, more than once, in his disappointment, that he wouldn't have give a supper had he known only so few would turn up, noomye! Paper table napkins were provided—"What be these yurr: handkerchiefs?" en-quired the elder of the Gammon brothers.

After the plates had been handed up, and the air was thicken-ing with smoke, a young farmer was asked to sing, but refused; and after an interval, a short sturdy man, with ruddle-red face, neck, hands, and clothes—he was a stone-cracker—jumped up and said he would oblige the company. Cries of "Order, please!" and some shout for quiet; and waiting for a moment when no voice was raised, the nervous singer, whose eyes for nearly a minute had been fixed in the corner of the ceiling above the multishapen liqueur bottles, began his song.

He sang in a high falsetto voice, the top notes of which were stifled and alarmingly forced. Like the other songs (with one exception) which I had heard the men sing on Saturday nights—after lowering several pints—this song was in a minor key, a song learned in youth and sung at intervals since. It might have been popular at the London music-halls at the end of the nine-teenth century. It was a favourite song, and applauded with shouts, and boots stamped on the lime-ash floor. Immediately afterwards, not waiting for a break in the noise, the singer began again. As before, the song was without vitality. In talk, as I knew, the stone-cracker spoke good and simple English; some of his phrases, the plain common phrases of the country, I wrote down in my note-book at the time, and later was astonished, and delighted, to find the same phrases in Shakespeare. (He had not taken them from the book Shakespeare; but the living Shake-speare had taken them from common speech.) Sometimes in talk, when meeting a friend in the lanes, I would ask for a phrase to be repeated; and almost invariably the speaker would hesitate, deprecate his own language, and explain, "That's how us says it; the rough way, you know; it ban't the educated way of saying it, no doubt." Also with what is called dialect words—they hid them sometimes from strangers, believing them inferior; some of them probably in English use before the Norman conquest, others as old. *Fitchey* (stoat), *dreshel* (flail), *weest* (dreary), *dimmity* (twilight). *He was as proper a man as ever trod ground. Wait until the ground's in temper* (i.e. the garden soil warm and loose for digging); *it's no use mucketting.* The exact and simple speech of their forefathers, until they understood I was finding value in it, was deprecated; the wording of the daily newspapers, arriving every midday in the village in canvas bags slung across the rear wheel of a red bicycle pushed by a small boy—the job changed hands about once a month, and so the pushing boy was always small—was considered the educated way.

The stone-cracker was singing his song as he had sung it scores of times before. Its title had been announced, *After the Ball.* I drank a draught of beer, and considered the problem:—had he ever understood what the words meant? If so, why did he sing them as though they were the words of an incomprehensible language? Perhaps he thought they represented the true and sad history of a gentleman's life—that strange and wonderful being who did not feel or work as common men like himself. Too late—after the ball—the cause of jealousy was found to be baseless: the man who had handed her a glass of water was her brother. So the lilting and stifled falsetto of the singer declared, in a minor key. At least, that is the impression I had of the song. The first few bars told me that it was not a real village song; his voice, heard above the many subdued but insistent head-to-head arguments, was like the magnified but varied noises of a mosquito in the smoky fug of oil-lamp light. I hid my grins, exchanged with an imagined companion of old time, in the handy beer-mug. At last he stopped in a rumble of applause, while the shouted talk and laughter immediately redoubled in volume. "I'll tell 'ee fur why—" "Wait a bit now, what about the cost to the ratepayer?—" "Yes, and if he's got all that land, can't 'a spare an acre?" "'Tis always the likes of he—"

The singer was going to sing again! The landlord, after a visit to the barrel-room, whence he returned licking his moustache, called upon the chairman to give another chap a chance; and having risen to my feet, and shouted for silence—momentary—I thanked the singer, and called upon William Gammon, one of the masoning brothers. They laughed. Bill Gammon cried in his gentle voice, "I ban't ready yet, zur. I wull later on, surenuff, midear." And after nine pints Bill did, sure enough, and had to be pulled off his feet; only force could stop his broken bellowing. He was the most popular man in the village—in the Higher and Lower Houses, that is; for outside there was no popular man. There were men owning property in cottages and fields; men going regularly to Church or Chapel; men who thought, and said, that the dancing (foxtrots) of maids and young men in the new Institute was wicked; men who "paid their way" (they all did this); but no popular man, unless it were the village schoolmaster, and he was a little apart from the village. William Gammon owned no property; he was a grief to his father, the tall and handsome John Gammon.

William Gammon was a Celtic type, with small head, hands, and feet; black of hair and moustache. He had more than a dozen children; he had the reputation for being a heavy drinker. Towards the end of the week, however, he drank hardly at all. He had no money towards the end of the week. When first I knew him, he lived in a cottage between the village and the hamlet of Cot; he used to go home part of the way with a yeoman farmer whom he called Jack, talking about the weather, the crops, the new cottages being built and "the opening of the place up" with the prospect of regular work, and with many bellows of laughter accompanying his thickish words. At the entrance to the farm they would wait perhaps a minute or two minutes, while the talk slowed up; then in a pause one would say, "Well, us mustn't bide yurr talkin' all night." And the other would say,

"Well, us must get to bed sometime." The other would reply, "Well, 'oomwards!" and they would abruptly separate, Billy round the corner of the high leaning orchard wall, Farmer Jack to his farmhouse glimmering beyond the walnut tree and the stone walls of the barn.

Farmer Jack—the absent Chairman on the night of the Rabbit Supper—during the years immediately after the War used to amuse the Lower House with his experiences in the ranks of the Royal Defence Corps, when he was stationed with his company at East Ham in London (Ham, *Anglo-Saxon* Hame, Home —would our remote village of Ham in Devon ever become a suburb of London like that other disverdured Ham?) on anti-aircraft work. " 'Cor blime mate,' I heard a soldier say, arriving on leave from France during an air raid. Yes, this man, he says, while all the others were scattering like a lot of bloody rabbits, this man says to me, cool as you like, as I was on sentry there, 'Cor blime mate,' he says to me, 'Cor blime mate, strike me pink if a bleedun Zellepin ain't dropped a bleedun egg!' Cockney talk, that's it: they all talk like that in London."

After the laughter Farmer Jack would repeat the story again, for all stories were told twice over in the village.

While I was recalling those days when first I came to the village—Farmer Jack had long since ceased to repeat the story of the Cockney soldier and the Zeppelin bomb which wrecked a dozen or more houses in its stupendous glaring crash—there were calls upon "Mr. Chairman" by the landlord "to invite some other gennulman to oblige with a song". The singer of society life and the noisy Billy Gammon, together with the fug of tobacco and the beer, had by now produced an environment in which song-shyness had vanished; and now there were several voices raised for singing. One of them, belonging to a stuttering grey-haired man, with the light blue eyes of a jay, an ex-mayor of the neighbouring village of Cryde (which office was held by any man who, leaving the streamside inn at night, chanced to fall into the water), seemed depressed that he had rivals.

"I don't c-c-care n-naught about it, I shan't sing if they d-d-don't stop their rattle, that's all," he kept stuttering. "N-n-no, I don't t-t-trouble!"

Cries of "Order, please, gennulmen! Horder!"

And in the slightly diminished noise the singer fixed his eyes on the rim of his ale glass, and stuttered threateningly, "Order, ulse I w-w-won't g-g-go on, n-n-noomye!" He began his song, which I managed to write down almost illegibly on the inside of the cigarette packet I had hastily ripped open.

> The butcher went to market
> To purchase for an ox;
> The cunning little cobbler
> As sly as any fox,
> He put on his Sunday clothes
> And a-courting he did go,
> The butcher's wife along with him
> Because he loved her so.

> With his ring a ding a die
> Me right to re de laddio
> Foll de roll de raddio
> There's whiskey in the jar.

After the first verse there was a cough in the silence, and immediately a chorus of cries, "Well done, Tanglilegs!" "Order!" "Order gents, please!" "Give a man a chance, customers all," and other exclamations filling the room. The singer went on, after a hasty but deep gulp of his ale, in a more stentorian voice. Unfortunately I missed the next verse, while transcribing the first; but the song concluded,

> He chucked the cobbler in the pen
> The bull began to roar
> The butcher began to laugh
> He turned him o'er and o'er.

VILLAGE INNS

With his ring a ding a die
Me right to re de laddio
Foll de roll de raddio
There's whiskey in the jar.

With hardly a pause for half a pint taken in three gulps, he
began to sing again. The song was popular in England during the
Boer War; and afterwards he declared, with wet explosions into
my ear, that it was called *D-D-Dolly Grey*. The din increased, but
he sang on; song after song of the music halls of twenty-five
years ago. He had learned them as a youth somewhere—perhaps from a phonograph—and obviously considered himself an
excellent entertainer. Well, he was, indirectly. I scribbled many
notes—afterwards indecipherable—as he sang, for the place was
rich with life for me. I remember the almost mechanical singing
of Tanglilegs being silenced by the apparition of Billy Gammon
on his feet, his glass eye fixed in a sideway shine, bawling
Roamin' in the Gloamin'.

"Aw, t-t-tidden no sense," stuttered "Tanglilegs" Pearse.
"Ah, can't zing a zong p-p-p-properly, with all this b-b-bliddy
row going on."

He was invited to have his glass filled up by Mrs. Taylor, and
he held it out. "Thank you, m'am. 'Tis better to give than
receive,' as old Pass'n Hole preached one Zunday. 'He meaneth
a toe in the ass!' cried out old 'Sparker'. 'A did, 'a did!" he exclaimed, while all who had heard him laughed. "That's as true
as 'm sitting yurr! 'He meaneth a toe in the ass!' that's what old
'Sparker' crieth out, in church and all! He was a heller, sometimes, was old 'Sparker'. I minds the time, when I was a b-boy,
when 'Sparker' and my father hanged up eighty-eight p-p-
pence during a swampy harvest in this very house! 'Tis true
what I be t-telling you! Tidden no lies, mind! You can write
that d-d-down, for it be true!"

"Aw 'tes true what 'a zaid, 'tes true," interrupted Billy
Gammon, in a voice suddenly melancholy. "Eighty-eight
pence—they drank eighty-eight pints between them one day,

when 'twas raining so they couldn't cut the corn—'tis all true."

"Aiy aiy!" cried a voice, "'twas in the Exeter 'Gaz-at-ee', as 'Sparker' allus called 'n."

From another corner of the room, by the dart-board, came cries of "Will the Way-ver! Will the Way-ver!" A man standing there with a black felt hat on his head suddenly began to smoke furiously, and to give uneasy glances round the room. His pale face faintly flushed and sweating, the blacksmith, after several more cries of "Will the Way-ver", brushed the beer from his moustache, and muttering that he didn't know it, prepared to sing the song they had delighted to hear since early youth. For three years I had been asking the blacksmith to copy out the song for me, and for three years he had been declaring that I should have it to-morrow. He was busy, of course, with bellows and anvil and tempering trough, while his fowls walked among the litter of rusty iron on the coal-dusty floor. The blacksmith had heard his father and grandfather sing it; "'twas a song they old chaps zang up to pub when I was a boy. 'Tis an old village song, surenuff."

One day he brought it to me, written in pencil, on some lined sheets of paper that may have been torn out of his grand-daughter's school exercise-book.

WILL THE WEAVER

Mother Mother I am married
better if I'd longer tarried
for the women do declare
that the breeches they will wear.

O loveing son no more discover
but I pray go home and love her
give my daughter wats her due
and let me hear no more of you.

VILLAGE INNS

Il give her gold
Il give her diet
Il give her all things if she is quiet
and if again she does rebel
Il take a stick and bang her well.

A neighbour ran all for to meet him
A purposely all for to vex him
saying Neighbour Neighbour Il tell thee how
and all I saw with the wife iust now.

There I saw her and Will the Weaver
laying love with each the other
They lift up the latch of your own door
They went inside and I saw no more.

Then home he ran all in a wonder
tearing down the door like thunder
Get me some beer for I am dry
this to his wife he did reply.

o then he did his best endeavour
for to find out Will the Weaver
He searched the rooms and Chambers round
there wasint a soul there to be found.

then up the chimney straight he gazed
there sate Will like one Amazed
A wretched soul he spyed there
sitting across the chimney bar.

O I am glad that I have found thee
I will neighter hang nor drown thee
Butt Il stiffle thee with smoak
This he thought but nothing spoek.

VILLAGE INNS

Then he put in a roaring fire
iust to please his own desire
and she cries out with free good Will
Husband Husband a man youl kill.

o then he did put in more fuel
and she cries out my dearest jewl
if I am your lawfull wife
take him down and save his life.

then off the chimney bar he took him
and most merrily he shook him
and every stroke these words he spoke
come yurr no more to spoll my smoak.

there never was a chimney sweeper
half as black as Will the Weaver
face and hands and clothes likewise
he sent him home with two Black eyes.

During the evening our host beckoned me into the barrel-room, and after filling my glass, he said in a low voice, "I want you to do something for me. I want you to write about this Rabbit Supper, and put it up on the papers."

I said, "Yes, but I don't know if you would like it when it is written. I should write it exactly as I saw it."

"You could get it up on the papers, couldn't you, 'Nry?"

"I will try, Charlie," I replied, while his grandson, a boy of seven hiding his thoughts behind wide and simple eyes, smiled at me. He was keeping very still just then; blown out with ginger beer, he was hoping not to be noticed and sent to bed. It was nearly midnight—a roar was coming from the bar, but as it was a private party, the policeman's sense of duty had not prompted him to knock on the door at one minute past ten. Indeed, I had seen the policeman in the corner; I think it was the policeman who had said "Proper" when I had finished singing *The Trumpeter.* I used to sing such songs in those days, when excited, "with tremendous power and pathos", as the local paper once reported—an ironical report having been sent in by a fellow-poet, then living with me in Skirr Cottage.

Speeches of thanks to our host and hostess were then made; while emphasis was laid on the fact that such generosity was most remarkable. The speaker ended by saying that Mr. Taylor was a proper sport, and he hoped that Mr. Taylor wouldn't feel it too much amiss that some hadn't turned up.

"Shouldn't 'v give it if I'd known," the truthful host was heard to mutter, while Mrs. Taylor, from her position behind the bar counter, said, "Well, boys, you've enjoyed yourselves, haven't you?"

"Proper, proper," exclaimed Billy. "It was the swatest little rabbut I ever tasted. It was!"

"You've had a good time, and plenty to ait?" insisted Mrs. Taylor. This to try and cheer up her old man.

"Aiy! aiy!" they answered, while the polite Billy Gammon said, "Proper, proper. Couldn't be better, I don't care who hear me say it, I don't. 'Tes all proper. Aiy, aiy. 'Twas the swatest little rabbut—"

"The supper pleased you, didn't it?" persisted Mrs. Taylor, while Mr. Taylor shouted, "Order, please, gennulmen! Horder!"

"Order! Order! Gennulmen, please! Order for Mr. Taylor! Speech! Speech!"

Mr. Taylor was standing up beside me, in an heroic attitude. He looked as though only by a superior power had he managed to get on his feet to make his speech. I do not mean that he was partly overcome by the excitement; but that to make a speech was an ordeal for which he had been fortifying himself for the past two hours—if I had read his abstract gaze aright, and his periods of sudden hilarity. Mr. Taylor's face had gone pale; he stood transfixed, slightly shaking, and stared before him with half-closed eyes. Whenever he laughed his eyes almost vanished; but he was not laughing now. He breathed deeply; his pipe clutched in his hand like a pistol pointed towards the top button of his waistcoat.

In the silence he said, in a voice curiously hard and brittle, "Gentlemen and sports." He paused, while the sweat broke out on his brow. "I want to say as how—I'm proud to-day—to see Billy's boy 'Arry Gammon back from China. Also that we and the Brish Empire was in the Great War" (a longer pause) "that we're celebrating to-day." (Pause.) "Every man here did his part well, gentlemen and customers all, and we went through and conquered, I'm glad to say." He had gone paler; his gaze descended slowly, and met the eye of 'Arry Gammon who had recently come home from Malta, a time-expired soldier. "Well, gentlemen and sports, we've all paid the supreme sacrament." Pause.

I wrote his speech down as he spoke, it was so slowly delivered, with long pauses. In my notes, scrawled on the inside of a matchbox, the word *Incredible* is underlined thrice. I suppose I emphasized this as I realized that a literal transcription would smack of exaggeration and distortion for the purpose of obtaining comic effect. Fragments of what he had glanced at in his newspaper were passing out of Mr. Taylor's head: the usual Armistice attitude, dissension about the Revised Prayer Book confused with the term supreme sacrifice, etc.

He went on, a bit easier,

"I hope you've all had a good time. I can't do no better than I have done." (Pause, and cries of "Hear, hear!" "I'm sure we're all grateful, Mr. Taylor", "'Twas the swatest little rabbut I ever—", etc.) His voice lost its strained and brittle quality. "Well, all I can say is, if they boogers outside don't want to come they can bliddy well do the other thing! I don't trouble!! Noomye!!! That's all, gentlemen." He sat down, rapidly swallowed a pint of beer handed to him by his sympathetic wife, and lit his pipe vigorously.

Then arose off the bench an old man with a grey beard, setting off a noble face: an old man with swelled hands, who had entered on shuffling wood-soled boots, with the aid of two sticks: an old man who had said nothing noticeable hitherto. The old man laboriously got on his bent legs, shuffled over to Mrs. Taylor, and solemnly shook hands with her.

"Thankee, midear, thankee," he said, and laboriously adjusted himself to go in the direction of Mr. Taylor, and shake his hand. He was too old to work, and the blessing of an old-age pension had kept him alive and free in his native village since before the War. I had had a conversation with him one early autumn about his solitary pig, the problem that worried him being, he felt he was going to die before long, he was very bad; and he could not decide whether or not to kill his pig, which would not be "fit for kill" until December. If he killed it before then, and lived over Christmas, it would be a loss; whereas, if he died, he would miss a nice bit of fresh meat, beside the bloody pie. The problem worried him much; and in the end he decided not to kill the pig before its time, but to let it grow until it was properly fat. That was two years previously: he had had two pigs since, and each autumn, when the leaves and the rains fell, his joints became more painful and the problem of the pig arose again in his mind.

"I've always found good neighbours," he said, shaking the hand of Mr. Taylor, who said, "That's right." "But you must be a good neighbour yourself before you can expect good neighbours," added the old man in his slow, thick voice.

"That's true!" cried Brownie. And when the old fellow had shuffled away, "As good a man as any in the parish!" he declared, his eye staring as though to quell any dissent. "As proper a man as ever trod ground!"

Some time afterwards Charlie Taylor, overcome by the risen memories of the past, was holding the hand of his wife, and singing. It sounds ungracious to liken his voice, or rather his prolonged notes of an (again) incredible melancholy, to the howling of one of the dogs of which he was so fond and proud; but really, it was exactly like that. Moreover, his dogs in the yard began singing in sympathy, and when I went outside for a moment into Church Street it was difficult to tell which was which. On my return I saw the tears streaming down the faces of Mr. and Mrs. Taylor. They were overcome by the power of old days together; they saw their lives as something that inevitably declines and vanishes, made beautiful by tenderness and union; their tears dissolved the things that unhappy men and women say and do to each other. He called her "Mother". I felt nearer to him then than I had ever felt before.

And so began my friendship with Charlie Taylor, which was to last for the rest of our lives, although we saw each other seldom. I had not liked him when first I came to the village; I thought him a brutal and unimaginative boozer. How wrong I was! I remember how, a few months after the Rabbit Supper, I saw the great green arms of a fern growing in a corner of his stable yard, and was surprised to hear him say, "I love that fern, I wouldn't have anyone shift it for any money. Noomye!" Later I learned of his regard for a thrush that sang outside his window every morning; and, most revealing of all, that he hated the idea of a badger having its throat cut after being dug out. "If I had my way, I'd let every one go, I would!" He loved his dogs, especially "Old Jack the Mullah", which used to lie in the sun in the road, scarred and toothless and happy, heedless of motor-car wheels. Charlie gave up the drinking of spirits; and when I saw him last, he was mellow and humorous; he loved the village life: a shot at a rabbit or partridge, a clay-pigeon shoot, a quiet pint of beer, a game of skittles, pride in his grandson Mustard in a deep-sea trawler, and a sleep in trousers and shirt-sleeves every afternoon.

Chapter Eight

THE VACANT FIELDS

When it left the adjoining hamlet of Cot, the road from Ham rose its lonely way along the back of the high ground, suddenly overlooking miles of estuarial flat and marsh—the old wide river-bed—lying green and misty to the shining sea. Farmhouse, cottages, barns, were left

behind. The narrow road, with its ferny banks topped by low
ragged hedges, bordered by ivy-frustrating telegraph poles, was
empty as the sloping fields. The solitude of the sky was upon the
hill. A coal cart, or the red mail van, might pass; but the place
remained as it had been for centuries. Here the spirit, confined
and dulled in a house, could spread into its ancient elements,
and be thoughtless in its true life.

Usually when I travelled along the road I was on wheels, and
in a hurry, to get a new wireless battery, or a kettle, or a new
bottle for the baby (remembering "a No. 5 leech-bite teat"), or
something that took me from the fields. A quick glance at the
distant mist arising off the Pebble Ridge, at the lines of white
surf along the shallow coast, at the sea at high tide resembling
an immense grey skate whose tail is the estuary, at a kestrel
hovering down the hillside; these glimpses were all I might take
for renewal until the steep Norman's hill descended before me.
But sometimes I was free, pressing the turf under my feet: I
could forget shops and houses and paper and ink, and free myself into the wind that buoyed the lark aslant its shrill rising
song. One such walk comes to mind.

There was a new colour on many of the fields, which lay to
the far sea like a faded Joseph's coat. A heavy pallor hung over
the hills, for the snow clouds were waiting, and the winds which
brought them were gone. Above the sea the light was copper-
coloured; the headland was blue and distinct. A swirl of birds
like snowflakes drifted over the newest dark brown furrows a
mile away, following a tiny moving man and horses; the gulls
were scrambling for wireworms and chafer-grubs.

As I looked, I saw that other plow-teams were at work, too,
in the gracious air of spring. Pale green of pasture, yellow-grey
of arrish, or stubble, these were being changed into new dark
brown rectangles of plough. There were not enough gulls to
float and drop screaming behind all the plows. The many small
fields were divided by grassy banks topped with thorns and
plashed elm and ash saplings. England has had many owners! As
I walked south, dreaming of the centuries that had known just

such a February ploughing scene as this, the soft rustling scrape
of a plow-breast on damp earth and stone came over the hedge
in front. It was a sound that opened the furrow of hope in the
heart. Two horses drew the plough, the barrowquails swung to
their sturdy trampling, the ploughman walked behind. Beautiful
it was to watch the travelling wavelet of earth turned up and
heaving over. With the noises of a myriad blended small rootlets
breaking, the coulter cut through speedwell, bindweed, dandelion, stroyle, and rotting sheep-nibbled roots of rape. At the
headland the ploughman cried hoarsely, *Whoa! Git back you!*:
the horses turned slowly and patiently: the curved breasts of the
one-way plow, like petals of a great silver sunflower, changed
over: a new furrow was started. Five wagtails and a chaffinch
flitted from clod to clod along it. The brown earth took a lustre
from the metal in the sun; it was very beautiful; but soon the
airs and the dews would break and dull that living shine.

Two days after my happy walk, I went again on foot over the
fields. The clouds were gone, the sky was radiant with the hot
blinding splash of the sun. And yet it was not the dream-giving
sun of my walk two days since. The day was blank, the sunlight
harsh. I noticed without real interest that lapwings walked over
the distant fields, pausing to watch, and running forward to
pick up insects or worms. They walked quickly, their greenish
plumage concealing them while they paused. Gulls walked
heavily behind, as though shepherding the flocks. Each gull
kept its yellow eye on the same birds. Occasionally a lapwing
would nip the head of a worm, and pull it from its hole; the
waiting gull would dash at the bird, and filch the worm from
under its beak. Noises like the scrupeting of ungreased axles
arose over the field, the threats of chasing gulls.

Curlews stalked in other fields, with starlings, and golden
plover. The gulls were spread out amongst them, not searching
themselves, but exploiting the labours of weaker birds. Such
was the law of life: the race was to the strong, and the meek
would inherit the earth only when the earth inherited them as
dust to dust. Now I was walking almost as a task. The fields

were as I had left them two days before, partly ploughed. The plows lay against the hedges, their shining breasts dulled with the faint yellow rusts of the dew-fall. In such fine sunny weather, it was strange to see them lying idle. The sunlight hurt my eyes. I turned back home, my mind like a sick squirrel in a cage.

On my way back to the village I saw a cat sitting on a bank, watching for a rabbit to come forth; and in another field a cattle dog was loping with a spaniel down the hedge. The cattle dog turned tail and ran away when it saw me, but the spaniel watched me from behind a furze bush. They, too, were after rabbits. Then I saw a barn-owl drifting over the hedge in front, as it sought mice in the sunlight, and farther on, I saw its mate. Nothing unusual in any of these sights, but they gave a strangeness to the deserted ploughs, the empty fields. My head was heavy as brass in the sunshine.

In Cot, by the red letter-box in the barn-wall, I met the oil-man, who, with horse and dog and cart of brooms and pails and crockery, passed that way once a week. I remarked the silence of the place, the waiting gulls, the poaching cat and dogs, the daylight-flying owls (which no farmer would shoot, knowing their habits).

"I can't sell no oil," he told me. "There be no one to answer my knocks. 'Tis a wind-floating business, I reckon, this influenza, for every farmer and plooman in Cot be to bed with it. 'Tis the same to Morte and Cryde and Crosstree, 'tis the same wherever I go: the schools be closed, with no one to teach, and the childer all to bed. And I've seen other owls about on my round, too—the white owl, you know, what roosts in the lin-hays. 'Tis so quiet in the farmyards that they venture forth, that's my way of thinking. 'Twas never known, I reckon, such an epidemic of influenza, since the last year of the War when ten of my mates died in the Veterinary Corps in France."

He sneezed; and feeling a shiver down my back, I hastened home. February, 1926: that was the time of the influenza epi-demic: the month my son was born.

Chapter Nine

VILLAGE INNS:

THE HIGHER HOUSE

When Mr. Taylor—or Charlie as I was first privileged to call him on the night of the Rabbit Supper—had first settled in the Lower House, he bought a pony and dog-cart, some ferrets, and a couple of terriers. I used to watch the pony being "broken-in" by the young man who drove the first "Taxi" in the village in 1919. He used to canter the pony up and down Church Street, tugging on its mouth, cursing it, hitting it over the head with a stick; Mr. Taylor watched, knowing nothing of ponies, except that this one was a booger to go. "I tugs to the right, but it won't go right: bloomin' thing's no use to me," said Mr. Taylor. Soon after the Rabbit Supper he asked me if I would care to ride it, and I said yes, and thanked him. It knew none of the usual aids, it nearly pulled my left arm out of its socket, it threw me into the stream at Cryde, and chased a mare across half a dozen fields, most of them barb-wired, with me as gooseberry on its back. It was what is called technically a rig; and was certainly what Charlie had described it. Soon afterwards he sold it, and bought a motor car in which, periodically, he used to go off with his famous terrier, the Mad Mullah, badger-digging. Often he invited me to go with him: he felt lonely, I think, and knew I was lonely, too: but I never went with him.

In those early days, neither of us felt easy with the other. Our sets of ideas, the motive forces of our lives, were different. I knew I was not good company, not a sportsman. With the landlord of the Higher House I was more at home. Albert Gammon was truly of the soil; he had the natural courtesy and charm of the countryman interested in a number of things. Pleasant it was to sit in the Higher House during the winter evenings. Sometimes I wrote parts of my books on the long table, whose lines of grain stood up sharp with much scrubbing. The room had a low ceiling and a lime-ash floor. A great beam, a single tree rough-hewn and showing the five-century-old adze-marks along its length, crossed the ceiling. Once upon a time it was the habit of a local visitor, who had bought a bit of land and built a house by the sea with money made from his tannery business, to ask strangers to the inn the height of that beam. He would say that he was five feet eleven inches high: now could the other pass a hand over the top of his head and judge the space? It was his idea of a great joke to push upwards, and to crush the stranger's fingers between bone and wood. He was a big man, with fair hair and ruddy cheeks, and a long nose. Another joke of this gentleman was to creep upon a man sitting in a private place, open the wooden hatch in the hole in the back wall, and strike into the opening with a handful of nettles, causing shouts of indignation and rage. "Was there ever a fight over that?" I asked. "Noomye. For 'a was a girt strong fellow, strong as a bullock. He just did it for divilment. But 'a was a proper gennulman, for 'a would give the chap a gutful of beer afterwards."

Queer things were done "in they days", the blacksmith told me one night, as he sat in the shadow of the corner seat near the door.

"I minds the time when Squire Priddle lived out to Annswell. A proper pup he was, too!" The squire lived in the white manor house among the pines in the valley beyond Windwhistle Cross.

"One day," said the blacksmith, "the squire went into a barn where a man was wimbling wheat in the winnowing machine. 'Turn the handle the other way,' he suggested, 'and see if it will work.' The man said that it would not work. 'How d'ye know if you haven't tried? Turn it backwards, and let's find out.' The man turned it backwards. The corn-dressing was spoiled of course," said the blacksmith, "and the chap had to do all his work over again, for the doust was all mixed up with the corn.

And the squire, he just walked away and forgot all about it. A proper pup, he was!

"A terrible obstinate man he was. You couldn't tell him anything. One day he had a oaken post which wasn't long enough, and he told the men to grease it in the middle and tug at it, to lengthen it. He kept the men tugging for a quarter of an hour, and proper fools they thought themselves, too; but they had to do it, 'cause the squire employed them, d'you see. A proper pup, he was; chucked all his money away and went to live in a cottage, and drank away what was left until he hadn't a penny piece to his name."

Death from drink, sometimes in extreme poverty, was the end of many West Country squires towards the end of the Victorian age.

On the bar of dark-painted wood was fixed a nickel engine for drawing corks; it was seldom used. On shelves behind the bar stood earthenware jars holding whiskey and brandy. A set of pewter was hung on nails below them—quart, pint, half-pint, noggin, half-noggin, quarter-noggin; they had hung there for more than a century. Through the door beside the bar could be seen the 18- and 36-gallon casks in the barrel-room. When first I knew the Higher House we drank from pink or blue china mugs; later, only from glasses. The air in the barrel-room, which opened into the kitchen and sitting-room (the "best room", seldom used), was less thick than in the bar, and here farmers went to talk quietly with the landlord. Here the mild-voiced schoolmaster came for his nightly drink and half an hour's talk and smoke before going out, as he had quietly come, through the sitting-room.

The windows were rarely opened in the evening, even in summer. They preferred a fug of twist and shag tobacco, stale air, and dim-seen faces. Being tall, the dim, hot, exhausted air made my eyes smart, and my breathing uneasy. It was the same in the Lower House, but not so bad, as the ceiling was higher there. Even the key-hole of the Higher House was stopped by a wad of paper: for the air of heaven will get where it can, and before the plugging of the key-hole it used to scream into the hot smoky room. Men began to come to the Higher House about eight o'clock, when talk would be low and reflective, when a speaker would be listened to. Perhaps the landlord or one of his daughters would be leaning over the bar, talking to old Muggy in the corner under the lamp, waiting for a game of whist. His hat was weather-worn, like his face and hands—he was never without his stick and handyman's basket. After wandering round the world he had come back to the village of his forefathers. Muggy had no convictions about life, having outworn them all.

Both in the Lower and Higher Houses the game of table skittles was played. Nine wooden pins were set up on a diamond-square block of wood in the tray, and a wooden ball, on a string swivelled to the top of a stick a yard or more tall, was swung round the stick in a wide parabola which the experts repeated almost every time—with the result that the pin at the apex of the nine was struck a glancing blow of such a niceness that it knocked over four pins to the right, while the ball, scarcely checked, scattered the four on the left. That was the desired result—a "floor-er". Sometimes two or three pins remained standing, and were "scutt" by the second ball, resulting in the satisfactory "spare" for the third and final ball—a "spare" being the nine pins set up again. Three balls each player, turn and turn about. The score was pegged with burnt matches on a block of wood drilled with four lines of holes—up and down for each player. Game was best of three up-and-down bouts; usually played for a pint of sixpenny ale.

Charlie of the Lower House was one of the best players in the parish. I have seen him "scatt" nine pins with one ball again and again. I doubt if he would have been equally skilful on the table of the Higher House—but he entered the Higher House as seldom as Albert entered the Lower House. It was the spirit of the village, of the age of the "little ego".

Sometimes the village of Ham played Cryde, or the team from Crosstree came up and played for the local championship.

Then it was most interesting to watch the styles of the players: the long swings, the neat and precise cross taps, the easy circles that just clipped the three outside pins, like a sharp scythe laying ripe corn.

On Saturday nights the Higher House was usually so crowded that the skittling tray was put on the small circular table in the corner; its usual stance was on the long table that stood almost the length of the room. In the midst of the smoke and noise of these nights, between half-past nine and ten o'clock, a strange figure would unobtrusively appear among the ruddy-faced men. It responded to, but seldom answered directly to, the name of Appy Arry. This man was small and thin, pale and woeful-eyed, hollow of cheek, and like a black bat flapping out of the night as he slipped into the room in his long frock coat and dragging boots. Sometimes the ankles of his sockless feet were raw with chafing. He had a small thin sallow face, with black uneasy eyes, and in a frail voice he answered the rough jests, all of a personal kind, of the men. He would pull a paper out of his bag and hold it opposite his customer's waistcoat until the twopence was put into his hand. Sometimes he produced a small chipped lens, looking like the glass of an electric torch, and screwing it into an eye, appeared intently to be reading one of his papers. Then he would glance up, catch someone's eye, and in a sad thin voice would offer the limp, smudged sheet. "Paper? Paper? Mr. Peto's speech against the Reds? Look!" Afterwards he slouched off to his home eight miles away, which he would reach at one o'clock in the morning, with his bag and frock coat lining bulging with paper scraps he had picked up by the wayside.

In the Higher and Lower Houses I heard many tales of falcons, foxes, badgers, ravens, men, which afterwards I wrote as stories. In the winter night, with rain driven against the windows by the south-west wind, and the room heated by the pale blue circular flames of an American oil-stove—so that a blast of air smote the incomer as he opened the door—I used to sit with Tom Gammon, who knew more about rabbits and ferrets than any man in the parish: a thin, blue-eyed, narrow-headed man, rude in argument as a schoolboy, generous and spendthrift, and very proud of his children. When, during the War, he thought he would be conscripted into the Army, Tom grew thin; he had lived in the parish all his life, and knew every tree and rabbit-bury, and every stone in the wall. To leave his wife and children —the idea was deathly. *Dulce et decorum est pro patria mori*—but also it is sweet and proper to want to live in your own village. The shadow passed from over his home, and Tom, as a mason, earned more money. Sometimes on Saturday nights, when he had travelled from Higher to Lower House about half a dozen times, he would whisper proudly in my ear, in a thickening voice, "Best childer i' th' parish I've got. No whoring in my house! Proper maids they always was. No whoring in my house! I never allowed it. That eldest maid—Bob Baggot's wife—her be the most grammatical speaker i' th' parish. Ed'cation, that's it! Most grammatical speaker i' th' parish, her be! Her saith long words ban't grammatical speaking: but her can say long words if her's a mind to, you know. Splendid sons and daughters I've got! Best childer i' th' parish." His voice would thicken, and drop away. "Wull, oomwards," he would grunt, and rise, pull open the door, pull it to behind him, impelled by urgent reasons; and afterwards, oomwards, homewards—thirty steps up Rock Hill to his cottage.

Tom Gammon's elder brother, William—Brownie—was another of my friends. He was gentle and sympathetic and sweet-voiced; except when he sang! One night the door of the Higher House was pulled open, and sounds like the screeching crow of a cock were flung in. Brownie got up obediently, and followed his wife; it was raining outside, and all the boots of his many children leaked. Poor Mrs. Gammon, the village used to say: her's had a proper hard struggle to bring up all they children!

In one corner used to sit Thunderbolt Carter, who spoke little, being deaf, and afraid to commit himself. "Aw, haw," he said once, before a General Election, hearing that a Labour candidate was standing for the first time. "Not they ould Socials!

No good being Social! Aw, haw, I won't have it about they could
Socials!" He read the weekly local paper, every word of it, including advertisements, for which he paid twopence. He was
the man who sold one of his two fields to Billy Goldsworthy;
the two sat up all night, by the light of a candle, counting and
recounting the price in small silver, sixpences and shillings.

Then there was Porky, the genial and goggle-eyed stander
of pints of beer, hundreds, thousands of pints of beer, in the
spring of 1921: one of the former mayors of Cryde village, who
was hospitable, on dud cheques, to the extent of £200 for beer
within a few weeks. And Mr. Copp, one of the Rating Committee, an individual with a long nose and cold blue jackdaw
eyes, who underrated human nature as he underrated his own
property, who, seeking re-election, used to appear in the Higher
and Lower Houses just before the elections for the local councils,
and ask everyone to have a drink with him—and nearly everyone did. The Zeale brothers—now unhappily parted since the
boot was thrown at the clock; Mr. Alford, the serious and garrulous and inflexible District Councillor, and a score of others
without subtlety, plain-spoken men mostly with understanding
and tolerance for human acts—unless their property were particularly concerned, when their understanding narrowed to
their own points of view; not forgetting "Tanglilegs" Pearse,
the stuttering trapper who at mowing and reaping used to crawl
home at night on hands and knees.

Then there was "Tiger" Kift, one of my early friends; I used
to see him frequently during the first years after the War—a
fierce-eyed fisherman, nervously tapping his foot on the floor
and shouting with sudden gusty guffaws. Tiger used to scale
the precipice for the young of raven and peregrine falcon. He
was already old when first I knew him, and had not been to the
headland for many years, except once to show a farmer the holes
drilled in the rocks under the cliffs where his ropes, made fast to
lobster pots, had been hitched. His father used to take the
young peregrines before him; and Tiger told me, with great
guffaws, how he remembered as a boy going with his parents

to Bag Hole, above which was the eyrie at the back of a ledge of rock. His father and mother had quarrelled that morning, and when the man was thirty feet down the rope, he looked up, and saw her leaning over, sawing at the rope with a carving knife she had hidden in the basket. He watched one strand snap, and then he yelled, "You wait! This rope cost good money! You booger, you! I'll trim 'ee when I come up!" The words made the wife laugh, and she recovered her good humour, and ceased to cut the rope. The sea was three hundred feet below the cliff top.

Another friend of mine was old Granfer Jimmy Carter, bent double, who was miserable because he could work no more in the fields, since his rupture a year before. In his garden, with fork or shovel or drill-line, he was happy, although most of the time he stood about. One year he planted out a row of stocks and sweet-williams in his garden, and his son Revvy was silent when he saw that: father had never done that before. He died a few weeks later.

Sometimes, on entering the inn, I would see standing there a tall and narrow man with large feet and hands, long and loose of arm and leg, with a thin prominent nose, like a red lobster-claw, between two eyes intensely blue. His sandy hair stood up untidily on his long narrow head. He spoke in a loud cracked voice—he jerked his head like a grotesque hen as he spoke. His conversation with me always sounded like a series of astonished squeaks. This was Clibbit Kifft, a farmer, whom one passed in the lanes, riding an Exmoor pony eleven hands high, with his immense leather-and-iron boots on the long thin legs only a few inches off the ground. He was said to be a generous man, who would "give anything away"; and he combined with this unusual generosity a temperament that was amiable in his own farmhouse only when he was drunk, and not always then. When sober his temper was uncertain; he was liable at any moment to thrash and kick his horses, his dogs, his wife, his children, to upset the table, smash up the dinner, throw about what chairs, plates, cutlery and pictures had remained unbroken in his home.

He had several children. His eldest boy on reaching the age of fourteen at once ran away from home. His wife was plump, with fresh cheeks and big brown eyes of a maid untroubled and tender; but she talked of him in a hopeless voice, without the consolation of happiness after death that is assured to some church and chapel folk. Her younger children were plump, and had her brown eyes and rosy cheeks. The girls had short hair, like the boys, and wore spectacles through which they squinted. The mother cut the hair of her children with sheep-shears; in her forearm were two scars where once the points were driven by her sober husband. What gnawed at his inner life, I used to wonder. "His vather were the same before him, and treated him rough: 'tis quite hopeless, you see," said Mrs. Kifft to me once during the auction at Fig Tree Farm. Below the farm the old Jacobean water-mill was grinding the barley as we walked down to Cryde together; the building trembled with its inner stone-thunder. There was an old runner-stone lying in the grass; and the pond above. Many references to mill-stones were made in the Chapel Sunday-afternoon sermons: but when I passed by, and heard fragments of these easy judgments, I used to wonder what it was that gnawed at the inner life of the father.

The men being paid for the week's work on Saturday, those nights were the loudest with laughter and shouted talk. They came to the inn washed and shaved, wearing the clean shirts which would be worn until the next Saturday afternoon. Collars were not worn; Sunday was collar day. Studs or buttons held the neck-bands neat; they were loose from Monday to Friday. At first they talked quietly, sitting on the benches. It might be about the good grass of Higher Ham fields, owned by Jonathan Furze, fields which let for £4 10s. an acre from 1st May to 1st September—grass that "topped your boots" in the first week of May; unlike the fields of Lower Ham, only fit for sheep, "no bullock bite in it". At nine o'clock the low-beamed room would be thick with men, their smoke and their dark clothes and their voices, the scrape and clamp of iron-shod boots on the stone floor, and sudden laughter—real laughter, not the chuckles of subtle wit, but the bellows of plain humour. At half-past nine most of the men would be talking at once, pushing with loud voices their opinions down the throats of men who were only half listening, and awaiting the least pause—sometimes not even waiting—to give their own opinions on the matter—the opinions being usually what they had read in newspapers, or what they had heard their fathers tell before them, were the subject of politics. On questions of the fields and the village each man had a deep store of knowledge, although it was often in dispute. Some lied deliberately, if their pockets were concerned.

Fists were banged on the table; mugs and glasses were rattled for refilling; the whist-players under the yellow lamp slapped down their dirty, worn cards, and the losing pair usually argued after each hand.

"Why didden 'ee play out th'ace before? Corbooger, gone to bed wi'n!"

"No 'twasn't so, it kept back his trump, don't 'ee see? If 'ee'd trumped that king o' glubs, us'd won the game!" The losing pair paid for a pint of beer each for the winners.

None of the beer in the Higher or Lower House was home-brewed as in the old days; it was chemical stuff; it left a tang in the mouth, as though saltpetre had been added to it, to give a false thirst for more.

By ten o'clock, when the landlord, who had been a corporal of a yeomanry regiment, the North Devon Hussars, whistled "lights out", and said to his customers, "Time, chaps!" the fug was loud with song—always some voices bellowing longer than others, and making discords. Out they went, bidding loud or quiet good nights, some to stand on the rock outside and argue for ten or twenty minutes, while the helmet of the constable, still against the southern stars when the first man had pulled open the door, moved down the short hill to the Lower House. A tale caused much laughter against the new policeman (when absent). Mr. Bullcornworthy, as he was always respectfully called, was said to be eager for "cases". One summer night Mr. Bullcornworthy heard snoring in the churchyard, and went

among the mounds and stones to arrest the drunk man sleeping
there. Mr. Bullcornworthy searched for a long time, finding no
one; for drunkenness is rare in the Higher and Lower Houses as
good fellowship is common, and the noise had come from young
white owls in the elms, awaiting the return of the old birds with
mice and voles.

Chapter Ten

A FARMER'S LIFE

I

One morning I climbed up the worn and narrow stone
steps of the Norman tower of the church, past the
bells in their oaken cage, and so to the leaded roof.
From the top of the church tower there was a starling's view of
Ham: the starlings which in autumn began to forgather along
the battlements, the flag-staff and its wires, the gilt weather-
vane. The village lay below, formless and casual in winter, with
dark brown thatch, uneven slopes of worn slate roofs, new red
tiles, and pink asbestos roofs. Gradually the eye from this clear
loftiness traced the shape of the village, which lay under the green
hills at the head of a valley. The valley opened into the sea a
mile and a half to the south-west. Cottages and bungalows, cob
and stone and brick and corrugated iron—ancient and modern
—stood beside the roads, which made the outline of an old-
fashioned swan-neck spur. The slightly hollow space between
the higher and lower lanes—the horns of the spur—was divided
by a stream, down to which sloped the ragged and flat winter
gardens, cluttered with old pails and boxes, tubs, oval baths,
broken and rusty, hiding early rhubarb, dung heaps, fruit trees
lichened and dishevelled with wild wood, gnarled and blighted,
never sprayed, never pruned. The swan-neck of the spur was

the lane leading past the church and turning up the lane called Rock Hill.

To the church tower various noises arose from the enclosed hollow of the village. The noises varied with the seasons, and with the light of the sun. There were the rooks, in the trees whose tops were below the tower; the belving of cows in the shippens of Hole Farm, and the barking of the young cattle dog shut in a barn; the clack and rattle of straw ropes being twisted by the village carpenter helped by small boys; the evening shouts of my good friend Revvy, the labourer, to Ernie and Madge in the water, or sneaking green gooseberries, or otherwise in mischief; the extraordinary bawling roar of a heavy red-faced youth singing the popular songs of the moment, *Yes, we have no bananas*, or *Show me the way tu go oom*, as he cleaned his motor cycle in the lean-to shed just beyond the churchyard gate; the faint ringing in the pail of jets of milk; the occasional loud report of a shot-gun; and sometimes, in fine weather, the singing of Alice, the hard-working daughter of Hole Farm, as, happy in her thoughts, she got the washing ready in the furnace, or copper-house.

There was another woman in the farmhouse, her mother; but the mother never went out. For many years she had never left the farmhouse, except in the early morning to sweep the slate slab of the threshold, and after rain to brush reddish water from the puddle in the roadway below the barred dairy window. The puddle was always filled in wet weather, for each brushing helped to deepen it; yet every morning after rain I used to see the small pale face and the expressionless dark eyes of the little body with her besom. If I happened to be passing, she gave me the least glance, only her lips replied to my good morning; the door closed and she was gone. If ever there was a woman with a broken heart, it was she.

The village called her husband "Stroyle" George—a gaunt and solitary man, with side-whiskers and a nose like a sparrow's beak, who was usually either at solitary work in his fields, or talking to others in the lanes. He was the best plowman in the parish, and the worst farmer. He plowed straight because, as he said, "I couldn't drave the ploo otherwise." Nevertheless his fields were full of stroyle, and usually backward in sowing; the farm was too large for him, he was a tired man, a self-tired man, and he had no son to help him.

Stroyle is couch-grass, whose thick, sturdy, whitish roots, pointing and creeping everywhere underground, take the food of the wheat in the fields. Farmer George had one son, who sat in a window-seat all day, his frail legs hanging to the floor. The face of the farm-wife was a mother-face, the face of a woman who, like a flower, forgets herself in her children. Daughter Alice tended the poor crippled brother; it was Alice whose joyous singing I heard on the top of the church tower, now that the south-west had cleared of its rain drifting grey up the valley, and the sun had freed in leaf and wing and man the very essence of life.

On the big kitchen chimney of Hole Farm hung dead ivy, blackened at the top with smoke, withered and drab in its sap-less poverty. Behind it stood a smaller chimney, topped with extra bricks to draw up the draught—after four centuries of farm-wives in weekly discomfort.

As I stood on the tower, it being a Monday morning, the smaller chimney began to flow with dense white smoke. The south wind carried the smoke among the elms whose tops were below the parapet of the tower. The faint eddies and whirls mingled with smoke from other furnace chimneys, drifting in a haze over the tombstones and among the bare branches. Most of the "furnace" chimneys were drain-pipes, often cracked and loose in old mortar, leaning out of ramshackle "backhouses": nine o'clock on Monday mornings was their hour.

Standing on the lead roof of the church tower, I tried to recognise and count the smells borne past me in the gentle south wind. It was not easy, for the sense of smell soon dulls; but I recognised apple sticks, candle grease, paraffin fumes, rags, parings of horse-foot—this from the blacksmith's forge at the end of one horn of the village—the acrid fumes of paper. I must admit that my nose was helped by my memory, for I knew already what the cottage wives burned in their furnaces.

The heaps of old rummage collected by the cottage wives beside their furnaces were made up of bits of the village, which was decaying and being renewed in eternity. Boots boughten a dozen years ago, worn to the uppers, the lace-holes broken; small wood, too rotten to repair the gate with or the chicken coop; posts which the boring worm or the mildew had done with; bean stalks too brittle to kindle the bodley kitchen range in the morning; cleaning cloths that were dropping to pieces; rags discoloured with age; stockings which, having been darned with wool many times their original weight, and then used for polishing a year or two, were regretfully scrapped; old magazines, dog-eared by many fingers and thumbs, which came originally, years before, by way of one of the servants from the Rectory or the big house of Pidickswell; rotten bean sticks, or twigs blown down from the apple trees; old bird-nests; old envelopes; lengths of decayed rope and string; tufts of cow-hair found in flakes of mortar fallen from the outer walls; dried rabbits' feet; chicken feathers frayed by moths; rubber bands off potted-meat jars; fragments of long-worn-out corsets ripped into bits. All in dry and dusty heap beside the furnace: so careful was the housewife in hoarding.

But, outside the door of the wash-house, the garden path was strewn with coal cinders, which also were cast on the beds, with broken plates and glass: several hundred-weight of good cinders cast away every year, for few cottage wives would think of buying sieves.

In spring Alice of Hole Farm, busy with washing stick, sometimes saw a ruddock or a crackey—robin or wren—flit through the open door, seize a piece of hair or bark fibre, and flit away to its building. At night the mouse ran out of the rummage heap, searching, with sharp nose and delicate small paw, for paper and rag for its nest; and the beetle crept over the axe-broken lime-ash floor, scuttling home at the first light, long before the footfalls rang in the stone, and the basket of the week's washing was put down.

A match to the dry rubbish shovelled on to the flaked fire-bars under the curved iron bowl of the blackened furnace, the white fumes straying out until the flame suddenly rumbled and leapt up with the draught. The Monday morning smoke poured out of the chimney top, taking the cries of the lost little mice into the sky which hears all, and yet hears nothing.

2

"Stroyle" George's farm was in two parts: one field near the village where the 'bus stopped, other fields a quarter of a mile off, past Rock Hill. The field near the village had the best soil, and the most foul-grass, or stroyle. It sloped up gradually to the blue and white horizon of the southern sky. Cloud shadows fled over the brown harrowed earth, across which the farmer was pacing in a straight line. He carried a basket in the crook of his left arm. Every two paces he cast a handful of seed left and right in one throw, like the motion of a whisking horse's tail. When he came to the headland he walked back along his tracks, thus casting twice over the same area.

The seed hopped from the broken clods, but so exact was each broadcast that the field was evenly covered. In his own words, "the seed sowed home". Years before, when a young man, he had cast sometimes a little too vigorously, so that the hopping seed had lodged in his tracks, and sprouted fourfold where it should have been twofold. In his words, "the corn was oversown".

Once during a pause on the headland, which he called vor-ridge—the fore-hedge—where the stroyle grass was matted thick, he told me about the piebald mare, which would, on being taken out in the morning, harrow two and a half rounds only, and then stop. Nothing would make her move until, in the farmer's words,

"I flipped off the ploo chain, and give her a cut across the back. She drave round all right after that, but stopped again after two and a half rounds."

"Why was that?"

"I can't tell 'ee, midear. 'Tes a mystery. But my maid can do anything wi' the mare, you know. The mare will follow her anywhere."

He told me that he could have won many ploughing championships if "I'd a mind to it. Why, my dear soul, I can't go wrong. So long as I could zee a stick in the vorridge, I'd drave straight to'n, straight as a gun-shot."

When he was plowing I used to walk to the field, called Foot Park, to see the smooth gleam on the new-turned furrows, while the gulls swirled like snowflakes immediately behind the tall stooping bewhiskered figure, alighting to take worm or grub and nervously jumping up into the white swirl again. On the return I heard the ripping of the coulter through the weed roots behind the soft thuds of the mare's feet. Farmer nodded, horse and man walked past, the snow eddy veered downwind, and the turf was rearing up and curling over like a wave breaking aslant a shore, and diminishing the soft shearing noise of the bright ploughshare. By the hedge lay the sack he had brought lest it might rain, watched by Ship, the cattle dog. Fifty yards away the gulls were unafraid again, alighting and walking in semicircles round the plough, flying and gliding to the new furrow, reforming the screaming swirl. The yellow-white cut points of stroyle grass lay in the quick-drying furrow. At the vorridge the gentle voice of the farmer:—"Whey, Prince! Come on up!" The off-side horse swung inwards, and walked up the furrow. The dog came over to smell and see anything interesting, and rolled on the beautiful new-turned earth.

3

Hearing the repeated ringing of a hand-bell in the village one sunny morning towards the end of May, I went out to discover what was happening. By the stream stood Alice, the daughter

of Hole Farm. She was talking to Mrs. Revvy. Both were look
ing up into the sky. She would ring the bell vigorously, and
hold her head sideways, as though listening. "They're playing,
you know!" she said thrice as I approached, a smile of the upper
air on her face. "Lovely sounds! I like to hear it, you know."

"Will you get them, do you think?" said Mrs. Revvy.

The girl shook the bell again; and listened rapturously to the
humming in the tree-tops.

The soft south wind rustled the leaves of the churchyard elms,
and the pale blue sky beyond the tree-tops could not be seen
except through the eyelashes. The humming filled the bright
celestial air of morning.

"Our bees are playing!" said Alice, turning her shining eyes
to me. "I like to hear them!"

The other woman looked amused; and then doubtful.

"You'll lose them, won't 'ee?"

The girl shook the bell again.

"'Tes better if you can give them rough music, ban't it?"
asked Mrs. Revvy.

I had not heard the term applied to bee-calling before. Rough
music had gone out of the parish life. It used to be given outside
the cottages of people who were disliked: such as a single man
who got a young woman with child and denied it, or a married
man who neglected a sick and subdued wife for another woman.
The instruments for this rough music were of the percussive
type: old pails, baths, cans, and troughs were banged and clattered under the windows of the accused, and sometimes thrown
at the door.

"Oh, they'll come to the bell if they come at all," replied the
girl, ringing the bell again.

The minutest dark specks were playing about the tree-top;
wandering down in whizzing curves until they were seen as
bees, as a succession of bees, as a menace of bees buzzing too
near my head. They were a community in mystic revolution,
agitated and without city, a swarm of selfless life-specks whose
sight-memory was as a gallery of bright and living mirrors now

unfixed and broken, and glinting with dangerous shards. They had left the security of dark galleries and cell-civilization for the unrealizable void, filled with a mystic and delirious urge for— what? What the spirit urging them forth on the frailty of wings iridescent and tenuous as the pale summer sky?

A dark Assyrian beard began to grow on one of the topmost twigs of the elm. The bees were clustering about the new queen. The girl ceased to shake the hand bell.

She was about twenty-seven years old, slightly built, wearing heavy leather boots, with her hair drawn back tightly, almost severely, from her forehead. I never heard her say an unkind or even an angry word to anyone. She passed dogs, men, children, women, with a smile and cheery words. The farmer told me that once, years before, the doctor, who had come to see the crippled brother who sat all day in the window-seat, suddenly called the shy little girl to him and "began to feel her head all auver", much to the farmer's concern. "Your maid has a very fine head," said the doctor.

The farmer told me how this early prophecy had been borne out. One evening up to the Higher House, he said, was sitting Stanley Zeale, a wonderful clever scholar he was supposed to be: and Stanley Zeale asked him that evening how long it would take him, the farmer, to count a million sovereigns, counting sixty to a minute. "Now, Stan took a stump of a pencil and a thunderin' great sheet of paper and scored all one side with figures, and then spread himself all auver the table on the other side; and when all the paper was covered with figures Stan gived it up. So I came home and told my maid, and she worked out the right answer in no time. Why, 'twould take a week reckoning a million sovereigns the way you or I would do it, you know!"

What life had the girl? Her brother died; her mother died; she was alone with her father, a farmer going downhill, a morose and bitter man, who had not hesitated to use his leather "girdle" on his daughter when, a girl of seventeen or eighteen, she had been seen walking out with some young man of whom

he did not approve. Now he was alone; and she would not leave
him. Why did the horse stop when plowing? It had not
enough to eat. The stroyle grass was sturdier than the oat plants
growing from the corn he broadcast; the stroyle might have been
growing inside his head, choking him.

4

As summer declined and the corn was cut and carried, long-
continued screams of pigs were sometimes heard in the village.
In days gone by only the earlier squeals were clearly audible, for
in most of the cottages the pigs were killed in the kitchen. The
big hooks by which the animals were pulled up were still to be
seen in the beams crossing the ceilings. Later came the pig-
form, a narrow wooden bed standing on four legs, on which
the pig was thrown, and tied, and then killed.

Another method, which I observed once behind Thunderbolt
Willy's cottage, was to tie a rope round the upper jaw of the
animal, pull it out squealing from the dark and mucky pig's
house, pass the rope over the lintel of the door, haul it up until
only the hind trotters were touching the ground, and then,
moving forward with rolled-up shirt-sleeves, firmly and steadily
thrust the knife into the shrieking throat. I remember the shrill
cries of Willy's sister, because she had missed, with the bowl she
had been holding ready in her uneasy hands for many minutes,
the first dark spurt. "Catch'n! Catch'n!" she cried, thrusting the
bowl into the hands of her brother. The blood was stirred vigorously, lest it thicken and clot.

The blood was needed to make what used to be called in the
village Bloody Pot. After killing his pig, one October morning,
the farmer of Hole Farm explained to me that there were "two
kinds of pot to a pig". One was the long pot, and the other the
gut pot. Three days, at least, was needed to clean the pots. I used
to see Alice kneeling on the flat stone under the little fall of the
stream, pushing a stick through the "pots" like a long finger
on an endless glove, washing inside and out. Blood, groats,

heart, liver, chitterlings—all these made the savoury Bloody Pot or Bloody Pie, which, fried with bacon, was considered a rare treat.

Once, when I heard the screech of a pig coming out of Hole Farm, I went into the yard. There the black pig was lying on its fat back upon the form, its snout twisted by a rope, its legs kicking, its ears flapping, gulping its life out. A neighbouring farmer, a devout chapel-goer, and a handy man with the knife, stood by it, relief on his kindly face. It was a job that both men were glad to finish. While the last shuddering groan came out of the flabby carcass, I enquired why didn't he take the blood? Thereupon Stroyle George looked at me, and said solemnly, "Touch not the blood, for it is the life thereof."

I said I did not understand.

"Touch not the blood, for it is the life thereof," he explained.

"Is that in the Bible?"

"You know it be! Didn't 'ee learn that when you was a boy to Zunday School?"

"So that is why you don't collect it for Black Pudding?"

"Aiy."

I looked at the pig, at the red trickle spreading away into the hoof-beaten mud of the yard, at the wild eyes and spread nostrils of the horse standing with ears strained back in the upper half of the stable door.

" 'Touch not the blood, for it is the life thereof'," he quoted again, while the other man wiped his knife on some straw. "It be in the Bible. There's no gettin' away from that, you know!"

I thought of the expressionless face of his wife, who once had looked like Alice, alight with the love of life when the bees were playing: the face of his wife, all the light gone out of it.

"But perhaps that meant, originally, a commandment not to kill animals?"

"There be no questioning the truth of the Book," he replied. "That's the only truth, you know!"

When I went back I found a small double sheet of printed paper lying on my table. It was the *Monthly Bulletin of the Parish*

Church of Ham Saint George, as the new Rector had recently decided to rename the village. Glancing through it I came to an item under the heading *Parish Matters*, which in its unconscious irony was immediately significant:—

"The Diocesan Inspector of Schools reported as follows on our Schools:—'The Infants showed a keen interest in the Bible stories and in the pictures. The teaching has been carefully given.

" 'In all the standards the children were attentive and their answers showed that the syllabus had been covered. Unsparing efforts have evidently been made to secure a general level of efficiency, and to make the religious teaching *of real practical value*. Attention was good and interest strong and there was a very reverent atmosphere.' "

5

The cow walked to her milking along the lane, Stroyle George walked behind her, the dog walked behind the farmer, all at the same slow pace. The cow was gaunt, with shoulders and hips protruding. The farmer looked like his cow. A worn and pathetic pair, man and beast. There was a dumb fondness between them, based on habit.

After the milking, the cow walked slowly out of the farm gates and up the lane. Twelve steps from the gate she stopped, and turned her head to stare at the broken gate, its bars tied together with string and old rope. For months the farmer and a piebald horse had come out of the gate, a horse which walked as silently as the cow on the lane, for its hoofs were unshod. Every night for months the gate had been lifted open: the iron bar, with its rusty worn ring, had clattered: the dog had barked with needless violence, and been cursed by its master: the door clattered to, and a procession of cow, horse, man, dog, had gone up the lane.

This night the piebald horse was not there, and the cow lowed vainly for her companion. Dog barked, running violently at the cow—a big collie dog, frightened of every other dog in the village—and snapping at her heels; the farmer shouted; the cow turned her head, and swung up the lane. At the top of the rise she stopped again, and lowed.

The next day a motor van backed through the gate into the farmyard, and came out again with something under sacking that shook to the uneven roadway, and wobbled clumsy feet. It was said in the village that the piebald horse had fallen down in its stable, and been unable to rise because of weakness. And three nights later, the gaunt cow, after lowing each evening when the gate rattled and no piebald horse came out on its horny feet, lay down in her stall and just died.

A little boy, one of the many small sons of Brownie, the mason, lived in the farmhouse. Boykins, as he was called, slept and ate his food there, lit the fire in the morning and swept the kitchen, and helped Farmer in the farmyard and along the lane. The farmer's daughter washed his face and brushed his hair, smarming it with water, and sent him off to school; never had the boy looked so smart. His mother was paid sixpence a week for his services. Boykins said, "The old cow only had a bit of straw to ait and slape on. The hay had gone black as your hat, and there was only straw to ait."

Horse and cow had grown weaker and weaker; they had survived the bitter winter, but were doomed by it to die in the spring. And now it was April, the dryest April for years, and the farmer's fields were still unploughed. Other fields had been harrowed and sown and rolled during the dry easy days; but not those of Stroyle George. So many of his irritable hours were concerned with the errors and wrong-headedness of his neighbours that he had no time to farm his land as others farmed theirs. He had no plan of farm work. If he borrowed a hurdle, to stop a gap for a day, until he could make up the gap, the hurdle would be there a year later. If he gathered in his hay before the July rains rotted it where it lay, he would not thatch the rick before the September gales, and it was blown open, soaked by autumnal rains, and rotted when it was most needed.

When a new farmer took the farm at Higher Ham, and

started with a horse and cart to sell milk at cottage doors in the morning, Stroyle George, it was said, wrote to the Sanitary Inspector and suggested that the drains of the Higher Ham farm, together with the beasts, should be inspected. The Inspector came out, found nothing wrong with Higher Ham Farm, and called upon the informant farmer, where he found his advice was needed. Stroyle George was not concerned with rivalry, for there was none. He felt he was old-established in the village, and could therefore assume duty, like some letter-writers to newspapers, *pro bono publico*. Fault-finding in his neighbours was the substitute for finding and removing the faults within himself.

One morning he brought a bunch of daffodils from his orchard to my cottage door with the warning, "They'm for the baby—mind! For the little boy!" Long afterwards I saw the reason of what to the village was a waywardness in his nature, making him interfere with others; the secret was in the flowers. Gaunt, worn, irritable and argumentative, deemed morose by many, such was the farmer: what hopes were tangled and lost hopelessly in his heart?

Chapter Eleven

VILLAGE CHILDREN

I

After the unnatural stillness and restraint, the village children always ran out of school with glad cries, thinking of play. How the wheel fascinated the young mind, especially the boy's mind! When first I came to the village I used to observe the fun that Ernie, the boy of neighbour Revvy, got from a pair of worn-out perambulator wheels. Out of them he made an ingenious vehicle, steering with a long stick used as a tail. He was, in effect, a wheeled tadpole with a stiff tail. He lay on the stick, resting his elbows on the axle of the rattling wheels, and came down Church Street at a speed which alarmed all spectators over the age of twenty years. With swift and skilful ease the four-year-old boy moved his slanting tail-stick left or right to avoid the feet of the aged and ageing; but occasionally something seemed to go wrong: there would arise shrill cries, a rattle and a crash, and then I knew that Ernie and his "moticar" were in the stream.

As he grew older, so he designed other wheeled forms of pleasure: long rakish things with boxes nailed and tied to the simplest of chassis, usually on the same type of decrepit wheels which were invariably to be seen lying in the stream when all their spokes had broken from the rusty rims. I used to try and keep the stream by my original cottage free of rubbish: in vain.

When most of the young masons in the village changed their bicycles for motor cycles, the boys' vehicles changed in design. Like huge wheeled grasshoppers, they moved swiftly and in comparative silence, but the end of all wheels was the same: the smooth rubbery circle became the rattling rusty oval, twanging and rattling itself into shapeless disruption and finally lying in the stream with rusty tin cans, broken bottles, and the wan waving tags of pig's chitterlings which Alice used to poke at and wash on the broad kneeling stone under the little waterfall.

We had much fun together, the children of Ham and I. There was "Babe" Carter, who appeared in the village at the age of two years to be looked after by his grannie and grandfer. I used to see him running through the angular bowed legs of the poor old man trying to till his tetties in the garden beside the stream. Granfer seemed to be shouting at the child all the while they were in the garden together, always the child was crying, or, locked outside the gate, was screaming with rage or misery.

He went to school when he was $3\frac{1}{2}$ years old, becoming furtive, cheeky, full of swear words, and "wickedness" arising from his furtive thoughts. Sometimes I heard passing grownup people chiding him for his words; and then he would become defiant, and in due course more words came off his tongue.

"Oh, you dirty, rude little boy, Vivian! I'll tell the schoolmaster!" So seeds of more "wickedness" were sown.

Sometimes from my window I used to see him, with penny spade and pail, absorbedly digging in the red mud scoured by rain to the roadside under Stroyle George's barn wall. His imagination was free; his mind bloomed like a flower, and drew smiles and gentle friendly words from those who had chided. These people responded without thought of what they had done.

At the age of seven Babe had passed through the uneasy fascinations of his mind, and never swore except in fright or anger.

The wheel was alluring at all ages. Tikey, the bold and merry Tikey, was the first in the village to fit himself into a worn-out motor tyre, and revolve, a human swastika, down Church Street at an incredible wobbling speed. Others imitated him, but few dared the slope down past the lych-gate of the Church, which was as the Cresta Run to the novice. The less adventurous preferred to roll the rubber tyres with their hands, like the old-fashioned hoops.

The first motor-tyre craze passed with the song *Yes, We Have No Bananas*, which was reputed to have made thirty thousand pounds for its composer. After a period of wheellessness came the age of the rusty bicycle. Second-hand motor cycles being so cheap, an older generation of masons—but not the oldest—began to buy them, and several old push-bikes were given away or sold cheaply. The senior boys of the school, from eleven to fourteen years of age, held races round the village on machines with real tyres, even if the spindles were worn and often without balls. The less fortunate trundled round on what was really no more than rusty wheeled frames, clattering and grating on the buckled rims. Now as I write in the midnight silence of the village, with the voice of the corncrake in the glebe field sounding strangely loud in my writing room, and Antares the star beloved of Jefferies, like an ember low in the southern sky,— the first frame, stripped of handlebars, saddle, wheels, chain, and pedals, lies in the grave of all worn-out toys, the village stream.

Like some of the earlier wheeled inventions of Ernie, my pen on these childish things has run away with me, but no farther than the stream where so many small feet and hands have played. The waters of the stream, bearing so much in dissolution, flow away down the starry valley and are lost in the glimmering sea; the children grow up, and change, I with them; what has not been written in those years, is gone for ever. A few sketches, a few notes, and I have not the heart to do more than transcribe them.

2

The Bucket.

Appearing one morning in my cottage doorway,
"Mis'r Wisson!"
"What?"
"My bookit (bucket) sin your place (garden). Kenni go an' get un?" (very sweetly).

The Drasher.

Ernie playing in street. Noise of traction engine, drawing threshing machine, remote in distance. Ernie rushing home, shouting at top of his voice, in greatest alarm, to little sister Madge, aged 2:—
"A drasher! A drasher!! Come in, Madge! Quick, or it wull zscratch your brains out!"

The Worm.

One morning Ernie appeared in my doorway, and said, "Look, Mis'r Wisson, me 'ands is dur-rty, but I got a great big high norman (enormous) worr-um for Daddy's zupper!"
Hearing that eels lived in the stream, and ate worms, Ernie set out to get one: and failing as a fisherman, Ernie brought the bait back for Daddy's supper. Hence the hands being dur-rty.

Pigeons and Owls.

"My daddy is gwin to get some li'l small teeny li'l pixigins. Then can fly on the backs of cows. I zeed one vlying on a cow.

They be brown on the back, and white on the front. An' if you let un out an' give un some corn, they can—they can fly to Exxer (Exeter) and come back in the morning. They be only li'l smally teeny li'l things, but they can vly on a cow's back and on the road again."

"An oil (owl) can't eat a pixigin. It can eat a rat. I zeed an oil looking out of your dark hole, just now, Mis'r Wisson." Dramatically. "My God! I didn't half run!"

At this moment the spaniel ran past barking at another dog. (In tones of awe to his sister Madge) "My God! Ah'll kill Mis'r Wisson's dog one day, ah wull!"

Death.

Ernie calls graves "pits". He tells me that dead men have a "good tea first, and then they take their boots off, and put them in pits. They can't see nobody any more, because the earth be in their eyes."

He says he will never go into a pit, because "he can't never die. Jesus said so to him in church on Sunday." (The beautiful sweet luminousness in his brown eyes as he says this: but beware, O sentimentalist, for this is no case of rare precocious genius but memory functioning effortlessly in a truthful, a father-loving, a non-shy child.)

I repeated Ernie's words to his mother. She laughed and said that the Sunday-school teacher had shown the infants' class, on the previous Sunday afternoon, a picture of the disciples, wearing sandals, eating corn on the Sabbath.

Ernie said of the flooded stream that it was "quick as the sand-water". Just before this, he had paid his first visit to the sea and the sands.

Dialogue, 1923.

Me. "Hullo, Ernie."
Ernie. "Mis'r Wisson."
Me. "I'm bad. Do I look bad?"

Ernie. Nods.

Me. "Are you ever bad, Ernie?"

Ernie. "No, I'm happy all my time."

Me. "Always, Ernie!"

Ernie. "Yes."

Me. "What makes you happy, Ernie?"

Ernie. "The fag cards I get." Holds out dirty cigarette cards.

Me. "I see."

Ernie. "'Ave 'ee got any fag cards, Mis'r Wisson?"

Me (looking). "No."

Ernie. "I've got two gingers—two ginger marbles. Look!" Holds out two ginger-beer glass stoppers, and runs off when a boy's shrill voice calls outside.

7 Years Old.

Ernie lying on his back in the road, his jersey and pockets bulging with green apples, holding one in hand, and languidly chewing. Several gnawn apple-cores scattered in the roadway about him. Through my window open to the quiet autumnal sunlight I overheard the following dialogue between Alice of Hole Farm and Ernie.

"You'll be ill, Ernie, eating all they unripe sheepsnoses!"

"I be ill already," replied Ernie, languidly chewing a sheepsnose.

3

My cottage gate was one of the chief points of interest for the children of the village: for at any moment there was likely to be a shower of apples, a chase, a dangerous and exciting journey in their rickety semi-communal perambulator, Baby Wee and his toys to watch.

Among the children usually there, was Babe, the cousin of Ernie, Madge, and Megan. Whenever I ran after Babe with a stick, pretending to "trim him up" for some cheeky words or extra boldness, he ran away vigorously, glancing over his shoulder every few steps. As I gained on him, stick in hand (a long thin whippy stick), his pace slowed, fear came into his blue eyes, and when he saw he couldn't escape to earth in Ernie's cottage, he would sink down suddenly.

"Ah, don't 'ee, Mis'r Wisson! I won't swear again! Aw, please don't 'ee hit me. I won't do it no more."

I gripped his wrist (not much thicker than the stick upheld in my other hand), in order to lift him up, for he tried to stick to the ground. Had the force of gravity come to the aid of this shifting and twisting mite? Although so light, a few pounds of bone and flesh, it was astonishing how difficult it was to raise him up; really astonishing how he used gravity to protect his rump. All the while he assured me of his reformation, and begged me not to hit him.

"Why should I hit you, indeed? What have you done? I can think of no reason why anyone should hit you, Babe."

I tapped him playfully, dropped him, offered him the stick so that he might trim me. Certainly I needed trimming, I told him, for scaring the mind of an immature man.

"No, I won't trim 'ee, Miss'r Wisson!"

He darted after me, and held my hand.

"Give me an apple, Miss'r Wisson! Give me just one, Daddy Wee! A sheepsnose. I do like a sheepsnose. Just one. Aw, do!"

Why shouldn't he have a sheepsnose? I had several hundred apples in store; and I didn't care much for sheepsnoses—greenish-yellow apples shaped like a sheep's skull. The wasps liked them, carving hollow the yellow sweetest apples as they hung on the tree above the garden steps; the starlings came for them, and pecked greedily, while fluttering to keep balance. The children liked them, too; but I was tired of the cries for sheepsnoses.

As I didn't tell him to stop his rattle, or shout a loud and resolute No!, Babe thought he had a good chance of getting a sheepsnose. He wheedled the more anxiously as we got near the gate, where Baby Wee, bib round neck, apple in one hand and cheeks full of pieces of another, was rattling the string-tied latch in order to escape into the immensities of the lane.

"Daddy Wee, give me a sheepsnose. Wull 'ee? A sheepsnose. Just one. Oh, do. Please? Wull 'ee? Give me . . ." etc.

"NO!"

Other feet were approaching rapidly. The dreaded chorus was about to begin. Ernie, Madge, Megan, Hen-ry the oft-beaten with his hands behind back wriggling forward, cousin Clark in his American cowboy's overalls ("Are you a tailor, Mis'r Wisson? My daddy in Noo Yark's a tailor"), Tikey, Boykins his infant brother, and others.

"Give us sheepsnose, please! Oh do. Lovely sheepsnoses, just one!"

The dreaded chorus had begun.

"Go away, or I'll trim you all up!"

"Oh, Mister Wee," cried Tikey, in a mock-plaintive voice. "Please give me an apple, Mister Wee."

Ignoring them, I climbed the garden steps, banging the gate behind me. Gentle voice from lower window murmured,

"Your lunch is getting cold."

"I shan't be a minute."

"Daddy Wee's having sausages," remarked Ernie. "I saw Freddy bring'n down from Arty's."

"Daddy Wee's having sassages," remarked little sister Megan, who was learning to speak, as she had learnt everything not of instinct, by imitation.

"Oo, I kin smell 'm," said Tikey, a sort of rapture in his voice.

"Look, he's getting sheepsnoses for a scramble!" whispered Madge.

Rapidly I was gathering windfalls, hiding the wasp-hollow'd apples in my coat pockets, together with the rotten brown cider-smelling apples which had been lying there for weeks: and so many grinder teeth and so much "tongue-water" (as Ernie used to call the gastric juices of the mouth) waiting to act on them! Those rotten brown sheepsnoses, soft as though they had been baked, were my favourites. They burst easily, they didn't hurt, and a direct hit gave much satisfaction. Ostensibly I was picking up fair sheepsnoses.

"I'm ready for the scramble, Mister Wee!" cried Tikey, the strongest present.

"Then look out!"

Tikey was the best target; merrily defiant as he dared me to hit him. Plap! Splosh! They burst against the curved wall of the cattle shippen of Hole Farm.

"Hit me! Chuck at me! Ha-ee-air! Coudden hit'm, tho!"

When the brown apples and the hollow apples—which whistled as they flew—were all thrown, good yellow sheeps-noses were dropped down, and they scrambled for them.

"Don't shout!" I shouted. "For heaven's sake, don't make such a damned row!"

"You sweared!" said Megan. "I'll tell Mr. Bullcornworthy. He'll take 'ee away!"

"Ah'll lick you for cussin'," cried Clark, in his musical American brogue.

"Ha-ee!" jeered his cousin Babe. "Clark says 'lick' when he means 'trim'!"

Clark the cowboy (Woolworth's) had been unlucky in the scramble, and so I gave him one of the best sheepsnoses. "Boo-ger," shouts Baby Wee, rattling the gate fastened with string. "BOO-GAH!"

"Baby Wee's swearin', Daddy Wee," says Babe, with a glint in his eyes. He had made that remark many times before. "Don't be silly. You know very well that booger is baby's word for an apple."

"Booger!" yells the infant at the gate: he is made quiet with an apple. Would he get colic, eating so many boogers?

I went to the sausages; not very good sausages. Arty Brook-ing the butcher put too much oatmeal or bread with them; and pepper, much pepper, much too much pepper, seemed to be the only flavouring he knew of. The hungry ones outside sniffed, and ate the sausages in imagination. At half-past one the school-bell rang, and they ran off, to my relief.

173

4

The littlest children came out of school again at half-past three; the older ones at four o'clock. My garden was raised above the lane, held in by a wall six feet high. I was "skinning" the heavy mat of stroyle grass, dock, and dandelion roots, which for years had bound the soil on the wall-top, when the children began to pass below.

After tea the wheels and tyres went rolling and bobbling by. The groups of players shifted from before my cottage to a slope of shale rock up the street—another place of interest. There was an interval of silent peace; and then I heard yells of protest from Megan, aged 4, and peering down, I saw her struggling on the ground with cousin Babe, aged 5. What an age to begin!

"Babe!" I shouted, suddenly angry. Immediately I thought, Why am I angry? Is it fundamental sexual rivalry? Babe at once sat up, apart from Megan, who immediately forgot her temporary discomfort. Babe's ruddy face was suddenly pale.

"Wasn't doin' nothing," he challenged me.

Almost before I could think, I heard myself repeating, but without conviction, the voice of the village adult in such matters. "You know what happens to people who do that sort of thing, don't you? They get taken away."

"I know," he whispered, his eyes wide.

Feeling very mean, I said, "It is my duty to tell Mr. Bullcornworthy."

"Oh, don't 'ee do that!" he implored. "Don't 'ee tell!"

"I must. It is the law that grown-up people must always report such things. To save you from yourself later on in life, you know."

Yes, I was thoroughly despicable, I told myself: a slight sadistic feeling possessed me. I went into the garden room, and typed a line of letters, while the child stood below and trembled. I came out, folding the paper. The sight of the paper put something beyond fright into his eyes.

"I won't do it again," he gasped out of a dry throat.

"Give me an apple," said Megan, smiling with the first cunning of Eve. With the impatience of faint contempt I threw down a sheepsnose—a bruised one.

"I—I won't do it again," repeated Babe. He had taken my broom, and was desperately sweeping the lane, where strings of stroyle grass, and other weeds which I had dropped down, lay with scatterings of dark earth on the reddish surface.

I went down the steps, and showed him the paper. I read the words,

MILLSTONES GOING VERY CHEAP EVERY DAY IN HAM.

"I didn't say that!" he cried. "Look, I'm sweeping up your dirty passelolmores for you."

"I did; and it's very true. Come here, Babe."

As he came to me, dragging the broom, I remembered his dead grandfather, who had called a collection of weeds a "passel olmores", which I had disentangled into a "parcel of old mores" (roots).

"Listen, Babe. I am much bigger than you; and therefore I can bully you. Now if I tell your Grannie she will beat you. But it would be very wrong to beat you for that. I was beaten for the same thing when I was a boy. It is like a puppy rolling on a dead rat, when his strong sense of smell is beginning to develop."

"You'll tell Grannie," he whimpered, not understanding the priggish lecture, but realizing that he was going to be let off.

"I won't."

"You'll tell! I know you will!"

"I won't, really."

"You will," he whimpered, hiding his wet eyes with his arm.

"Seven million men of my generation had to die in order that you should not be whipped for what you have done, Babe."

"Promise you won't tell Grannie?"

"I promise, Babe."

"You'll tell," he wept.

"I won't, really."

"I'll tell—I'll tell—Stroyle—I'll tell Stroyle George it was you who—who drowed the rotten sheepsnose after him last night, if—if you tell Grannie," he threatened, his face brightening.

"Stroyle George knows already."

"You won't tell, will you, Mis'r Wisson?"

"No."

"I won't tell Sparrow, either."

"Thank you. And you'll forgive me?"

"Yes, 'a wull."

We shook hands.

He insisted on sweeping the lane for me. I insisted on giving him a basket of the best sheepsnoses. He ran up to the slope of shale rock, to give an apple to each of the children; and ran home to give the rest to his Grannie.

5

Again and again the plaintive voice called below the elms and the gravestones. "Hen—ry!" And again, "I want you, Hen—ry! Henry. Come here, Henry!"

Many times a day I heard that melancholy voice calling the name of Henry. The voice belonged to Henry's mother, who came from her native Malta to the village a year ago with her husband, Harry Gammon, a soldier "time-expired" from the British Army.

"Hen—ry, where are you? Hen—ry!"

She found her three-year-old son in that forbidden place, the stream, playing with a broken glass jam-pot and an old beef-bone. Henry was wet and muddy to his waist.

Henry was cuffed, thumped, and pinched; he rolled shrieking on the road, and was kicked (but not really hard) when he wouldn't get up; he was dragged into his cottage, and dragged out again, with a towel and soap; he was stood on the stone slab under the waterfall by the road, where buckets were filled, and was forcibly washed. He jibbered and yelled and danced in his misery. He got backhanders and forehanders, miniature upper-cuts and jabs to the ribs. He tottered sideways under a rain of blows, but before he could fall, he was sent tottering back against the churchyard wall. His wet jersey was pulled over his head, his ears and nose and hair nearly going with it. And never did the assault of words and blows on Henry cease.

I saw it from my sloping garden. Anger and pity rose in me. I gave a feeble shout. The shout was feeble because I understood how worried and anxious Henry's mother always was. Her husband, a Class A reservist, had been in Shanghai since the spring; and no one knew when he was coming home. Her nervous strain after living months alone in a strange remote country village was shown in her actions. The poor woman was not popular. She was dark, short, and fat. So far from sunny Malta!

Half an hour later Henry and a transatlantic relation called Clark were rattling my cottage gate, and talking to my baby. They did not see me.

"Give Baby Wee a dapp," suggested Henry.

"Noo. Daddy Wee will lick you," warned Clark.

"No he won't! You give Baby Wee a dapp!" said Henry.

"Noo," said Clark. "You!"

"Look," said Henry.

"Oh, durty!" said Baby Wee, innocently, for Henry was doing before him what his mother had just succeeded in training Baby Wee not to do anywhere indiscriminately, but only in a little white pot. "Durty" was a comprehensive term, including earth on hands, milk spilled on the bib, Daddy's moustache, and the spaniel's muddy footmarks on the lime-ash floor.

Many times Henry had been called a dirty beast, and been made too conscious and ashamed of part of his body; and this attitude, with the beatings and scoldings he received, caused a repression of which this was the reaction. Henry grinned, thrilling at his own "badness".

"Oh, durty!" repeated Baby Wee, adding amiably, "Pot!"

Whereupon Henry picked up a stone, and threw it at Baby Wee. Baby Wee thought this fine fun, and laughed. He toddled nearer, and came within reach of Henry's arm thrust through the wooden bars. Henry hit him. Baby Wee's lower lip protruded at this unexpected discourtesy; he went to the dampest corner of the garden, and stood with legs slightly bent at the knees. I knew that attitude of misery.

"Henry!" I called sternly from the window. A brown face looked up at mine. Fear widened two Maltese eyes which were like two balls of chocolate.

"It was Clark," said Henry. "Mus' go now."

So saying, Henry ran away—or rather, he hurried away at his fastest pace, which was like that of a very old man. I caught him by the seat of his oversize (economy) trousers, and squatting level with his subdued and dirty face, gave him words suitable for his age and distorted outlook. To finish the job properly, I brought him back, and gave him a piece of cake, *via* the hand of Baby Wee (who never having been whipped, always did what he was asked).

Afterwards, in a benevolent mood, I allowed Henry the great treat of coming up into the garden to watch me trenching the damp, cold potato patch. After a minute of standing still, my guest finished the cake, and said:

"Mus' go now."

He went a few yards and sat down on a cold stone. I fetched him a mat to sit on, and permitted him to eat a half-rotten apple he pointed at in the grass. When he had eaten it he said:

"Mus' go now."

I gave him a cigarette card, with the picture of a footballer on it; and having stared at this, he tore it up, and said that he must go.

"You're cold, Henry," I said. "Come into the warm room."

I led him into the apple-room, which was my study, and sat him on a chair. Then I switched on the wireless, to give him, surely, the greatest treat of all. It so happened that an act of a Shakespearean play was being broadcast to schools. Henry stared at the loud-speaker, burst into tears, and sobbing that he mus' go, he went.

At the gate he stopped, looking at Baby Wee. He rubbed his

eyes with his hand, and then picked up a stone. A plaintive voice floated through the quiet air of the village.

"Hen—ry! Where are you, Hen—ry?"

Henry drew back his arm.

"Don't throw the stone at Baby Wee, will you?" I said gently. "Throw it over there," and I pointed vaguely at the road.

Knowing that he was observed, Henry walked away obediently. I went back to my work. Shortly afterwards I heard the sound of a stone striking a wooden door, and I saw Henry running away round the corner. In his haste and terror he fell into the stream. Just as he had scrambled out, the door of Hole farmhouse was opened violently, and Stroyle George's voice cried,

"I'll lay my girdle about your backside if I catch 'ee 'eaving stones at my door agen, you young limmer, you!"

"What 'as Hen—ry been doin'?" enquired his mother plaintively, coming round the corner.

"Throwing stones at my door," replied the voice.

"Hen—ry, you naughty boy," said his exasperated mother, dragging him into the cottage; and by poor Henry's cries I knew he was going through it all over again.

Chapter Twelve

OLD WOOLACOTT

"Ah well, us must all take the rough wi' the smooth, mustn't us?" said Old Woolacott in a voice wherein still faintly trickled the sweetness of his simple and unvaried life. He stood huddled on the threshold of the cottage he was leaving. He spoke through bare gums, and when he had finished, his shapeless lips went on opening and partly closing. The skin of his face and neck, from which nine hairs, each a solitary, wandered out in curls and twists, was drawn and rutted with extreme age. A blue hand, half covered by a woollen mitten, clasped a stick which bore part of the weight of his body muffled in thick waistcoat and pea-jacket of black West-of-England cloth, and held him from swaying. He was waiting for the cart he had hired to take himself, his wife, and his belongings to another village five miles away.

"'Twas only four years agone us had to go from t'other place in Lower 'Am, wasn't it?"

I nodded, remembering that cottage in Lower Ham. It used to stand beside two cottages built together with a common wall, its back half turned away from them, and leaving a wedge of space scarcely wide enough at its point for a cat to slip through. Perhaps its cob walls had been slapped-up on an ownerless space, while jealous and less bold eyes regarded it with curious resentment. It stood by itself, a little offset from the others, a monument to the dominant spirit of the village, which was the spirit of property, whose roots were underground, and the sap rising therefrom was bitter. Resentment of what a neighbour might come to own before yourself; hard secrecy of what money you had, either on deposit in the bank, or in the chest under the bed (in silver pieces, perhaps gold, but no paper money); envy and resentment of those who got on ("What do'm want all that for? Haven't they enough already?"). A spirit that having built the chapel, decreed that Old Woolacott and other common labouring men owning nothing should sit in the back seats; that maintained therein the letter which, being fixed, killeth natural growth. A spirit that was hard as the rocks on which the cottages were built; but even rock softens and crumbles in time.

The sense of property in the village was not kind to the human nature it dominated. It was less crude to-day than when the cottage was built four or five hundred years ago, for wider ideas were now in the air, and drifting into far places; but the cottage with its back turned away from its older neighbours, with its wedge of space through which the wind moaned and sighed in weest nights, was an expression of the village-spirit made manifest before all eyes. "Do what you like, so long as you keep away from my property"—this was the answer I received from an old woman on her way back from church, when I sought permission to walk on her grass the next morning for the purpose of hauling on a rope to raise a wireless pole, which was to stand against my wall dividing our gardens. I had to wait for this yeoman's daughter to die before I could hear Beethoven from the Albert Hall in London; and then the ten-minute trespass on the long rank withering grass was observed by "Stroyle" George, and reported to the heir, a builder of rows of houses in a seaside town, who wrote and warned me to keep off, or be summoned before the magistrates. Nothing personal in this; it was the usual thing in the older generation.

"Maybe if I'd a-done as other volks all me days, I'd a-be in me own place to-day," said old Woolacott, never moving.

The dominant spirit of the village had turned him out of the cottage in Lower Ham; Old Woolacott whose seventy years of plain work in the fields—he was earning eleven shillings a week just before the Great War—had not enabled him to save enough money to buy the home where he had lived so long. At the auction he heard, with fear and unhappiness, the bidding rising quickly to his fifty-odd pounds saved during more than half a century, heard it pass on into the sixties, and fall to the mason-builder, whom the village knew would have it, for ninety pounds. Had not this grey-haired man with the uneasy eyes and slinking walk, one of a family whose roots were already spread under many walls, been seen scores of times to stop before the cottage, and cast his eyes over its roof and then down to the garden, peering about. Fifteen year old, that thatch; his father, hale and active at seventy-five, remembered everything about all the village property. Father might be bidding for it too, but for the age of the thatch; Father was not one for new building, preferring to keep his money on deposit, where it had always been. Even then, Father would not have bid seriously against son, although the appearance of brisk rivalry at the start might give the idea that here was serious opposition that would run up the price too much for others.

OLD WOOLACOTT

So Old Woolacott moved out of the cottage, for although the new landlord's application for ejection before the magistrates failed, the constant thought of his insecurity wore away all peace of mind. The father of the new owner suddenly offered him one of his cottages on Rock Hill, at a lower rent, for father and son had seen something in the local paper about the subsidy for new houses being lowered shortly; and Old Woolacott, with only the Old Age Pension to live on, accepted after many anxious hours' meditation, or rather mental anguish: for he suspected a trap. However, the offer was genuine enough; two loads of a handbarrow shifted his belongings over the couple of hundred yards of rising roadway.

At first the old labourer enjoyed the change. On warm days, muffled and coated and clumping carefully on wooden-soled boots and stick, he used to go down to watch the breaking-abroad of his old home, and the building of a new tall subsidy house, while his thoughts moved behind shapeless lips, and remained wordless.

Although the cottage on Rock Hill was as comfortable and dark as the one he had quitted, Old Woolacott did not find the ease he had hoped for. He lived in expectation of being given notice to quit. As every quarter-day drew nigh he became concerned and agitated for the security of his time, labour, and vegetables—his property. Another root, but stagnant, of the family he feared lived next door, and whenever Old Woolacott saw the grandfather walking up Rock Hill, he swallowed the spittle in his mouth, and his thoughts began to shape words. When the landlord had taken his pound rent in small silver, and given him a receipt in pencil, that made the middle of his lips slightly purple by wetting the point, and departed, Old Woolacott used to speak quite genially to his neighbours—to the wife and family of another son of his landlord, who spent thirty shilling a week on beer, and therefore had built no houses—the stagnant root. Should the ball of the youngest child happen to fall in his garden, and be retrieved without permission, Old Woolacott would not sulk for a week, as before quarter-day, but merely tell the little nervous grinning girl that she had no right in his garden—his property.

Thus three years passed, and every quarter-day, when he had paid the rent, and received no three-months' notice to quit, Old Woolacott used to stand in the doorway, or look out of the window if the weather were weest, thinking of his garden in front. With six months clear from Lady Day, it would be safe to put out first early tetties (potatoes) on April the first, and plant kidney beans on Kidney Bean Day (May 1); and after Mid-summer, it would be safe to plant out winter greens; after Michaelmas, the digging-up of the garden, and the winter sow-ing of broad beans; and then after Christmas, he would think it safe to buy half a load of dung, and rat (rot) it down in the corner with the slops and the cabbage stalks.

The eldest son of the stagnant root was a mason like his father, and earning $1s. 5\frac{1}{2}d.$ an hour at his work; but the young man never went into a pub. Old Woolacott used to watch him every fine Sunday, when he came home from the village where he worked and lodged, bringing his girl on the back of his motor cycle. He was a quiet and steady young man, taking after his mother and sisters. His grandfather had declaimed against pubs; his father had spent most of his evening leisure in them, sometimes causing his mother unhappiness because there was no money for food and clothes; the son wasn't going to behave daft, like Father, noomye! He was going to get married as soon as he had saved enough money to buy from his grandfather the cottage where Old Woolacott dwelt.

Someone—Charlie Tucker, another one-man builder—told Old Woolacott about the proposed sale of the cottage. Charlie Tucker sincerely sympathised with Old Woolacott, saying what a shame it was: that Gammon family owned too much already: Old Woolacott heard the news a week before the fourth-year Michaelmas quarter. His landlord said nothing about it on quarter-day; but on the first Sunday in October, a day of warm still air and deep blue sky, the grandson, after leaning his motor cycle against the wall, and speaking to his girl, went up to him with a smile, and told him that he was hoping to buy the cottage after Christmas, and live in it next summer, when he was wed. He said he had told Old Woolacott then, to give him plenty of time to look around for a new place.

Later the same afternoon Charlie Tucker went to see Old Woolacott, to assert that this was not proper notice, nor was it given at the proper time. Charlie Tucker, unsuccessful bidder for the pulled-down cottage, advised Old Woolacott to take no notice of it. So old Woolacott was in a dither.

Christmas came, and the grandson, now the owner, took the rent, but said nothing about notice. In the dry windy days of March, the ground being in temper, men started to dig up their gardens in the evenings after work, but the garden of Old Woolacott was left wild. And a week before Lady Day, saying nothing to his landlord about the cottage his son-in-law had taken for him, Old Woolacott made arrangements with a carter to take him to the village of Morte. He had taken an old cottage there.

"It be a shame vor to turn out old volks like us be, bain't it?" he said to me, when I went to say good-bye to him.

"Were you turned out?" I asked.

The small head, with its eyes shrunken like a slow-worm's after winter sleep, was unsteady on the neck enwrapped with the double folds of a muffler. The lips continued to sip at nothing. His skinny body under the heavy coat remained fixed and unmoving on the wooden tripod supporting it—wooden soles to boots, besides being cheaper, kept out the damp. Other words were shaping themselves, and a few moments later he said, "'Tis a pity they cauliflowers wasn't let bide vor to come to full head, bain't it?"

Old Woolacott had eaten the cauliflowers when they were small, not wanting to leave any behind when he had gone. Weeds covered the ground strewn with white china shards, between the stalks, leaning and stripped, of sprouts and kale. There grew speedwell with its tiny flowers of blue; shepherd's purse and scurvy-grass, both white in bloom; ground-ivy showing purple; and yellow disks of dandelion. Looking at these weeds, Old Woolacott said, with long pauses while his lips faltered, "There be a garden to the place to Morte, where I be goin', but there'll be a passelolmores (parcel of old mores, or roots) to skin off 'fore I can till out my tetties. Volks won't skin'n if they'm leaving, wull'n? Yet tidden right vor lave (leave) ground vull of dirty weeds, be ut? 'Tis a lot of work vor an old man to do, bain't it? Tidden like as though I be gwin at Christmas quarter, be ut? 'Tis time the pays (peas) was in. But I be gwin on me own choice. Tidden as though I got vor to go, be ut? No one gimme notice vor to go, as some be zaying."

The face of the young owner, over the stone wall between the drangs, held a mild grin behind the fag he was smoking. He felt happy and secure, owning a house and a motor bike, and well suited with the maid he was to marry in July. He had the pots of paint and the rolls of wallpaper for the doing-on-up already paid for; a table, a pair-of-chest-of-drawers (always so-called in the village), chairs, and a sofa, boughten at auctions; a new shovel and a garden fork with white handles. Granfer said he ought to sue old Woolacott for the quarter's rent, because he hadn't given a quarter's notice of leaving; but let it bide.

All the young man cared about was the moment when Old Woolacott's cart would rattle off down Rock Hill, when he might go into his own house, and kiss his girl with joy as they looked at the ceilings, the floors, the shelves of their very own cottage, and think of all the happiness before them.

Chapter Thirteen

THE FAIR: MORNING

I

The important days in the village of Ham were those which were "a bit more lively" than usual work-a-days: Easter Sunday, especially for the village maids, for then the Church was full of flowers, new hats, frocks, artificial silk stockings of varied colours, and the thought of Bank Holiday on the morrow—the natural thought-festival of Proserpine; Whit Sunday and Monday, for the same reasons, but not with the fervour of Spring; the August Fête, pronounced Feet, in the glebe field, held nearly every year in order to raise money for new Church work. The word Feet appeared to be established in the word-store behind most village tongues of the time, although once an effort was made by the new London-born Rector to french-polish the name of the summer pleasure meeting into *Ye Olde Englishe Fayre of Ham Saint George*. The older people, with their beautiful precision of speech, still spoke of it by its original name—*Ham Revel*. The revel brought to mind wrestling, balm cakes, white-pot, ale skitting for a live pig, "tanglilegs" (courting), and the rough fun of olden time.

Then there was Christmas Day—the day of great eating, whose jollity and feelings of brotherhood were enhanced by going to Church in the morning, since contrast was the salt of life. But Barum September Fair was the greatest event of the village year. There were three days, Wednesday, Thursday and Friday, but Friday was the main Fair Day, being market day also. Friday was the most exciting time of all the year, because of its fullness and variety of life. The school children had an extra holiday on Fair Friday.

The farmers' daughters drove into Town in their fathers' motor cars or jingles—the two-wheeled carts were becoming scarce. They might go in one of the new fast green omnibuses, the ticket for the twenty-mile return journey costing twenty-seven pence. Some walked to Crosstree village, three miles over the hills, and went in by train—but the railway carriage was a lesser social place than a bus; and the bus took us from outside the village shop-post-office to the first booth of the Fair.

The Fair ground was roughly the shape of a crescent moon between its first and second quarters; one horn resting on the railway station, the other by the western entrance of the town. As the bus rolled on its pneumatic tyres along the road and approached the western horn, we got a view of the town's rubbish dumped in a rushy field where rooks and sea-gulls were walking and flying. In time it was hoped to raise this swampy ground several feet, and turn it into a good friable soil. Farther on a great notice-board invited us to inspect the artistic earthen-ware products of the town; but the advertisement was inartistic, too glaring. Then a row of post-war houses, each one different from the others yet scarcely distinguishable one from another; through two rows of pre-war houses each like the other; over the bridge across the pill—muddy arm of the estuary—whose stony bed at low tide was lumpy with weed-covered tins and pails thrown there by the more untidy of the town's inhabitants. Through the white gates of the level crossing and over the lines of one of the smallest railways in England, which puffed its slow and serpentining way through the valleys to Lynton and Lyn-mouth. As the bus slowed we got out a little quicker than usual: the myriad sights and noises of the Fair confused and excited us. Here we were at last! We must keep our money hidden away: for the first thing we read was a temporary notice-board with the printed words

BEWARE OF
PICKPOCKETS!

2

Beside the notice a crowd was waiting. Above the crowd, and in its centre, was a Ford motor car; and in the car stood a man, maculately clad in morning coat and vest, striped trousers that were invisible below the bulging pockets, a winged collar, and a tie of the Brigade of Guards. He had a wide mouth, he was unshaven, his forehead sloped back into a close mat of short dark curls, he had a big nose more fat than curved, and he spoke in a hoarse voice, while fixing his chocolate-coloured eyes upon a man standing before him. The interest of the crowd was centred upon these two men; the man in the frock coat was bland and persuasive, while his false-twinkling eyes roved around the faces. He held a yellow watch in one hand, wrapped around with a pound Treasury note.

"You give me back my pound," said the man standing before him—a pale-faced man obviously trying to look calm as he clenched his teeth on a dead pipe. "You give me back my pound."

"But, my dear sir, you bid me a pound for this watch. For the past ten minutes I have been standing here, demonstrating to you this excellent gold watch, warranted perfect in every part, and jewelled with the finest jewels in every hole; a watch, let me tell you, that you couldn't buy elsewhere for under two guineas at a minimum estimate. I ask you, ladies and gentlemen, am I standing here to be made a fool of?"

"You give me back my pound. I never bid for the watch. I didn't want no watch. You asked to me lend you a penny, and I did. Then you asked me to lend you two shillings, and I did. Then you asked me to lend you a pound, and I did. I never bid for no watch."

The roving eyes of the Frock-coated Jew swept the crowd. A look of surprised indignation, almost of pain, came into them. The Frock-coated Jew took a deep breath; he nodded his head, his lips being tightly pressed together. Then, with thumbs in upper waistcoat pockets, chin sunken on his collar—now we know why it was so grimy just there—forehead wrinkled, he prepared some devastating remark. But he changed his mind; the smile broke out again.

"I'll tell you what," he exclaimed abruptly, holding out the watch wrapped in the pound note. "Look here," as his face widened in a grin. "I'll make you another present! Look here! Ladies and Gentlemen, obviously this gentleman is a business gentleman. Well, so are we all! We all want value for our money! Look here, sir. You see this watch?"

The pale Pipe-clenching Man, after a period of fixed silence, admitted reluctantly and cautiously that he saw it.

"You see this pound note?"

The Frock-coated Jew slapped it with his other hand.

"Yes, I see it."

"Good. Look here, just for an advertisement. I'm going to make you a handsome offer. Just to advertise the goods of my firm. Will you bid me a pound for this watch *and* the pound note. There, I'm giving it to you! You bid me a pound note for this pound note *and* a watch. Never mind about robbing me. I'm here to advertise my goods. You want something for nothing, that's what you came here for, wasn't it? Well, now's your chance! And may you sleep easily o' nights ever afterwards!".

He waited, smiling: the crowd waited. A watch and a pound for a pound. Why didn't the man accept, quickly? But the Pipe-clenching Man repeated monotonously, "You give me back my pound! You said you would make me a present of the watch! Well, I don't want it, even as a present. You give me back my pound, or I'll call a policeman."

The pipe shook in his hand, his face was as pallid as the under-side of a flatfish.

"Oh, you'll call a policeman, will you? And you've had all the other free gifts, and now you want this gold watch, also as a free gift, eh? What do you think of that, ladies and gentle-men?"

"Oh, dirty, dirty!" promptly cried a man in the crowd—a man with a swivel eye, broken lips, and unclean collar.

"Dirty! dirty!" echoed another man on the outskirts, as he shook his head. He, too, wore an unclean collar, and grimy canvas shoes.

"Dirty!" exclaimed Swivel Eye and Canvas Shoes together, shaking their heads.

"You see what these ladies and gentlemen think about it, don't you?" suggested the Frock-coated Jew. "Here am I, a gentleman what has to work hard for a living, and you come here and try to get a gold watch for nothing!"

"A twister!" suggested Swivel Eye, significantly.

"Twister!" agreed Canvas Shoes.

"You give me back my pound, or I'll call a policeman! You can keep the penny and the two bob!"

Eventually the pound note was screwed up and tossed back contemptuously to the Pipe-clenching Man; the crowd eddied away; the Frock-coated Jew descended from his Ford car and strolled to where Swivel Eye and Canvas Shoes were talking together. They appeared to have forgotten what had just happened, as they munched sandwiches. Their faces were almost human again under the marks of their trade.

3

The crowd shuffled on slowly, towards the central blare and stridor of the Fair, where in the distance and over the heads of the people great circular coloured structures were revolving under a drift of steam and coal smoke. The booths stood side by side along the slowly widening horn of the moon-shaped Fair Ground. At the back of the booths we had glimpses of a jumble and congestion of motor and horse caravans, tents of faded grey canvas, cooking fires, unwashed brown-limbed babies, children with bare legs and arms and matted hair, lurcher dogs with long legs and narrow heads; but we had come to see the front of the Fair, not the back. A thrilling sight! A fat woman with rouged cheeks, black plaited hair, ear-rings, neck and arm bangles, and the name of Madame Montana, beckoned us to come into her tent, to have our fortunes told. Nothing doing; we know our own fortunes, and not having love's sickness at the moment, we do not need to hear about a dark or a fair woman.

The crowd began to thicken. We had to work our way through a dark-suited press of bowler-hatted farmers, stout mothers, young men, girls and children. Why did the older people wear such thick drab clothes, why were their teeth either false or neglected to the brown stumps? Yet how good-humoured and polite they were, these people from the villages in and under Exmoor, shuffling along slowly, mildly regarding the varied and multitudinous side-shows! Bells rang; rattles were swung crick-crakkering painfully in our ears; reed and klaxon horns scraped away the privacy of our thoughts, if any. The innumerable small coco-nut shies and hoop-la tables appeared to be disregarded. How did the owners live? They were the small contented folk who made the large majority of human beings on the earth, making a sufficient living in their work and finding contentment in every day.

Farther on were the larger booths, the gaudy colours, the sensational painted headlines. LANGUID LILY, THE LADY WHO CAN'T MARRY ("If you ask her the Reason, she will Tell you Why"). A sad-looking man took the threepences in the entrance of the flapping tent. Languid Lily had wrists as thick as a man's thigh. Dressed in a monster sort of little girl's frock, and weighing nearly a quarter of a ton, she stood on a tub and slowly heaved round, while grey-bearded farmers gazed at her colossal calves and yellow curls.

"Eef any lady or gentleman desires to ascertain the legitimate reason whai Languid Lily is unable to undertake the vows of heuly matrimony, and should care to ask her whai, she will be pleased to whisper the aforesaid reasons in his yar," announced a woman with the figure and garb of a pantomime principal boy of twenty years ago.

No one desiring to ascertain, picture postcards of Languid Lily were offered for sale at a penny each. An old Exmoor farmer with the innocent eyes of a sheep dog put his hand laboriously in his pocket and bought one. It was the only sale. Why did he buy it? Would he guard it secretly when he returned to his lonely farm in some combe of the moor, or would he put it on his chimney-piece and talk about it until next Fair?

We shuffled out of the tent again, leaving Languid Lily quietly descending from the tub. Next door was Mademoiselle Gaby Desvoeux, who had appeared before the Royalty and Nobility of the World. Draped in a velvet cloak, she stood on a raised platform before the entrance to her marquee, looking round at the crowd. In a hoarse voice her manager, beside her in dress clothes and opera hat, declared that she had appeared before All the Crowned Heads of Europe—("Both of them," remarked a wit, loudly, but we could not think so quickly as that) —and had more marks to the square inch than any other lady in the world. The price of admission was only threepence. At the mention of the sum the Tattooed Lady allowed her cloak to fall slightly open and reveal part of her corsage. This artistic touch decided some, the old Exmoor farmer included; others hurried away.

Inside, the cloak was removed to show the broad blue-wormed limbs and torso. In a voice of incredible and almost painful refinement she told us the facts and statistics of the tattooing. What shape was her tongue? In the midst of her contorted recitation the back of the marquee opened and a young face peered in. "Ma!" it said, addressing the vast blue-and-red-scrolled back, the jungle of snakes, flags, anchors, ships, houses, flowers, trees, which surrounded and suffocated the Prince of Wales—"Ma! Baby's crying!"

"Get away, you young cuss!" hissed Ma, and how relieved we felt. Outside again; what's this one—boxing? Ah, boxing!

4

The crowd was tighter and thicker by the boxing booth. Upturned faces regarded five men standing with folded arms, on a platform outside a marquee. They wore greyish-white jerseys and grey flannel trousers and rubber shoes. The man on the left was the heavy-weight, then came the light-weight, two middle-weights, and a fly-weight. One of the middle-weights was a negro; his the only face unbattered.

The manager, whose nose was flattened, challenged the crowd. He would pay two pounds to the man who remained on his feet after three rounds with any of the five champions. Marquis of Queensberry rules. Also exhibition boxing between the Dixie Kid and Boy Ovey from Cardiff. After exhorting us he blew a tarnished bugle. A man held up his hand.

"I'll do three rounds with the middle one."

"Exhibition or fight?"

"Fight. For the two quid."

"You understand what you're up against?"

"Yes."

"You're quite aware of what you're asking for?"

"Yes."

"All right."

A pair of gloves was slung over our heads. We determined to see this fight, and fumbled in our pockets for sixpence. Someone said that the challenger was an out-of-work man from Bideford; we hoped he wouldn't be knocked out. He looked rather thin with worn blue eyes. He looked as though he had survived torture, but that maybe was our fancy. The champion he had challenged, Boy Ovey of Cardiff, had a thick muscular neck and eyes that looked on the world as an easy place.

Other pairs of gloves were tossed into the crowd; and suddenly the line of five dingy white men—the negro wore the dingiest jersey—moved with interest: and one of the middleweights said to the manager:

"You know who it is, Fred? The Terror of South Wales."

"I know it."

"Right! Exhibition?"

"I'll fight, by Cripes!"

The manager hesitated, glanced at the heavy-weight on the left of the line, who said in a deep Welsh voice, while frowning:

"I'll fight if he wants a fight."

The man in the crowd who shouted out "Fight, by Cripes!" grabbed at the gloves flung to him. He smiled or rather grinned. He looked like a negro bleached white. His big canine teeth looked as though they had been filed. His cheeks and brow were nicked with old scars. Each ear was like the much-pecked comb of a cock, only pallid like his bald head and grinning face.

We went in, and waited ten minutes while the space around the raised saw-dusted ring was gradually filled with men, and sometimes a young, frank-eyed girl with her brothers or friends. At last the flap was closed behind us.

"Ladies and gentlemen, during the bouts to follow I ask you

to refrain from makin' any audible comment or noise, but to express your appreciation at the end of every round by the clap of the hand. The first contest, ladies and gentlemen, is three exhibition rounds of three minutes each between the Dixie Kid and Bill Burbridge of Cryde."

Gloves were tied on by seconds, the referee-manager called "Time", and the first round began and continued with the clopping of the Cryde champion's boots on the boards, the soft slurring of the Dixie Kid's rubber shoes, the slapping of gloves. The Dixie Kid was easily the master; the wild blows of his nervous opponent glided over his cropped head; he breathed easily and none of his actions were forced. He was merciful and good-tempered and smiled as half-playfully he tapped his opponent in vital places. It was soon over: the Cryde ploughboy hot and breathing fast; the negro quite unaffected.

"Ladies and gentlemen, I think we all agree that Bill Burbridge has fought in a sporting manner, and I ask you to put something in the hat that he will now bring round to you."

Quickly Bill Burbridge donned his coat, slipped under the ropes and was moving with his hat among the onlookers. How many times had he done it before?

Now for the fight. The terms were announced again. "And if the Bideford Lad is on his feet after three rounds, he takes two pounds. Ladies and Gentlemen, I ask you to refrain from making any audible comment or noise. On my right Boy Ovey of Cardiff, on my left the Bideford Lad. Seconds out. Time!"

They crossed gloves and shook; stepped back and squared up.

Very soon there was blood on the cheek of the booted Bideford out-of-work, who fought in his ordinary clothes, except that he had taken off coat, collar, and waistcoat, and rolled up his shirt-sleeves. His blue eyes looked more worn; we heard him breathing hard. Most of his blows were avoided by Boy Ovey, who hit him again and again, but not really hard. Smack, thud, clump—the booted one was driven into a corner. "Time," shouted the referee, looking up from his hand, and some of the onlookers lighted cigarettes in relief. Others declared that he was getting only what he could have expected. Meanwhile one of the Bideford Lad's seconds was flapping a much-used towel in his face, and the other was sponging his cheek. The fighting man's eyes seemed a more haunted blue; perhaps he was hungry. Perhaps—but pity, like whiskey, can be a falsifying stimulant. We want the good plain water of facts.

"Seconds out! Time!"

How tired were his arms, how harsh his breathing! Towards the end of the second minute Boy Ovey was hitting him where he liked, but never so hard as he might. Suddenly the Bideford Lad shook his head, and the referee thrust his arm between them. The Bideford Lad leant back on the ropes, wiping his brow with his right forearm. Boy Ovey stood easily in his own corner.

"Well, ladies and gentlemen, I think you'll admit that it was a sporting fight, and that in stopping it I did so only when there was no doubt about the issue. Ladies and gentlemen, show your appreciation by the clap of the hand. Now I think we all agree that the Bideford Lad put up a plucky fight, and deserves some token of appreciation, so I'll ask him to step down among you with his hat. Thank you, ladies and gentlemen."

Quickly the Bideford Lad slipped under the ropes and came among us, saying "Thank you" for the chink of coppers in his hat.

Later I saw him fighting again. He appeared at many of the bouts. Perhaps it was arranged that he would neither be knocked out nor receive any money except the coppers in his hat. He must have taken several pounds' worth of copper coins during the three days.

The fight between the young heavy-weight, the Champion of the West of England, and the Terror of South Wales came next. That, too, must have been arranged. The powerful young Welshman stood half a head above the old Terror, whom he hit several times, with what appeared to be a vigilant respect. The old man's head was bald, scarred like his face; he grinned and grinned, while the taller man danced round him, frowning, and keeping him at arm's length. Once they got close and "mixed it"; there were noises like a badger, like many badgers, grunting; the younger man clinched. When they broke he sprang back, and the shuffle-dance around the grim and grinning prize-fighter began again.

Suddenly the upcurving right arm of the Terror seemed to fill the ring; it was a terrific swing, swishing six inches off the other's ear. *Bang!* went the Terror's boots on the floor, and a buzz broke out in the tent. The Terror grinned wickedly, wrinkling his bald head with its scarred ears; his opponent smiled grimly. "You old booger!" he muttered. Was that swing, with all the tigerish force of the Terror of South Wales behind it, in the arrangement? The young champion danced around more nimbly, and pushed the old man in the face with a long-reaching arm whenever he could.

He frowned.

"By Cripes, you won't put me to sleep, you young heller, you!" grinned the Terror.

After the third round two notes were handed over to the grinning Terror (he must have been nearly seventy years of age), who took his coat, celluloid collar, and tie from his woman standing by the ring. Her hair, piled up like a great pine-apple, was a very bright yellow. She wore a feathered hat. The skin of a fox was slung round her shoulders. Between her and the Terror then ensued a short sharp dialogue which ended only when the two notes had been thrust into her handbag. She must have been his wife. He followed her out of the tent, grinning like a ram in wolf's clothing.

At night, and especially the last night of the Fair, the fighting was fast and hard. Young men, having had a few pints, were liable to challenge recklessly. I remember one such who, on the first cry of *seconds out!* jumped up and took a round swing at a negro called Jimmy James of Harlem. Jimmy James stood still, merely lowering his head, over which the blow swished like a scythe in grass. Flung off his balance by the desperate swing, the ploughboy fell into his corner; his hand struck the post, and the force broke one of his fingers.

Jimmy James was a terrifying object as he moved in a sinister crouch around the ring, with his left elbow crooked across the upper part of his face, and his right arm held out like the padded claw of a coal-black lobster. His eyes had the intentness and inscrutability of a lobster's eyes. Furious swipes were aimed at him, hitting his shoulders and glancing off that bony right arm. Desperate blows were rained on his skull. He heeded none of them, but moved after his opponent, avoiding the blows, spending no strength himself. Sooner or later—usually sooner—his opponent would make an extra wild swipe at the curly nob and yellow-white eyeballs: instantly the muscles of the pacing black torso would set in their power: instantly the hard ebony arm with an effortless sweep would drive all consciousness out of the other's skull. It happened; and the other man was lying on his back, slightly writhing, and Jimmy James of Harlem was looking unconcernedly at the crowd.

Towards the end of the Friday night, when the naphtha flares were smoking ragged and tawny in the wind, and mazed drunken voices bawled and cheered, a most amusing fight occurred. The Champion of the West of England, the deep-voiced young heavy-weight Welshman, was challenged by a small skittle-pin of a man dressed in a sailor's uniform. Skittle-pin's head came up to the Champion's shoulders, and he was much under his weight.

"Hell, I don't fight little boys," said the Champion, contemptuously.

"Wind up!" jeered Skittle-pin's friends. "Frightened you'll lose your two quid!" "You said you'd fight all comers, you long streak of p—— in a gaspipe!" These and other taunts were shouted at the frowning Welshman.

The naphtha flares lit the moving faces. It was nearly midnight, and already many of the smaller booths were being packed up. Angered by the taunts, the Champion said he would fight.

The tent was crowded to watch it. The sailor stripped to the waist, revealing an armour-plate of blue tatooed muscles.

Hardly had the referee called "Time!" when he smote the Champion on the nose twice, causing the crowd to roar. This infuriated the Champion, who slashed the smaller man; but he could not hit him. Laughing and taunting, the tattooed Skittle-pin slipped all the Champion's blows; and, getting under his guard, punched him on the ribs so fast that not one blow could be seen. The Champion grunted, and clinched; but the smaller man laughed, twisted out of his clasp, and hit him until he grunted and sagged; and then a round-arm blow reached upwards, clicked and jarred the Champion's jaw, so that he sank down and remained down for the count.

"Any more want to meet me?" grinned Skittle-pin in the direction of the Champion's seconds.

Jimmy James of Harlem clapped his hands, grinning widely, the crowd roared and cheered; the Champion was lugged to his feet and sat sagging in his corner. Soon he was smiling, and shaking the winner's glove. "Who the hell are you?" he asked.

The little man was the Light-weight Champion of the Royal Navy.

5

For threepence you might enter another booth and see the dwarfs. There were two, presumably male and female. They were about a yard high. They were supposed to be married, and to have a baby. Every year there was a baby in a perambulator inside the pen with the blue-suited dwarf and his doll-like wife; a fat baby with a head shaped like a vegetable marrow, obviously an ordinary baby. The eyes of the dwarfs were round and large, their voices were tinny, and their attempts at familiarity made you feel uneasy. The female was a tragic and rickety little middle-aged figure. A local doctor told me that when he had to attend the female dwarf for drinking too much brandy, or it may have been methylated spirit, she was coyly amorous towards him, asking him to sit beside her, to hold her hand. "Come on, be matey," she squeaked. Although he did not show it under his impersonal cheery manner, the doctor was repelled and humiliated within himself; and although he tried to feel pity for her, he really felt that such an unfortunate physical state should not be permitted to survive its infancy. So a distorted and dwarfed plant on a wall strives to put out a blossom; and so strong chickens, ignorant of any reason, will peck a weakly bird to death.

6

The mild, almost personal, English sunshine outside, which seldom or never entered the dwarfs' booth, soon restored the nervous force that had been taken from me unconsciously. Soon upon me was thrust the essence of the jungle sun, a harsh and crude sun, which stirred and vitalized until it wearied with its overmuchness—the chaotic jazzy blaring of three roundabouts together. Primary colours, chiefly yellow and red and blue, revolved and noisily sinuated before my eyes, while the smoke of the steam-engines driving the dynamos rose and drifted away behind them. These were the engines which drew the roundabouts and the caravans to the Fair Ground, and tore up the tarmac surface of the road with the oblique tracks of their great iron wheels. Now they stood with humming fly-wheels and whirring driving-bands, panting and shaking against the wooden chocks. For threepence I found myself beside others in a sort of chariot and was jolted up and down and around a circle about a dozen times, while decisive notes of the pipes smote *Show Me the Way To Go Home* on my ears, and the dummy figures in pale blue and pink clashed the brass cymbals and struck their hammers mechanically near the heart of the engine. Afterwards there were the horses of the rival roundabout, which whirled us round to the shining metallic noise-shafts of *Yes, We Have No Bananas*. Beside the horses were the roundabout swings, whose wooden seats, held by two slender chains, whirled one higher and higher over the people below, while thoughts of what would happen if the slender chains were to break gripped the spine-bases of some of the village girls, causing them to utter shrieks of fear and laughter.

Higher and wider the slender chains took them: the funnel of the engine driving the dynamo beside the fence of the Fair Ground gushed smoke and quivering air under their outflung feet: they tried desperately to be themselves in a confusion of drab and coloured squares, circles, polished brass rods, black bowler hats, upturned faces, ships and water, green fields in the distance, all whirling above perpetual noise.

Then there was a smaller, out-of-date roundabout, which only the littlest children used, a drab and humble affair set in motion by an old man turning a handle. The hands that took the little boy's penny were as hard and yellow as cow-horn. The wooden horses were chipped, their paint faded; the canvas awning was split and rotten. Some children perched there solemnly; others smiled with enjoyment. I watched the old man for an hour; he took tenpence during that time. At night, when the electric lights studded the great noisy trundling giants with brilliance, this old man would be sitting smoking his pipe in the caravan where he was the lodger, hearing little of the din outside, as he browsed in the worn fields of his mind. One day, after the departure of the Fair from one of its many visiting grounds, the old iron framework of the ancient roundabout— its woodwork stripped for firewood—would be left standing among the cinders and paper litter; and who could say where the old fellow would be then?

7

As I pressed through the people on my way to the booths and stalls lining both sides of the street, I had to run the gauntlet of the gipsy girls who were in charge of the rifle ranges. For any youth or man under seventy years of age it was embarrassing to glance at their eyes; for then they darted forward with a lithe and seductive motion, holding out a small rifle for him to take.

"Come, my fine gentleman! Try your luck, my gentleman! Only sixpence for four shots! Come along, my gentleman. I've had a hard time, my gentleman, and only taken a shilling all the morning."

Many words were poured softly in my ear. I tried to be firm, and avoid the tigress-eyes and tongues, looking straight ahead, murmuring continually, "No thank you, no thank you." The farmers disregarded them, and were seldom appealed to. The word "gipsy" in the village was usually spoken with slight contempt. Gipsy girls, the sun and the wind, golden brown faces, plaited coils of hair like ripe wheat, strong and supple figures— my thoughts were my own, and alas must remain thoughts.

8

Then came the stalls where heaps of gaudy sweets were piled, with the brown curled toffee fairings which I must buy and taste for old times' sake. There were dozens of children darting about to whom it could be given. Pass on to the Hoop-la awnings which took a score of sixpences for every sixpence-worth of cigarettes, chocolate, jewellery, opera glasses, vanity bags, etc., handed over to the lucky ring throwers. Then to a modern toffee-making machine, smart with nickel and paint and gleaming aluminium, where a pretty girl in white cap and over-all, working serenely in the gaze of many people, mixed the butter, the sugar, and the treacle—or it might have been the coco-nut grease, the glucose, and the treacle—which was then cooked, rolled flat into trays, and passed into the clicking machine to drop out in paper-wrapped cubes.

"It's lovely toffee!" declared a rather tired voice. Who could have spoken? Could it be this young man, who stands in front of the modern factory on wheels?

"Sixpence the quarter, or a shilling the half-pound box. It's lovely toffee."

The young man showed no interest in the little factory. He glanced at his brogue shoes, at his stockings, at the overplus of his knickers, at his cuffs, at his nails. He moved about, shifting a matchstick on the ground with his toe, crushing a cigarette stub, scraping the bare earth with first one shoe, then the other. "It's lovely toffee."

So impersonal and remote was he that I believed him, but I didn't want any toffee. I went away, I came back. "Sixpence the quarter, a shilling the half-pound box. It's lovely toffee." Suddenly I found myself buying.

"Sixpence the quarter, thank you."

It *was* lovely toffee.

Other sweet-stuff sellers, other methods. Here at my elbow as I chewed, wondering if the temporary filling of my tooth would be pulled out by the toffee, stood the sinister figure of the silent Masked Man. He was dressed in black! The orchestra was in perpetual overture behind him, the two blaring tunes crashing into each other and disintegrating. Was this tragic or comic opera? *Show me the way to have no bananas.* A tray was slung from the Masked Man's shoulders, resting against his celluloid shirt-front. On it were the packets of mystery, wrapped in plain white paper.

> I AM DUMB BUT MY GOODS SPEAK FOR THEMSELVES
> I AM UNDER OATH NOT TO OPEN MY MOUTH
> GREAT AND SURPRISING VALUE
> ONLY SIXPENCE

I passed the dark figure many times during the day, and never saw anyone spending only sixpence at the dumb counter. Those boots! How far had he walked? Why didn't he make it three-pence? His pursed lips, his glance through the mask was disquieting. Would he be there next Fair? He would probably curse me if I suggested, in all benevolence, that his get-up was negative, disconcerting, too much blackness. His eyes were black behind the black mask. I could not make contact with him. The sixpence, fingered often, remained in my pocket. It was—the black hat, the black mask, the black stare, the down-at-heel boots! A man wanted to be able to feel happy at the Fair.

THE FAIR: MORNING

Let us observe how the positive method succeeds.

Here is the Chocolate Kid. He is smiling, in shirt-sleeves; his top hat is ruffled and dented; his gestures are big and confident. His name is printed large and bold for all to see. And curiously, he looks a Chocolate Kid. His face, under the top-hat stuck around with crumpled ten-shilling notes, is yellowish-brown, as though he ate nothing but chocolate. He thwacks a rolled-up newspaper on his palm. "Half a crown the half pound! Who'll bid? Half a crown? Two shillings. Only half a dollar?" *Thwack*. "Here, I'll tell you what—one and sixpence. One and six. What, nobody wants a half pound of the Chocolate Kid's best chocolates for one and sixpence? Here, I'll give them away at a shilling! Going for a shilling." *Thwack*. He gazes round at the semicircle of faces. "Here!" an extra loud thwack of the paper on his knee. "Sixpence! Right, sir. Thank you. Bill, give this pound box of The Prince of Wales's Own Special Chocolates to the lady over there. You, sir? And you, madam? Thank you."

When the sale is over, the Chocolate Kid begins again with another box, taken from the top of several gross of white boxes piled on the trestle table behind which, like a tin imitation of the Mad Hatter, he stands and addresses people all day and every day. Sixpences clink into his box. He will be there next year.

When I had given my box of Prince of Wales's Own Special Chocolates, less the solitary one I bit, tasted, and spat out, to one of the sparrow-like children darting about, I could buy grapes from the fat man who, with a white top-hat stuck on the back of his boar's head, was to be found standing on a cart near the station. I noticed that these grapes, which the fat man pulled out of a box with a rain of cork dust dropping from his enormous fingers, were sold to thirsty, inoffensive, and elderly parsons for a shilling a pound; but they could be bought, with a minimum of words, for half that price. This is the way to buy them:—

Let Boar's-head, whose waistcoat is burst and stretched twelve inches across the back owing to his exertions, talk himself out, which happens very soon; and then when he has, metaphorically and literally, burst himself again, hold out sixpence. You may remark, as the bag is dropped into your hand, that his grapes are very good; but he will be too hot to answer, and his eye, like that of a long white lop-eared pig, will be roving around the crowd—for the Annual Fair ground swarms with parsons.

Chapter Fourteen

WHAT THE DOCTOR SAID

I was getting fed-up with the noise and the faces, and decided it was time to eat something, so I went to have lunch of beer, cheese, bread, and pickled shallots at *The Ketch at Anchor Inn.* There I met a friend who was a doctor. Talking about cheap-jacks and quacks, he said,

"There was an old chap who used to practise in the village years ago who was called 'Butcher' Baggott. Half his maternity cases died. He used to say, 'There you are, I can't do any more: don't blame me for the anatomical design of the human body: wipe the blood up, and get the bedroom wall lime-washed.' "

It sounded stark; but such were the doctor's words. Outside the noises of the Fair were beginning to increase. He told me about a woman named Charity Vallance, who was a white witch —she helped people who were sick, and all her incantations were benevolent. Charity Vallance lived alone, and acted as a self-appointed unpaid parish nurse. Her treatment of sick cases was at least as successful, or unsuccessful, as that of Dr. Baggott. For kidney disease she would recommend applications of fresh cowdung, which, she declared, must be "caught hot". Once when the doctor asked her to keep a specimen of the water of a woman in an outlying farm suspected of diabetes—the doctor said he would be back in a couple of days—he returned to find the room filled with pots, pans, jars, and other receptacles; and the faithful Charity declared that she "had not missed a drop" during the forty-eight hours.

WHAT THE DOCTOR SAID

For rickets Charity would bake a mouse in the oven, grind up the cinders, and mix them with milk into a potion, while muttering "Mousie's din (hair) best colour inder zin (sun), so may the Lord make this chiel's leg straight as the zin's glance, Amen."

"When old Dr. Baggott gave up practising, he showed me his collection of queer letters. You can copy this one and print it in your book if you like. Notice the extra initial she gave him—the extra B, for Butcher."

Saturday Morning.

To Dr. B. Baggott.

Enclosed is 17s. to receipt Bill no doubt the Rector told you that he said it was a sad misfortune for me having such an awful blow to make me in this fearfull state I told him So the minute he and Mrs. Tigg helped me up and I have told you for 20 years if that jaw realeased its bearing it would be very serious as I was ten or twelve years suffering that side that the mussels and cords were strained to mere threads then the double blow the right side finished me something gave way and shuffled down my back and has settled at the small of the back causing me to be crippled and indigestion my hearing is knocked out my jaw and my sight is bad years ago you told me it was quite normal and likely to remain like it when you saw me for a long and expensive time the heavy brain pressure is causing it my headaches is awfull what you called *Rot* Oh that ever I should have went up for medicine when I was well strong and healthy as I had been for 50 or 60 years but thought a couple of Bottles of medicine would do my liver good as you said it was *rotton* you said my burning eyes was the liver Oh you bad wicked man you knew it was caused by the jaw releasing its bearing and so it remains no Specialist can do me any good now I am shut up for life and broken hearted being all on my own it is my wish to have a post-mortem when my breath stops which I hope wont be long.

Yours truly,

Victoria Garnish.

"Well, good-bye," said the doctor, "don't let any of those bloody rogues outside sell you a brass watch."

I was getting tired of the Fair, but decided to stick it out, for the sake of posterity: I wanted my record of village life in the nineteen twenties to be as comprehensive as possible. On the morrow, I told myself, I would follow the stream down the valley to the sea; I was weary of human beings.

Chapter Fifteen

THE FAIR: AFTERNOON

I

The narrow lane between the rifle ranges and the sweet stalls debouched into the square before the Town Station. Here stood an Open Air Mission, a Fish and Chip Engine, an Ice Cream Barrow, and laid-out heaps of clothes, boots, bridles, spades, tools, nails, and other country gear, arranged on pitches on the roadway. Beyond was a space wherein a man was being bound in chains and ropes. Beside the hollow human square arose the shrill voice of Maisie the American Master Mystic. Noise and confusion of sounds were everywhere. Scores of pedlars were selling balloons, toys, laces, studs, and innumerable other little things. And the insistent voices of half a dozen Human Spiders.

First I looked at the Master Mystic. She was a woman, with a thin face and red nose. I wondered if she had tried the many remedies for Indigestion offered about the Fair. She was dressed in a light frock which the wind blew against her thin frame. Her partner stood beside her on the platform. He was a fat man dressed in a blue, almost purple, suit, out of which emerged big purple hands and a very large purple face. Periodically he beat a gong, and then Maisie addressed, or endeavoured to address, the crowd in her thin, strained, high-pitched voice about the Unsolved Problems of To-day. The lips of the Purple Faced Man followed the patter of her words; and when her weak voice grew almost inaudible he banged the gong and shouted about the Spiritual Forces all Around Human Life To-day.

Most of the people under their platform were not looking their way, however, but at a ragged man with a cropped head and wide mouth who was hoarsely inviting any gent to tie his wrists behind his back, and to enwind him with chains, and secure the ends with a padlock. There were the ropes, the chains, the padlock. Any gent! The tighter the better. He stared round the ring of faces. Any gent?

I watched the ragged man hoarsely asking us to put chains upon him, but the powerful voices of the Open Air Mission drove me away. I returned, and stared at the sorrowful figure in chains. What was there about him that was disturbing? Then I saw in the slow, good-humoured movements the type of common soldier whose puttees were usually askew; the big-mouthed company clown who hated no one, and whom nothing could dispirit; the sort of mud-slabbed creature who crawled to his officer, many years his junior, lying cold unto death in an ice-ragged outpost-crater of the Passchendaele morasses, and muttered, "I'm wiv yer, boy." Here he was, with his wide smiling mouth, in his rags of uniform, chewing a quid of tobacco, grin ning as he submitted to the chains out of which he presently strove to twist and wriggle, shaking his head like a dog in play as he rolled on the wet ground while tugging with his teeth, and all for the penny that you might, or might not, put into the hat like a shapeless bag brought round by his chum, a man stumping on a wooden leg, and carrying a small child in the crook of his other arm. This old soldier looked at every eye as he said, "Thank you;" he read a man swiftly, and when he saw that more than a coin had been given, he gave you a deep look and a smile.

2

Offset from this hollow square were several groups, suggesting spider-webs thickly laden with dark-clad figures. They were the petty swindlers: like the fellow at the entrance to the Fair ground, they were dark, curly-headed, sloe-eyed, fat red-lipped men, with fat protuberant noses. In the centre of each web stood a man, or a human spider, shouting and gesticulating. All the shouting, the pleading, the slick humour, had but one object—to lure a few people forward so that the Spider might catch them and suck their economic blood.

The spinning of the web varied slightly with each Human Spider. One was just beginning to twist his main support-line. I stopped to watch his technique. A man with a blue-shaven chin and bad teeth, wearing a blue suit, a worn bowler hat rammed down so that his ears stuck out, suddenly bent down and gripped the arm of a passing urchin. The urchin, whom I had seen at several September Fairs, was remarkable in that he appeared to have remained the same size year after year, and that his head was the shape of one half of a crab's claw, exceedingly small, with scarcely any crown. Hair like yellow feathers fell over the narrow brow, half covering the bird-like eyes.

"Ho, where do you come from, eh?" loudly cried the man with the blue chin and oversized bowler hat.

"Yurr! You leave go me ar-rm!" cried the boy, struggling and grinning.

"Would you like a fly in an aeroplane ter night, and ter be dropped from a parrowshoot, eh?" shouted the other.

"Yurr! You ain't got no aeriplane! I knows that!"

"Ain't got no aeroplane? That's not the way ter speak, my boy. Ain't yer got schools in this town ter learn yer 'ow ter speak? I'll come and tell yer master, I will."

"Yurr! Leave go! You can't frighten I, maister!"

"Ho, I can't, can't I?"

Several people stood around, drawn by the sight and the loud voice.

"What's yer father, eh? Jus' you tell me that, now!"

"Feyther be a dustman."

"Ho, a dustman? Well, let me tell you this, that emptying dustbins is a very dry occupation. Does he like beer?"

"Aiy, when 'e can get it!"

"Do you like beer?"

"No."

"Ho, you don't, do you? Well, let me tell you this, I do, when I can get it! And shall I tell you how I'm going to get a whole barrel very soon, and what I'm going to do with it? I'm going to give it away! Just as an advertisement! That's what I'm going to do! And if any lady or gentleman"—addressing the now considerable crowd—"wants further particulars of this FREE BEER, I shall only be too pleased to refer you to my partner. Just to show we are up-to-date advertisers my partner will now distribute a few presents, absolutely free, gratis, and fer nothing."

He pointed to a man, standing up in a motor car, who slowly smiled. The smile vanished remarkably quickly; he began to speak loudly, as he flung some articles into the semicircle facing him—a few shaving sticks here, a couple of pipes there, fountain pens, small white boxes containing brooches and clasps. Each article was mildly scrambled for. Meanwhile Bluechin had disappeared.

"Now I want six ladies and gentlemen to form a committee, each member to lend me a penny! I'm asking six ladies, or gentlemen, to lend me a penny each! I am doing this to advertise my goods! Nowadays you've got to pay out if you want to sell anything, and I'm here to-day to do the paying out! Six ladies and gentlemen, to lend me six pennies between them! A shilling, sir, did you kindly offer? Thank you, but one penny will be sufficient! It is very kind of you, sir, to offer a shilling; it is very heartening, and shows that honesty is always the best policy. Only a penny, sir! Thank you. Now I want five more to join my committee.

You, sir? Thank you! Kindly come forward, sir, if you please Make way for the gentleman please."

O horror, his roving eye had fixed itself on me. His smile was bland as melting grease.

"Now, sir, I can see that you have plenty of initiative. You're not one of the shy ones, I'll warrant. Will you set an example to the rest of the ladies and gentlemen present, and come and stand here before me? Come, don't be shy."

The personal address, unless you have the moral support of friends beside you, is as gum tacking you to the spider-web. You do not move; you try to look unconcerned and amiable. You remember the poor show made by the Pipe-clenching Man.

"Just make way for the gentleman, please."

I stood still, and shook my head, grinning with fatuous amiability.

"What, won't you lend me a penny?"

I tried to change the grin into a smile.

"Here, take this!"

He tossed a cigarette case to me. I didn't want it, but I caught it, and continued to grin. I didn't want the damned thing, yet I held it. The Human Spider's gaze was fixed upon me. His bland-grease smile was going; it was gone. With a rancid look he shouted from his platform,

"Can't you even say 'Thank you' for a free present? Lor' lumme, haven't you got any manners?"

I shook my head.

"Here, I'll tell you what! Here's something else for nothing. If you don't smoke I can see you shave! Here's a stick of shaving soap! Here, catch!"

His partner held out a small cylinder of yellow soap.

"No, thank you," I said. "I don't want it."

"Doesn't like the look of soap, eh? Let the gentleman smell it, Sol!"

Sol, otherwise Bluechin, held the cheap little cylinder of soap under my nose.

"Nice smell, ain't it? Tell the other ladies and gentlemen."

"Very nice. But I've decided to grow a beard, thanks all the same."

And at the laughter, Bluechin says,

"Have another sniff," and with a slight upward movement of his wrist, and a leer on his face, he jabbed the soap under my nose. Tears ran slowly down my nostrils with the unexpected pain. I slackened my muscles, until the desire to punch him on the nose subsided. "Well, thank God they're not all like you," commented the Chief Spider, and glanced around, having forgotten me.

After another free tossing-out of gifts, he drew six people to the hub of his web; and yes, one of them was the old bearded farmer with the mild sheep-dog eyes, who bought the photograph of Languid Lily, the Lady who Can't Marry.

The Committee was now complete. The members were assured that they would be required to do nothing except to lend their pennies.

He held out an imitation leather box, stamped with gilt lettering.

"Who will bid me one penny—one penny only—for the contents of this box? Now, I'm asking you to trust me. I tell you there is good value in this box, and I ask someone to bid me a penny for it."

"I will."

It was the man who offered first to join the Committee.

"You will bid me a penny for this box and its contents, sir? Although you haven't seen inside it?"

"I will."

"You trust me, sir?"

"I do."

"Very well, since it Pays to Advertise, I'll take your bid. Perhaps you wouldn't mind showing the ladies and gentlemen what is inside your box, sir?"

The box was opened. Something glittered in the sun.

"What is it, sir?"

"A gold lady's wrist watch. Thank you very much!"

"A gold lady's wrist watch! A gold wristlet watch for a lady! What lady, I will not enquire, sir! This is a free country, although sometimes when I go home late at night I begin to wonder. Are you satisfied, sir?"

"Perfectly."

"So am I, sir. As I told you, ladies and gentlemen, I am here solely to advertise my goods. Now, I have here another box, a plain cardboard box, as you perceive. Now who will bid me a penny for this?"

"I will."

"Ah ha, sir, you want another watch for another lady! Dirty work at the cross roads, gentlemen! Well, sir, I'm going to ask you to bid me two shillings for the contents of this box."

"I will."

"Even if I tell you now that it may be empty? That there's nothing in it? Will you bid me two shillings for this box under those conditions? And be satisfied? Mind you, I'm stating that there may be nothing in the box. Are you still willing to bid me two shillings?"

"I am."

"Will any other lady or gentleman bid me two shillings for this box? Half a crown? You, sir? You? You? Well, what's up with you? I'm telling you it pays to advertise and I am here, on be'alf of my firm, to advertise these goods. Very well. You, sir, I think, bid me two shillings for this box, although I clearly stated in the presence of witnesses that it might be empty?"

"I did."

"You are still willing to bid me two shillings?"

"Certainly."

"Here you are, sir. I hope you are satisfied."

The satisfied man held up another wristlet watch.

"Now go to the nearest watchmaker, and ask his opinion upon that watch, sir. Jewels in every hole. Try and buy it to-day for two pounds, and would you be able to do it? I don't think so. I know you couldn't. I am here, let me repeat, to advertise my goods, and so I'm giving them away. Yes. I'm giving them away! Here, sir, is your shilling and your penny. Here, I'll tell you what. I'll make you a further present of them! A catch in it, I hear some sceptic say? Very well, sir, if you can prove that there is a catch in giving away two handsome jewelled gold watches with the sum of one shilling and one penny, then, sir, I will give ONE HUNDRED POUNDS TO THE NEAREST HOSPITAL."

During the pause after this important declaration, the assistant with the blue chin and hat-pressed ears gave him another box. The Advertiser, his gaze continually roving about the web of people, opened the box, took out something in tissue paper, unrolled it slowly, and then, as he declared his charitable offer, held out a third glittering watch.

"Now, sir," addressing another of his committee men, as he rolled back his cuffs and with pseudo-slim fat fingers opened the watch. "Will you bid me a pound for this watch?"

No answer.

"Come, sir, do not be shy! I'm making you a grand advertising offer. Very well. I admire caution. Will you lend me, for a few moments only, a pound note?"

"I will," said the man who had got the two watches.

"One moment, sir! I'm here to advertise my gold watches by distributing a limited number only. You have two already. I appeal to your sportsmanship and sense of British Fair Play to let others have a chance, sir."

"Quite right. I'll stand down."

"Now, sir, will you lend me a pound note? You shall have it back. What, you haven't one? Then I'll give you one. Will you accept this note, sir?"

The man shook his head.

The advertiser made a pretence of despair, and put on his hat.

He took it off again, and leaned forward.

"Will you lend me a pound note, sir?" he enquired of the grey-beard farmer. "I am only asking you to *lend* me a pound, remember."

Slowly the old man took out a note and handed it over. The Advertiser picked up another box.

"Now, sir, will you bid me a pound for this box, taking a chance whether it's empty, or whether it contains a gold lever watch jewelled in every hole? A watch that will tell the time more constantly than the sun itself. Look here, I'll tell you what I'll do. Here's the open box. It contains, as you can see, a gold watch. A gold lever watch, jewelled in every hole, such as millionaires the world over are in possession of to-day. Now you did not, I think, bid me two shillings just now for a similar box. Now I'll tell you what I'm going to do, sir, just to advertise my goods. I'm going to put your penny with this watch, and now I'm going to put a two-shilling piece with the watch and the penny, and now I'm going to wrap the whole lot round with the pound note. There they are. Now, sir, will you bid me One Pound for the watch, together with the pound note, the two-shilling piece, and the penny?"

For several moments the box and the money were held before the eyes of the farmer; until slowly the old man put his hand in his pocket and pulled out another pound note, and held it up towards the motionless Spider with the black curly hair, smiling and leaning down to him. A slow smile widened his bearded lips, as the old farmer nodded.

"Are you satisfied, sir?" said Spider, softly.

"Yesmye," said the farmer, and I saw his bright eyes as he turned away. The crowd, its curiosity satisfied, became unloosened from the web, and the Spider got down from his car and lit a cigarette. I knew, from a conversation with a watchmaker in Bear Street, that the petty confidence tricksters bought their brass watches, which were called "crash stuff" by the trade, by the gross, and the thing he had sold for one pound to the farmer had cost him about eighteenpence.

3

It had stopped raining; but the day was "dirty". The roundabouts blared in the near distance; my waterproof riding coat hung damp and heavy on me. After an aimless prowl around I

stood and watched a man selling something on a stall beside one
of the forsaken cheap-jack platforms. The man was without a
hat, and his hair was wild. He stood on one leg. The naked
foot of his other leg was displayed on a stool before him. He
addressed half a dozen people.

"I can save all burning of the flesh," he yelled. "For God's
sake take my advice."

The veins on his pale forehead swelled with the vehemence
of his shouting. There was froth on the corners of his mouth.
A big red-faced man, rolling the stub of a cigarette in his fat
lips, stood beside him, looking down at the naked foot, on
which several patches of plaster were stuck.

Four other people, including myself, gazed apathetically towards him. One of them looked like a farm labourer in his best
clothes: cowhair was stuck into the band of his bowler hat. It
was a sign to any farmer who wanted a man that he was waiting
to be hired for the coming year, Michaelmas to Michaelmas.

"I want your confidence!" suddenly yelled the man with the
veined forehead, staring at me.

"All you people go the right way to get it, too," I murmured
ironically to myself, preparing to move away. Supposing he
insisted on sticking plaster somewhere on me? Or gave me a
black eye?

"You'll be twisted everywhere else! But if you can't tell a
gentleman when he's speaking, what the devil can you expect
except to be twisted?"

Now what could I answer? I began to cough, but stopped
suddenly: for he might sell cough-cure as well.

"I am here to help all who suffer in the pedal extremities, or,
to drop medical professional technicalities, in the feet. No one
here, within sound of my voice, need ever to be a cripple any
more. My Paradise Corn Cure, sixpence the packet or three for
a shilling, is famous in this world and the next, for my firm has
been established over one hundred years!" His tones alternated
between frenzy and the smoothest persuasion.

Across the street a small man in white peaked cap like a

General's cap, and a white coat like a Surgeon's coat, began to ring a hand-bell. "I say! I say!" he cried, then relapsed into a moody pacing up and down in the gutter before his white ice cream cart. A few drops of rain fell.

I began to jot down in my note-book the statements of the vehement man about his Paradise Corn Cure. Just beyond the Ice Cream Merchant stood the Open Air Mission—a caravan on wheels, with an open side showing a raised platform. Four men and a woman sat on the platform out of the wind and rain. Religious texts were hung inside on the wooden walls. One of the men, with a heavy clean-shaven face and pince-nez spectacles, was playing a harmonium, and leading the singing of a hymn with a stentorian voice. The other men sang with loud determination. The woman's voice, frail but determined, was pitched an octave higher.

> *Throw the life-line!*
> *Throw the life-line!*
> *There's one poor sinner to be saved!*

The Corn Cure Merchant threw them a wild glance, and muttered to himself. Then he almost shrieked, as a gust of wind flapped the skirts of our coats,

"Christ Almighty, the weather! But God is good, and if it rains to-day, it will be fine to-morrow. With my Paradise Corn Cure I'll shift a corn in two nights, I'll ease a bunion in three, I'll clear a wart in four dressings! For God's sake believe me! You'll be twisted elsewhere."

" I say! I say!" yelled the Ice Cream man.

As I was writing down his words, I saw, over the edge of my note-book, a pallid naked foot come to rest on the ground beside my boot. Looking up from my writing, I realised that the Corn Cure Merchant was staring furiously at me, his pale face but a few inches away from my own. I continued to write for a moment, and then closed the book, and put it in my pocket.

"Ah ha!" said the wild-haired man, softly, and intensified his gaze into my eyes.

"I hope it will be finer for you to-morrow," I murmured.

Swiftly he made this astonishing reply, "Environment and thought tells me that you were writing about me in that little book!"

I coughed several times.

"Am I right?"

"In a way, yes, perhaps you are."

"Answer me!" he thundered. "Am I right?"

"Well, you see—"

"AM I RIGHT?" he shrieked.

"I'm hoping so: for I want to get the truth if I can."

He stared at me, one eyebrow twisted almost vertical, the other depressed and almost hiding its eye.

"And may I ask why you want to get the truth about me?" he hissed.

"Because any distortion would not be real life," I explained.

"Ah ha! You think me a bloody rogue, no doubt?"

Before I could answer he screaked furiously in my face,

"I wasn't brought up in a market, you know! I'm not just a bit of the scum of the earth like all these twisters you see! Environment and thought tell me that you mean no good to me by writing in that little book! My authority for psychology is Thomas Carlyle! Can you stand here and name a better?"

"Well, I really—"

"CAN YOU NAME A BETTER PSYCHOLOGICAL AUTHORITY THAN CARLYLE?" he shrieked in fury and despair. "Give me a straight answer to a straight question! You are speaking to a gentleman, remember! I warn you that any insults will be strongly resented. Well?"

"I wish I had Carlyle's first editions," I said, desperately trying to avert a black eye. "Do you collect first editions? If so, may I put you on to a good speculation? My novels have just been remaindered for 10d. each, and in a few years' time they will be worth £10 or more each. Really, I'm no twister."

"Who are you, to insult me like this? ANSWER MY QUESTION!

WHAT WERE YOU WRITING DOWN ABOUT ME IN THAT BOOK. I demand to see, at once!"

"Just a few notes."

He stared at me seriously. "Is that so? Indeed! Just a few notes! Ah ha!"

His head leaned at an angle of forty-five degrees, as he took a new bearing on me.

"Are you aware, sir that you have driven away potential clients from my business?" he said grimly. "Those people thought you were a policeman in plain clothes, and being but human they moved away, not wishing to be involved in anything beyond their control. What right have you, apart from the damage to my business, to write down notes about me? I consider it an unwarrantable impertinence, and I demand to see your book! Now this minute! What are the notes for, may I ask?"

"For a chapter in a book I'm writing. The chapter is called 'The Fair'. I'm trying to write truly about it for people to read in years to come, maybe, and to see what a muddle the white races were getting themselves into."

"And what sort of book will it be, if you write truly? What is truth? Answer my question, sir: *What is Truth?*"

"Well, I don't know; but I'm learning how difficult it is. For example, there is an old man in the village who repairs boots. You see him working in his cottage window. Well, this old man never goes to either of the inns. He keeps himself to himself. He is a very sharp man for his money—no harm in that—it's a good clock that tells correct time. I've been told that he distrusts banks, and keeps all his savings in a chest under his bed. His religion is like that over there in that Mission. Now for years I've had him weighed-up in my mind as one of the narrow, old-fashioned type, whose every thought about the world was on a level with that money hoarded under the bed, in the darkest corner."

"Well?"

"Well, one Sunday—it was Easter Sunday—I was with my wife and baby in a field called Netherhams, near the haystack. The baby was rolling naked on a rug on the grass. The Easter sun blessed him. The old chap came by, and stopped. I imagined he would strongly disapprove of the sunlight on the naked baby."

"Well?"

"His words were, 'There be nothing so fine for a plant or a chiel as the zin. For the zin maketh everything.'"

"Well."

"That was surprise No. 1. The Elizabethan precision and simplicity of his expression! Then I told him about my book, and said, not expecting him to understand, for his trade is different from mine, 'The difficulty is to get everything down exactly as it is, as the sun sees it, as it were.'"

"'I understand,' he replied. 'You mean you must neither exaggerate nor depreciate. Well, if you can do that, you'll write a good book.' Those were his exact words!"

"Well?"

"That from the man I had come, in some moods, to consider —unhappily, I must say, as I am always hoping to believe that all men are essentially the same under the rind and wrinkle of their different experiences—as justifying the kind of writing about country people which makes them out to be mean, selfish, dull-witted, and altogether inferior creatures to the superior author who analyses and portrays them. 'You must neither exaggerate nor depreciate.'"

"Probably he had been reading Carlyle!"

"I must ask him. So you see, when I write about the Fair, all I can do is to try and recreate it as it interested me."

"Quite! And I interested you, did I?"

"Frankly, you did. Your talk was so interesting that I intended to buy some of your Paradise Corn Cure for my little toe."

"I'll give you some!"

"That is very kind of you; but I feel, especially as I have frightened away some of your customers—the man with the healthy red face was looking most intently at your foot, I noticed—I ought to make up for it by—"

"Don't you believe it! That red-faced chap is my partner, that's all. Here, take three packets. What sort of corn is it? Blood or plain?"

"Plain, I think. But I must insist that you take this shilling."

"Certainly not, as one philosopher to another. Dog does not eat dog! This'll do the trick. It's really very good stuff. So I shall be in your book, shall I?"

I promised to send him a copy of each of my five books, for sixpence a copy; I had bought several for myself. After taking his address, we parted in an almost embarrassing atmosphere of politeness; and when I passed his pitch half an hour later, I saw the red-faced man standing with *his* foot on the stool, while the wild-haired disciple of Carlyle was waving his arms at a small crowd in which stood the labourer with the cowhair in his hat, and yes! the old Exmoor farmer.

"With my Paradise Corn Cure, I'll shift a corn in two nights, I'll ease a bunion in three, I'll clear a wart in four dressings! For Christ's sake believe me!!"

The froth was again in the corners of his mouth. The veins showed on his forehead like the roots of thorns. I knew that feeling. Suddenly he saw me, and the veins disappeared.

"You'll find it will ease your painful feet immediately, my friend!" he called out. "As it has eased the feet of hundreds of thousands of sufferers before you."

He bowed deeply towards me, and seeing the eyes of his listeners upon me, I assumed a slight limp before returning the bow.

Across the way the harmonium in the Open Air Mission had ceased; and the choir-master was now addressing the Open Air.

"No man or woman is so utterly sunk in sin that he or she cannot seek and find salvation," the stentorian voice declared.

"I say! I say!" cried the little man before his Ice Cream barrow, as he swung his hand-bell, and blew through his clenched hand. The cold north-west wind was flapping the tents, and driving its vain fish-scales on the water in the gutter. A wild voice yelled down the wind.

"Christ Almighty, doesn't anyone in this town suffer from corns, bunions, carbuncles, or warts?"

Dare I offer him the shilling again? While I was hesitating because of the sudden thorny despair on his face, the old farmer stepped forward and put his hand in his pocket, and the Cowhair Hat did likewise.

"Don't hesitate; you can be saved at this very moment, here and now!" cried the preacher of the Open Air Mission.

"I say! I say!" shouted the Ice Cream General, swinging his arms for warmth.

"I want one more lady or gent to complete my Committee!"

"My firm is the oldest in the West of England! I am here to advertise my goods!"

"Come unto me all ye who are heavy laden, and I will give you rest! Come now, at this moment, and be saved!"

Ah, if only it were as easy as that!

Walking among the people who, having come to enjoy the Fair, were remaining in spite of the cold grey wind and sudden showers, it seemed to me that acts of inhumanity made up what in olden time was called the Devil; and that all these acts were determined and shaped by outside circumstances. They did not truly arise from the inner nature, except where outside circum stances had stifled it. To be complacent about these circumstances, and merely to hate or despise the sad human nature illshaped by them, this seemed to be sinful.

Just as excess of alcohol magnified and distorted the dominant trait of each human character, so the Fair, the world in miniature, revealed the effects of a competitive civilisation, based on the money power, upon human nature. I watched the Jewish tricksters when they had stepped down from their motor cars and pulpits; their thoughts for their wives and children were apart from the callous, the cynical, the pitiless ways of swindling the poor.

The sun flung his beams under a cloud. Everything brightened at once. Human nature did not change, said the false and complacent prophet; whereas imagination, since the beginning of history, had been changing human life. Coral reef of thought upon thought, raised out of the bitter sea towards a life ever wider and more fair. The sun was so sweet and warm; never again would I disintegrate myself in the roundabouts of thought. I would be serene, I would—

"WASHED IN THE BLOOD OF THE LAMB," came the stentorian voice amidst the wheezing groans of the harmonium.

"I say! I say!" The Ice Cream General rung his hand-bell, then swung his arms in order to keep warm.

"There they go again," he grinned at me, jerking his head towards the Mission.

"I say! I say!" he yelled, giving them an imitation of a scowl. "That's the way to live," he resumed, with a wink. "Three pound a week and all expenses, and all they've got to do is to shout 'Come and be saved'."

"Have many been saved during this Fair, do you know?"

"Sweet Fanny Adams, that's all! People come here to enjoy themselves. My word, ain't it rotten cold weather! I've only sold a couple of ices all the afternoon. I say! I say!"

Cling-aling-a-cling!

"Do you think they feel unhappy about no one heeding them?"

"Not a bit of it! They're saved, and so they're quite happy, especially with three quid a week coming in regular. And they wanted to pinch my pitch this morning, the dirty dogs! I got the best pitch along here, and they claimed it!! But I stuck out for my rights, and here I am! I say! I say!"

The barrow of this alert business man was standing over a drain in the gutter, I noticed: and he appeared to have the length of the gutter to himself as well.

"I say! I say!"

Cling-aling-a-cling!

The sun was gone, the wind blew in cold gusts.

"Here, have an ice!" he said suddenly. "I'll give you one for nothing. I'll make you up a nice large one! I'd like to!"

Buttoning up my coat, I declined with exaggerated thanks.

Would he accept a copy of one of my books? Yes, of course I would write my name in it: yes, and I would send him a copy of each of the five books. Of course I wasn't kidding. I wrote down his name and address.

"Won't you really? I'd give it to you gladly. It might sell one if others saw you eating it, too."

Thanking him once more, returning the handwave of my other friend the Paradise Corn Cure Philosopher, I hurried away, for the 5.54 p.m. home was smoking in the Town Station.

Yes, I sent the books to the Corn Cure Philosopher and to the Ice Cream General promised at the Fair of 1927; and I hope they didn't throw them away, for in 1931 the market value of those first editions had increased by 20,000 per cent.

Chapter Sixteen

THE STREAM

I

The stream which flowed and murmured through the village of Ham rose in a field above Jonathan Furze's farm, where a spring broke out of ground trodden by cattle. Starlings settled there to drink, and splash among the leaves and blue summer flowers of brook-lime. The runlet of bright water, few inches wide, hurried down the sloping field to a sunken lane, passing a gate which overhangs a slough of hoofmarks, brown and stagnant except in the dryest summer. Then the stream, scarcely floating the ducklings hatched by the once-wild duck nesting in Farmer Furze's pond behind the rectory, trickled under ferns and a stone "ditched" wall. It passed a well, the overflow of which hastened secretly under the red road to join it. There the first trout lay, by the faint hollow drain-song.

The trout were scarcely so big as a boy's finger; yet they guarded the beauty of the water, for where the brown trout lie a stream truly is living. By its mosses and hart's-tongue ferns the rill flowed and murmured, by violets pale and long-stemmed in the shade of the rookery elms, above which patches of sky gleamed, and the high cirrus clouds drifted in still June days.

At the end of the avenue the trickle of water left the road, and, under open sky again, lost its lustre in the pond behind the rectory, where the tame wild-ducks—raised originally from a clutch of eggs taken from a nest in the distant estuary marsh—swam with the shy moorfowl. The moorfowl, most discreet and innocent of birds, lived on the pond all the year; there was no market in peace-time for their bodies.

Boys fished for eels in Jonathan Furze's pond, usually moving away when the farmer appeared. Mr. Furze never shouted at the boys, he was quiet, kind, aloof, hard-working, and the biggest landowner in the parish; therefore he was not popular; the village invariably repeated, "Furze by name and furze by nature." Once a boy asked of Mr. Furze permission to fish in the pond, which was readily granted. "Don't you get wet, or your mother will be after me," he said.

Under the fender at the pond's end the water slid through the rectory garden and another smaller pond, under the tall "ditched" wall of the churchyard with its nine elms, and past the cottage with the dark opening under the thatch of its end-wall, through which the white owls floated on summer nights. It fell beside the water-dipping stone, where the daughter of Hole Farm knelt to wash the "pots" of pigs for the making of hog's-pudding. Here the buckets were filled for washing lime-ash floors. The stream water was as clear as under the ferns above, but broken china and glass, rusty pails and cans, rags waving like grey weeds, roots of weeds washed clean, and parts of bicycles, lay among the stones. Shrimps flipped away from under the stones turned over by boys, or desperately wriggled on the wet shillets lifted up. Sometimes a male shrimp holding its smaller mate in its arms was seen, picked off the algæ-brown stone, and taken home to be shown; to be forgotten a moment later, and left to die in the sun which scorched away all movement, all life, but left them fast in death.

Usually an eel lived under the big flat kneeling stone. It was fine sport in summer to lever up the stone, and try to grab the blue ungraspable shape sinuating through the mud-tinged water. The sport did not always end with the escape or capture of the eel; for the stone was heavy, and the hands holding it upright were liable to slip, when the spectators opposite were shot with mud and water. Once Vanderbilt Will, Revvy his cousin and neighbour, "Stroyle" George of Hole Farm opposite, and seven boys were splashed together: a record.

Afterwards the shrimps settled again among the specks of rock and leaf and twig which the stream carried away under the culvert. Revvy Carter, called over from hoeing his aged father's garden across the road, declared that the tiny jelly-like creatures, half an inch long, moving in the plashes and against the sun-lined rillets, were baby elvers, recently hatched from eggs laid in the water-weed. He didn't deny that some eels might go all the way to the Sargasso Sea to lay their eggs: but here the Ham eels were, not long out of the egg, for anyone to see, and it wouldn't be long before some were grown as long as my arm.

"Why, they little threads of things, do 'ee mean vor tell they travel thousands of miles? Why, tidden sense, if you'll excuse my opinion, zur."

There they were, Revvy's baby elvers, some only a little more than a quarter of an inch long, wriggling in the shallow water of the Ham stream, which in a dry summer filled only four four-gallon buckets a minute.

2

Every two or three years there was a storm of rain, and the stream rushed and roared past his cottage, coloured red with ironstone mud from the road leading past the spring in Jonathan Furze's field, downwards from the high ground of Windwhistle Cross. Once the stream overflowed its narrow course, with its bed raised by years of accumulated rubbish, and swilled down to the dark pigs' houses and the back doors of Revvy and Thunderbolt Billy. The kitchen was filled over Revvy's boots. When the water had run away, and Revvy's stormy anger against the landlord had gone with the mud swept off the floor, an eel was found under the case of the grandfather clock. "'Twas a master gr't eel —'twas as long as me ar-rm!" declared Revvy, in the village street, as he set out at half-past seven to his work in the fields, a potato sack for overcoat on his shoulders. The outstretched arm, with a finger of the other hand laid on the biceps muscles under the green, once black, coat, demonstrated the exact length, and also the original excitement of the discovery.

Later I heard his four-year-old son Ernie, on the way to school, declare in his sweet treble, to his smaller cousin "Babe" Carter, "Cool but 'twas a master gr't eel! Didden he just twist and snack (snake) about on the vloor! 'Twas as long as me ar-rm!" He stopped, and marked the length along his little arm. And in the playground the eel was as long as Babe's smaller arm.

The stream flowed from the culvert and beside the wall of Hole farmhouse, and disappeared under an opening in the wall of the outhouse beyond the kitchen. This opening was used by the timid cattle dog of Hole Farm, who ran along the stony bed of the stream and so to the yard and barns unseen from the road. Every dog at the farmhouse had used this way. Old Jimmy Carter, the father of Revvy, and grandfather of Ernie and Babe, told me that he minded (remembered) more than a dizzen (dozen) dogs, every one called Ship, "that learned theyselves vor rin (run) thaccy way".

3

Away from the last house—West End Farm, where I made my first and last barrel of cider—the stream became wild again, marked by the green growth of rushes, meadow-sweet, yellow

flag-lilies, and umbelliferous plants. On the north-west slope
sheep fed on very green grass growing below the duct or
ditch which led from the village cesspool. Above the duct
could be seen another field, and then the village school, built
above the lane which leads down to Vention Sands.

Sometimes a heron stood on the rushy ground, overlooking
the stream, which now in places was a yard wide. The water
was clear in the sunshine. Children coming home from school
wandered by the banks, plucking flowers of ragged robin, and
yellow irises; gathering watercress, too, the leaves of which
were not so strong and dark as those growing under the sinister
patch of green grass higher up the valley side. Queer little fish
with big heads and fore-fins like arms clung to the stones of the
bed, coloured pale brown like the algæ—mullheads, or loach,
which ate the dead leaf nibbling grubs whose coverings of stick
and stone fragment were gummed to their bodies. Trout and
eels eat the loach; and one summer evening, while wandering
down the "river" (as Ernie called it), exploring it from source to
sea, I saw a satisfying sight. An eel even longer than Revvy's
arm was waving in the bright shallow water, waving and sinuating from its head buried under a stone.

I imagined the mullhead wriggling its way under a stone,
following a stick-caddis grub; the eel, smelling the mullhead
down the stream, moving up silently, following the scent washed
down. I had seen eels moving up a brook to the entrails of a
rabbit, thrown away by someone in Ham whose house was near
the stream, probably Mrs. Revvy Carter or Alice of Hole Farm
or Clib the grave-digger and postman.

The eel quested like a mute hound in the water. Slowly it
burrowed under the stone, its body rippling with the strength
of eagerness. I had been dozing on the bank, freeing myself
from village confinements into the light and warmth of one
of the rare and lovely west-wind days, when time is truly the
sunshine; and keeping very still, was watching the behaviour of
the fishes. Then above the idle murmur of the stream in the
hovers of the banks I heard a noise as of a dog shaking its coat,

followed by the sound of a heavy animal rolling in the rushes just below me. The west wind blew up the valley, otherwise the otter would not have been so careless. Wondering when he would see me, I kept as still as I could: it seemed that he must detect my body swaying from the waist, hear the breath in my mouth, and certainly start and sink away silently in the water at the noise of my swallowing. But no, he leaned down to drink. I saw alertness come into the loose brown form. The head appeared to sharpen from the nose, the whiskers to be sensitive to the water-writhing of the eel; for the otter, at the low angle, could not have seen it in the water beyond the cattle-broken bay where it stood on its low webbed feet.

It slipped so silently into the water, scarcely six inches deep by the bay, that I thought it must have seen me, and was crouching still under the bank; but craning my neck, I saw it swimming up to the eel. Then it was standing on its hind-legs on a mossy stone, with a black knot writhing from its mouth, and looking at me. This was the first time I had seen a wild otter so near, other than an otter hunted by hounds. It did not remain staring at me long, but dropped out of sight in the stream, the eel still in its mouth. I followed it, wanting to know if it was afraid; it ran through the rushes and up the slope of the hill, through a hedge, and into a small larch plantation, which I called Goldcrackey Spinney, since gold-crackeys, or golden-crested wrens, nested in the larches every spring. The plantation was overgrown with brambles, in which were many rabbit buries, or burrows, and although I peered and poked I did not see the otter again. It must have been used to sleeping there by day in a larger rabbit hole, for it ran to the spinney directly.

A few weeks later a friend told me that an otter had been found in a rabbit gin, in the field on top of the down over-looking the sandhills and the estuary to the south. The trapper had beaten it with a stick until it was dead; he said it took him a long time to kill it. Thinking that it might have been the otter I had seen, I felt very angry with the trapper; but later this anger seemed unjust, for field workers immemorially have been overcoming wild creatures which take from their livelihood, just as wild beasts had been preying on other living things.

The water flows everlastingly, wearing the stones smooth in its glides and runs; and so the sensibility is worn away, and life flows more smoothly.

4

The brook wandered down the valley towards the sea, passing its third farmhouse, which looked like an old manor house surrounded by barns, some with the "economical" roofs of galvanised-iron sheeting. The square stone chimneys were green with ferns, and one chimney-pot was a deep warm red, a pleasant sight among the trees. It flowed by a modern building erected before the Great War for a rifle range, later converted into a cottage. Below, it slowed and deepened into a muddy pond, the haunt of eels and trout up to a pound in weight. Part of the stream fell over a wooden wheel turning a dynamo for electric light for a house at the junction of two valleys, which was also the junction of two streams—the one I had followed from the pasture in Jonathan Furze's field, the other running down the valley from the hamlet of Cot. The junction was called Forda, which meant Little Ford; before the culvert was built the stream ran across the road, a refreshing sight for horses in the hot weather.

The stream flowed on, serene in summer, just as the brooks of London once flowed towards the Thames: they flow still, buried from the light, dead with street water in the sewers which contain them.

At the Little Ford, where the horses stopped and pulled at the reins, and driver or rider looked down complacently at the long thick muscles of the neck, a trout used to wait just below the parapet abutting the garden wall, ready to dart into the shadow within when the children coming from school peered over. One day Mr. Alford, the Chairman of the Parish Council, threw some quick-lime into the water and at once the trout was asphyxiated. This was considered quite proper, in a seaboard country where a generation before many lived on the wrecks of wooden ships lured by false lights on the rocks in a storm.

Green willows and ripe hazel nuts; a cattle shippen with a roof that had been gaping wider during the years I have walked down the valley. First the slates pegged with oak pegs to the battens; then, perhaps hundreds of years later, mortar to keep them together; then, with the coming of motor transport, cement; then tar and sand, the last stage. Afterwards, a new roof, or a ruin. Usually in Devon it was a ruin.

Under a great hill of furze and fern, where in two years of the Great War potatoes grew, after hundreds of patient hours had gone in swaling, uprooting, ploughing and hoeing; now the rabbits were numerous as before in their dense cover, and the line of the hillcrest dark and uneven with furze and bracken as a sea horizon in wind. Buzzards soared and wailed at sunset over Furzy Down.

Past a grey-walled square on the northern slope (where the southern sun swiftly draws up the green vegetables in spring) and the hamlet of Cross, with its dozen cottages—with Grannie Parsons its oldest inhabitant dwelling in the smallest cottage in the West Country—was left behind. By Cross were two unusual things: the ancient jawbone of a bullock in the hedge, hung on a bine of bryony, moss growing around the base of its loose teeth; the small crimson carcass of a mole flung in the lane. There it lay, a minute body, complete with tail, paws, sensitive snout, whiskers, nose, legs, veins, muscles, sinews, and shoulders; but without its coat.

Once I caught a mole by another stream. It squeaked in the cage of my hands, and pushing its long pink snout between two fingers, thrust its head through with surprising strength, levering with its forepaws. On the ground again, it hurried away with a quick miniature waddle, stopping at a hole in the ground and tearing away grass rootlets with pink paws set like fins against its body. Pulled forth once more, it squeaked and tried to wedge its head through the close fingers. It ran away again, falling over by the weight of its body and shovel-paws, scrambling up again, falling over once more, squeaking as it hurried away, to tumble into the stream and hurry across in a pattering motion between waddle and swim. It reached the other bank distant by one stride of human legs. There it rested, and shook itself, but it over-balanced and fell back into the water. Rapidly it emerged, and found a worm on the bank. It absorbed the worm with haste, squeaked, and hurried on again. After being picked up a few more times it became tamer, and ate worms given it in my hand; but always it squeaked, and was hasty to escape as before. With its tapered snout and thick furry body, huge pink hands, and bundling run, it was a comical sight; and therefore it seemed that this small body, stripped naked and forsaken, flung over the hedge into the lane, was a pathetic thing to be seen in a summer evening.

5

In the next field the stream divided into two courses. The upper stream flowed past elm trees into a lake made by one man, who for months was to be seen, solitary and silent, working with barrow and spade, wire-netting and concrete-puddle, making a dam across the hollow of his meadow. This gentleman, who bore the name of Ponde, was a retired colonel of the Indian Army, and a member of Ilam Parish Council. With immense labour from sunrise to late evening, and sometimes by moon-light, he managed to keep back about a quarter of an acre of water five or six feet deep at the dam long enough to encourage a pair of moorfowl to nest in the reeds which sprang up around the edge.

The dam then burst, causing the cottage dwellers in the village below to exclaim against the volume and colour of the water overflowing the narrow bed of the stream into their kitchens. After surveying the channered delta of his lake, Colonel Ponde began work again on a heavier dam, which was faced with an inch or so of concrete reinforced with rabbit-netting.

The rood of water shone placid once more in the beams of

the rising sun, and the moorhen returned and made a second nest in the rushes. Canadian willows were planted, for the red hues of their graceful withies, and the binding power of their roots; and one evening, as the colonel was moving around on the surface peering for any trout or eels which might be in his pond, sculling himself in a little collapsible boat made by himself of the skins of some animals, the dam burst again, the collapsible boat promptly collapsed, and the sudden release of water once again caused emotion in the peaceful dwellings below. As he crawled out of a whirlpool under what had been the spillway of the dam, the colonel is reported to have declared that at last he saw what was needed to keep the water permanently in the lake. In time the improved dam was made; and so effectively that the dam withstood the greatest flood known in the history of Ham, which occurred one June morning nine years after the first waterworks in Ponde's Mash, as the field was by then called in the village, had been instituted.

The left, or south, stream ran murmuring through another pond, which was dammed above the ancient grist-mill at the head of Cryde village. A stone-ditched wall held up a solid bank of turf rising steeper as the lane descended and turned a corner which gave a view of cottages, the mill-house, and the inn which for several generations had belonged to the family of John Smith, called "Muggy", of Cryde.

6

As I walked around the bend in the road, I heard a thundering and a humming. The mill was working, for what might be its last time; for Cryde was becoming popular, and there was talk of turning the Charles II millhouse into a modern boarding house.

I crept under the wooden casing which carried the flume from the pond, and watched the great wheel revolving. A cascade of water gushed under the fender, filling each elm-wood trough. The water fell in silvery plashing. On the wheel, with its rusty iron hub, dark green moss grew, and hart's-tongue ferns hung from the cracks in the stone wall behind. The water foamed and churned, the wheel turned ponderously as though in steps, the wall and spindle and bearings shuddered, and rillets of water fell from its rim in a steady pattering. From behind a cloud came the sun, and the falling water took its light and glinted gold, with red and blue flashes that held me watching there.

The miller, in apron and black beard a dusty white, allowed me to look over the mill. Cobwebs hung from the beams overhead, dusted with chalky white. The wheel turned iron cogs, which worked the upper or runner stone against the nether or bed stone. While the building shook and rumbled, and I shouted into his ear—he had long been deaf, perhaps because of the years grinding corn—a bell rang in the loft above. The stone needed more grain. He showed me his own invention: a leather strap fixed to a bell was thrust under a heap of barley, which dropped steadily between the stones until the weight of the pile became less than the weight attached to the bell, and it fell until checked by a cord, and so rang its warning. He told me that the mill had belonged to his great-great-grandfather, and that he did not like to give it up; he could just make it pay now, but motor transport made a difference, bringing cheap flour into the village.

I looked on the wooden steps of the Club room for Muggy Smith, but he was not there. A cheery voice called from across the road, where he was sitting in his shirt-sleeves, basket at feet, one leg cocked over the other, smoking a cigarette in his long holder.

"Here I be, midear: known to the police! If you please, zur, I want a word with you. Now please listen to what I be going to tell you. I want you, when you put me in your book, if you please, to say that I am Muggy Smith of Cryde: and will you please not forget to put in about the rats that ate into my food-box in my hut? That will please me very well if you do. Yes, sir."

I enquired about his business, and learned that he had extended it, yes, sir: he was now open to take orders for mill-stones; not for the necks of some people in the district (in a

louder voice, for the benefit of visitors passing), for there weren't
enough to go round. No, sir. But he could let me have a mill-
stone for a garden ornament, if I required it: he was the agent,
duly appointed: thirty shillings apiece he was asking: but no
delivery at the moment, as they were in use. His thumb jerked
over his shoulder towards the mill-house. Times was changing.
Progress, yes, sir. Had I noticed some of the new buildings in
Cryde village? Up to date, the place was being brought. Progress,
yes, sir. If London hadn't become London, Cryde would have.
Up to date, was all the talk to-day. Yes, sir. (And here his voice
grew very loud as he said slowly),

"Up to date, sir. The only trouble being that the date be
about 1890."

With these words the old man arose, shouldered his basket,
and walked slowly up the hill towards his hut; but he must stop,
turn round, and repeat his piece of wit; for that was the Devon
custom. Usually the repetition of a joke brought a second lot of
laughter; and it was genuine, not polite, laughter, the merry
laughter of children.

7

The stream ran beside the village street. Clapper bridges—
slabs of stone as long and wide as a coffin—crossed it to the
barns and cottages, thatched and slated. There was the barn in
which apples, fresh-picked, windfalls, brown-rotten, were
tumbled together into the slicing machine and pressed into cider
in the autumn; chickens roosted on the oaken press, with its
great central screw hand-cut when the ships were going down
the estuary to join Drake's fleet at Plymouth. Round cat-holes
were cut in the lower part of the doors; the race of rat-eating
cats were lean, sharp-eared, and half wild.

A notice-board stated that anyone throwing rubbish in the
stream would be liable to a fine not exceeding forty shillings, by
Order of the District Council. The notice was splashed with
mud, many handfuls; and in the stream were shards of cups,
plates, saucers, and other domestic utensils; heads and feet of

chicken, potato peelings, rags of petticoats and stockings, egg-shells, broken glass, and, justifying the general satisfaction that the village was being brought up to date, a motor tyre. Once I saw Muggy, over seventy years of age, laboriously picking the rubbish out of the stream and putting it in a sack, a job for which he was paid a few shillings annually.

Below an orchard wall the water hastened, where trees were cut down, and red-bricked cottages were being built; two culvert bridges crossed to them. If London hadn't become London, Cryde would have, said Muggy; I gazed sadly at the style of architecture. Past cottages, derelict of thatch and browed with ivy—the home of hundreds of sparrows and starlings—when I had first come to live in Devon, but now sold and restored and let furnished, to produce in two days of the summer season more than their yearly rent before the war.

Here the stream broadened, lapping on its farther bank a farmhouse wall, under which many ducks paddled and quacked. There was the new bridge, a wide structure with parapets which no bus could knock down. Not built of the red ironstone of the country, or of the grey shale, was this new bridge, but of grey concrete showing the grain-marks of the deal frame boxes which moulded it, like the German pill-boxes in the Salient. In this it was not unique; nearly all the new houses and cottages erected in the 'twenties were the result of a complete lack of what is called taste. One young lady, to whom once I mentioned such things, said to me, in an aside, "Don't say anything at all, will you, to anyone we may meet; you see, people think you are completely barmy." It was a kind thought on her part; she was expressing the general opinion of the times. There was also some truth in her remark: for to be untimely is to be a little barmy: eccentric.

8

Below the bridge the stream gained its freedom once more; which is another way of saying that the village and its changes were left behind, and I followed water running through a green meadow where willows grew, and cows stared in the shade, frisking their tails at the flies. A faint roaring was filling the quiet air, from the waves of low tide beating on the shore behind the sandhills ranged irregularly against the western shining sky. Winding and returning upon itself, as though loath to leave its individual life for the sea, the brook chattered and sparkled where the caddis grubs, within their rough-cast houses, speckled the red and yellow stones; and then, running quietly round a bend, it turned slowly in an eddy where sticks were lodged, and bubbles rode, and a deep-blue-winged dragon-fly rose and fell as though it were a hair-spring of the sun's invisible time. Regularly once a second, with wing-whir shining like something working with metallic precision, it rose and fell, each time dropping an egg at the edge of the water.

I sat down to count. One hundred times, and still the mystic rite went on. Egg, egg, egg, egg, egg, it went on and on, and I started counting in batches of twenty, for variation, checking them off on my left hand. This led to confusion with the five fingers to be added for the preceding hundred; it was hot with the sun on brow, cheek and forearms, and I was always confused by the basement work of mathematics. Egg, egg, egg,— and then *splash!* the marvellous and thrilling sight of a curved dark-brown gleaming back, blue head, and crenellated fan of tail, and the ripples flopping against the grassy hollows of the bank. A trout that size had never been suspected in this stream three miles from source to estuary, a stream leapable anywhere except at the cattle and duck shallow before the concrete bridge, and where it splayed itself as though in final abandon after serpentining through the sandhills. That trout must have been three inches thick through its back, and nearly two feet long. A rich life nourished it, with other fish in the holes and eddies of the bends. Grasshoppers, beetles, caddis grubs, shrimps; moths fluttering in from among the bracken of the burrows as the moon was rising; mullheads with fins like a mole's paws; the entrails of rabbits thrown in the stream by trappers; frogs, mice, and even moorfowl chicks.

9

Had this trout, with four red spots on its back fin, as I had clearly seen, had this trout begun its life far up by the drain where the rooks cawed in Jonathan Furze's elm-tops, and the tame wild-duck led her dappled babes in the coolth of the hart's-tongue ferns? Had it, as an alevin, with its yoke-sack consumed and shrunken in to become a belly, had it turned with the authentic flash and seized its first food, one of the strange white *animalculae* which used to be seen swimming in the palm of the hand which lifted a delicious drink from the well after walking down from Windwhistle Cross in the heat and fury of the August sun? If they were not *animalculae*, I always called them so; and *animalculae* they be, a dialect word if you like, but no doubt the trout ate them. As it grew, so it drifted downstream, through Jonathan Furze's pond and the rectory pond, past the churchyard elms and the kneeling stone, then under the wall of Hole Farm and down into the pleasant meads—pleasant they were: and as for the very green grass above, it purified or restored the balance of nature, which is ultimately serene dissolution—and, escaping the ducks, the wandering otters and herons, the pitchforks and pails of poisoning garbage of the village, the trout reached the slow-flowing water and eddies of the plain before the sandhills. The stream was still living; here was the trout, and no cannibal either, for when he rose again, serenely for a drowning moth swirled around in the little whirl-hollow which was the eddy's pivot, I saw the fat shoulders and the graceful olive head and blue-black mottle of spots.

I was content with life; the sins of man—pollution of the living streams of the earth, together with the living streams of the human spirit—had not yet killed this little English river. I sat there, feeling free and happy. Cirrus clouds were calm and unmoving in the height of heaven. With the first high flush of sunset, I walked slowly on the sandy sward, round the reedy bends where other trout would be lying. The plain was a beautiful waste-land. Summer was over; but I walked in the midst of summer again. Here grew burnet roses, low on the sand, with their small blooms of delicate ivory paleness. Bird's-foot trefoil and dove's-foot crane's-bill—quaint and ancient names given by what unknown English poet—the mosses turning bronze-coloured with the ardour of young summer, the nightjar arising from the brake-ferns, where those wilderness trees, the elder-berries, grew amidst the salt-wreckage of the old branches, and mullein plants grey-flannel-leafed and rising straight to their yellow cluster of flowers like a torch, the clumps of wild privet where rabbits ran to hide, the oases of greensward made fine by the nibbling teeth of a thousand years—the stream wound its way through the waste-land, coming at last to a gorge through the sandhills where the marram grasses and brambles made against the sky a fringe, quivering and seeming to dissolve in the heated air. The sea from an everlasting murmur became a refreshing roar, for the waves were coming quickly up the sands. Now the stream was preparing for its end, spreading wide and hurrying with multitudinous small leaps and cries over the stones of its delta. Here was its last bridge, of sea-eaten brown iron piles, supporting a footway of single planks. Every high tide altered the miniature estuary, which some days was narrow and at other times wide and noisy with its thousand stones washed and shifted anew, and the sand-cliffs of its banks collaps-ing noisily. Here a scour or sandbank arose, only to be cut away the next minute amidst a swirl that lifted the baby flatfish and showed their pallid undersides. Wider trickled the water, and more shallow. Now I might cross wearing shoes which would not be wetted above the welt. Gulls stood below on the wet sands; but where now was the water? Its brawling over, the summer stream was gone under the sand, to its immortality in the immense sea.

Chapter Seventeen

SUMMER AFTERNOON

I

Every hour out of doors was an hour of immortal life. If I could not spend at least part of every day by the sea, or within sight of the sea, I was restless. I must hurry to the sea, before the shadow of the headland darkened the sun in the sands, where alone I felt full freedom of the spirit or self.

Sometimes the slight wavelets of the ebb tide reared to curl and break very far away, hidden in the sun-mist of the flat shore. Walking down the sands, over the soft area of pools and runnels, I came at length to where the small waves were rearing each with its fragments of old marine vegetation. The stalks and glistening brown ribbons of the thong-weed lifted as each wave passed through their jungle.

At the low spring tide the sea was slack, cold, distained, a litter of death, anti-human. Monstrous jelly fish with purple interiors were awash in the marine litter; or, embedded and shrinking in the sands behind, were slowly being annihilated by the springing hordes of sand-hoppers. A baby seal lay in the wash, a dirty white and sloppy bundle with sad little whiskered face and hind-legs as though malformed. Was this species or race going back to the sea from the land, or to the land from the sea? Wrestled over by what imaginative spirits of earth or water? Or was it static, one of a million million species created within a space of six days, as the unknown writer of the Book of Genesis saw in his poetic vision? Meanwhile no dry sticks for the kettle-fire were likely to be found down here, where the limpets and winkles were thick on the rocks, and anemones in the rock-pools tried to clutch one's finger and draw it into their soft allurements of sea-devilry. The eyes of little fish caught in the sirenic arms stared dead in the clear water.

SUMMER AFTERNOON

Lying on a low flat rock, I saw the distant beach-party dissolve in the mirage. Now I was alone with the tricklings of the weed-hung rocks, which were literally being sucked away by the limpets, for where one had been chipped off by oyster-catcher or falling cliff-scree, a small crater was left. The presence of the dissolution awash in the listless sea was lifted when the brown vibrating mirage fragments cohered into the figure of the spaniel trotting to find its master. Nose to tracks of naked feet in the sand, the dog found the baby seal, and turning leisurely over on the pivot of its neck, began to roll luxuriously on the corpse.

2

In the late afternoon, when the sun's brightness had un-hardened and his rays were beginning to mellow, it was pleasant to climb over the rocks under the north side of the headland and await the tide coming up the hot sands.

The tidal lassitude was gone. Atlantic breakers swept up the yellow shore, swirling in the pits and pans of the morning tide's lapse, each retiring wave a net wide-cast to drag sand back to the ocean's verge. The air roared. Fountains rose and fell whitely on the peaks of rocks jutting sharp and black in the blinding sun-rays.

The wind was purifying on the highest ledge of the lichen-shaggy rocks, above the dash of the topmost wave of the highest spring tide. The spaniel followed, whining his uneasiness. At three-quarter tide the rock became an island, cut off from the headland cliffs by a narrow gorge. Here the press of waves surged and walloped, and *boom!*, the spray leapt high at the meeting of other waves surging around the gorge from the sands. To reach the mainland again the marooned castaway had to wait for the exact moment to step down on a wet foothold exposed at the drop of a wave, to leap forward to an opposite ledge, to clutch a pinnacle, and to pull himself out of the next up-flinging of gravel and water.

We had sat here often before. On the return the spaniel, after much shivering and yelping, usually jumped or rather scrambled into the water, and after being rolled under by many surges, crawled thin and red-eyed from sea to warm, dry, loose sand, where he rolled and rolled and rolled, before dashing happily to greet his uncaring master. Now, mindful of the return, the dog whined, and shifted uneasily from one squatting ledge to another.

The great jovial waves curled green and translucent before toppling in rushing white surge and pounding the rocks, flinging up their spray for the sun to charge with silver. The sea was living again. All life is imagination; dead matter shall be imagined into another form of life.

The heat and light of the sun-reflecting sea glowed on my face. I was alone with my dog on a desert island, without water to drink, and only the fleshy leaves of sea-samphire to eat. Patches of orange lichens were spread on the honeycombed ridges, and the sapless branches of other lichens sprouted from the dry and bare stone.

The sky above the sun-mist was a burning blue, against which the airy poise of a kestrel was like the slow curling flicker of floating tawny flames.

Upon the highest puffs of tide-breeze the little mouse-hawk rested his breast, tail, and wings. His small head, with his hooked beak and full brown eyes, was bent downwards in an intent scrutiny of the rocks below. For nearly a minute he quivered like a winged flame over the rock and the spray.

Curiosity, one of the instincts which probably has come unchanged from the post-creation slime, made me "freeze" on a knife-edge, beside the clump of sea-samphire, and watch for what the kestrel had been seeking. Then the fool-head of the spaniel appeared in silhouette on the topmost crag, and with a twirl the hawk was gone.

A large ninth wave broke upon the rock, and a sunbow came out of the pounded mist. It vanished, and the lesser waves poured in foaming cascade over the pitted lower crags. A red-and-green soldier-fly whirred to an orange lichen, shut and folded its wings, and began its hunt, a swift legionary over the desert of the rock.

I was following the restless movements of the soldier-fly when a small sand-wasp seized the fly; the rape was instant. I heard the click of the wasp's mandibles as it held the soldier-fly on its back and tore off its wings. With what looked like a single stroke of its head it ripped up the green-and-red fly and tore out its entrails. While I was regarding an act almost as ferocious as those performed by Man—such as the street beheading of Communist youths by the Christian Chinese soldiers in the war that this Devon sun would look upon plainly in a few hours' time—while I was watching, I say, both wasp and soldier-fly were mysteriously whisked into a larva-bubble hole.

Peering into the aperture, which was about the size of a penny, I saw the wasp moving its abdomen slightly, trying to use its sting in the pain and stupor and perhaps fear of death. A ticking noise came from the darkness of the cave beyond. The rock was hot and dry, and an adder might be within. After awhile I overcame my fear, and crawled down the steep side of the rock, approaching to observe beyond striking distance. Peering through the scope of one partly closed fist, in order to shut out confusing sunlight, I saw beyond the feebly moving wasp an open mouth with sharp white teeth.

A weasel, I thought, as the ticking continued, and small eyes shone out of the gloom above the teeth. Hoping that it would not bite my nose, I crept nearer and touched it with a pencil. The ticking increased to a frenzy of chittering.

I withdrew, and watched the hole. The wave-fountains rose green and white against the rock, the spaniel shivered, the vast undulations of ninth waves surged through the gorge, the sun was ardent on my bare legs and arms and head. Then a flake of burnt paper flittered from the hole, and I saw it was an aerymouse. The aerymouse rose and fell and turned over the gorge, enjoying the sound of the sea, the air, and the light. She came near my head, and I saw a baby clinging to her breast. It was like a game of consequences:—The soldier-fly came for his prey, the wasp seized the soldier-fly, the bat took the wasp, the kestrel hovered for the bat, the dog frightened the kestrel, the water scared the dog, and everything scared me—a game called by some the Harmony of Nature.

Uncaring for fly or wasp or fish, and but dimly aware of the Chinese dragon, I drowsed; harmoniously I drowsed, in the bright mist of the sea and the sun sinking down upon China—while my winged relative the aerymouse—for we are related through the common ancestor God, which nowadays is confirmed by Science—enjoyed herself over the waters of the gorge, bathing herself in the leaping showers of spray. Cutting a lovely curve in the blue sky, the kestrel came up into the breeze and lay above the rock; then she flittered straight to her larva-bubble home, folded her wings, and slithered within. The sun burned away in brilliance, and the air was sweet with the living sea.

Chapter Eighteen

A DAY ON DUNKERY

It was pleasant to rest in the bush of heather, near the summit, after the long toil up the northern slope of Dunkery Beacon. I lay among the small, bronze-and-green scaly leaves, while the vapour dragged past the beacon above. The sun was very hot when the wind, which is ever on the hills, had borne away the summer cloud. There was fortune in idleness, for while I lay there I saw a peregrine falcon cut through the sky far above me, suddenly to fall in a long slant upon some bird hidden in the coombe below—a curlew perhaps, or a stock dove.

There were lizards among the stems of heather, and on the hot grey rocks, dreaming with me in the heat of the sun. A pipit climbed to the sky to descend singing in its dive of joy, again and again. Wild bees burred among the pale bells of the ling.

After awhile I heard the sound of a sneeze; and peering up, I saw what looked like a small leafless oak tree standing against the line of the sky on my right. Through my glass the branches became antlers; a stag was lying in the sparse shadow of a rowan tree, growing out of a grey-lichened rock of granite. He was near enough for me to see that his coat was a ruddy gold. He kept shaking his head, for the flies tormented the sensitive antlers which had not yet hardened after their early summer growth. The brown velvet skin was still tender upon them.

If the wide-spread slot—the print of the cloven hoof—that I found pressed into the wet ground by a black water-filled soiling pit be his, then I know the stag has been warrantable two or three seasons at least; he is seven or eight years old, and in a few weeks' time he may have to run for his life from the tireless hounds ever following the scent that lies in the slot, and in the breath panted on the cotton grass of the bogs, on the mossy rocks beside the waters in the valleys, where he has soiled and shaken himself.

I called in to see the hounds in the kennels at Exford. The kennels adjoin the huntsman's cottage, in the porch of which were nailed the antlers and broken bony pates of stags killed in past seasons. How cool and airy were the kennels, with their straw-laid benches a yard above the floors of grey slate slabs, on which were lying the long-eared hounds patched with black, yellow, white, and tan. On the wheaten straw they rested, some with heads on paws, others squatting. All looked at the white-coated whip, who was lighter in weight than most of them. Their eyes moved to mine when I spoke; no friendliness in those eyes, only a dispassionate power that might, at any moment, fill with the yellow glare of the pack spirit. Two hounds jumped down and sniffed the sandwiches in my pockets—youngsters not long out of puppyhood, and still remembering the customs of those who walked them. The whip ordered them back to bed, while they growled, or looked on with clear hazel eyes, or continued to lick the head of a veteran tufter. They stared, blinked, nibbled their coats.

In another lime-washed kennel were the matrons and daughters of the pack. Many growled at me; their eyes glinted yellow. The whip told me that they quarrelled among themselves more often than the dogs. It was not wise to enter.

Behind in the cookhouse cauldrons of oatmeal and horseflesh for more than forty couples of hounds were being boiled. The horseflesh was shredded after cooking; the porridge was poured into wooden trays. Meals were eaten cold. The red-tiled floor was clean, the great wooden trays scrubbed white.

I was stroking the kennel cat when the dark place resounded with a deep musical note. Out of nearly ninety voices the whip recognised the tongue which had spoken. "Solway, calling for Sheba," he said. "They were of the same litter, and friendly."

Outside in the sunlit courtyard I saw Sheba, a ten-month puppy. She was alone, meandering round and round the yard. I called her, but she did not come to me. She continued her lonely amble, round and round the courtyard, sometimes tripping over her forelegs, and always leaning inwards. She stumbled into a wall, lurched away, and tottered round the yard. She bumped into me, shuddered, bowing queering as though in apology, and staggered on again. Her head drooped as though too heavy for her neck; her eyes were dull and grey, seeing nothing mortal. The yellow glint of a full life would never fill them now, for she was delirious with distemper, and would die before the night.

The afternoon deepened into one of those mellow evenings whose memory fills one with indescribable longings; the honey of sunset was very clear and still over the fields. I passed the kennels again when the sun had sunken. Something almost phantom was ambling out the last of its life in the silent dusk of the courtyard. The eve-star shone bright and rayless behind me, a thin little silver moon rested its lower horn on the hill-line to be climbed on my way to the dry hedge bottom where were hidden a blanket, a kettle, and a store of dry sticks. Whenever I stopped on the road the night was so still that I fancied I could hear the dew settling on the leaves of the beech hedges. For a moment it seemed that life was suspended in the summer twilight, a shape was gliding past me, a branched head glimmered, and it was soundless, like the phantom of a stag that had been killed on the moor a long time since, whose printless slot were luring the dying hound to the forests beyond the sun.

Chapter Nineteen

A DEVON HILLSIDE

I

After weeks of slanting grey rains drifting through the valley, of harrying winds, of cold and dullness everywhere, the sun is suddenly hot on the hillside. The guts of the grazing marsh below reflect blue sky, and gulls over the flooded river are a brilliant white. The heavy, damp mackintosh on my arm is a burden, and, after a few more paces along the cattle-path, so are tweed coat and shirt-sleeves. It is always so in North Devon—autumn and spring within the same five minutes.

What weather has passed over the hill and the grazing marsh! Weest weather, as they say in this country over-ridden by the south-west gales, where the crippled trees of the hills have the shapes of porcupines—some, licked by bullocks for the salt on them, have thrice as many roots underground as branches in the air. For days the swallows wheeled about the tiny church of Lancarse that looks like a barn, and I thought that summer was dead; and my thoughts, which had lived their own life in the sunlit airs, with the flowers, the trees, and the birds of summer, must now lie with the seeds and the chrysalises, whose hope is beyond the winter. For days the clouds dragged above the hills, the apples bumped down beside the silent bee-hives, with only the birds and the mice to take them. The otter-hunters came home early, with soaked blue coats and stained white breeches; they had drawn the mill-leat, without a touch anvwhere, and afterwards hounds had returned by the old canal-bed track beside the river, and so to the station under the hill. And then, this morning, before a rook had time to fly from hilltop to hilltop, the lusty ocean winds blew the sky clear, and the sun beat down on the hillside with the ardour of spring. Within an hour the mud of the cattle-path was firm and pleasant to tread, the shooting buzz of flies crossed the furze, dandelions opened, and grasshoppers were risping among the grasses and the pale green stalks of the broom.

The sun, blinding with spikes and splashes of light, the immense luminous thistle-seed rolling through space, means much to us, but how much more to the lesser things of the hillside! It is their all. The bee creeps out of her tunnel beside the mossy stone, the wasp flies swift and intent again, the gossamer spider throws its lines gleaming with red and blue, the bronze fly, pollen-dusty, basks on the ragged disc of the ragwort, the grasshopper flips from bent to bent, free of the air—for all webs of the larger spiders, tunnel, cartwheel, and tangle-net, are gone. It is the risping of the grasshoppers that fills the morning with the illusion of summer. They are so happy and excited, the little sun-worshippers, with their boatlike bodies and strange masks, and long fiddler legs scraping out their love-songs. One by my boot has found a dwindling rain-drop on a grass-bent, and drinks it away; and then a sweet blade to nibble, until, turning abruptly at the sound of wings, he meets all beauty mask to mask; and all else, even the sun, is unknown or unseen.

2

I meant to go down through the oak-scrub and the holly trees (in one of which is a ring-dove's nest with two fresh eggs) and to cross the marsh to the tide-wall. The river, tidal for another mile up the valley, lay like a great conger eel under the curves of the wooded hill, coloured with the brown fresh and glittering at its bends as with a myriad minute scales. Sometimes a peal, or a salmon, leapt out of the riding froth. I thought I might see an otter's seals in the mud, for one has been roving there by day and night after the migrating eels; and here I am on the hillside, sitting on a stone by the cattle-path, with the bright wraith of summer risen to disturb my mind.

3

A heron, one of the six which regularly fish the tidal waters of the Torridge, arrived at his pitch by a gut-sluice an hour ago, and has yet to catch his first dab; for he has been watching me ever since, with anxious turns of his head to observe first with one eye, and then with the other. Meanwhile the swift water, nearly three hundred yards distant, lapses lower and lower, but he dare not stalk down to the edge, for then he would not be able to keep me under observation. Another head has been watching from the bank lower down, a black head, with shorter beak and neck, but it vanished, and an oval series of ripples spread out from the muddy verge, to be swilled smooth by the ebb. Half a minute later a small fish leapt out of the water fifty yards downstream, and then another; the cormorant bobbed up, paddled into the current, and swallowed the fish. It was probably a little bass—locally called "thumb bass", pronounced "base".

There was a harsh cry of *Kack!* down the marsh and five herons flew up, one behind the other, with slow flaps of loose wings, and glided low over the grass before settling along the line of a gut. *Kack!* The heron by the river arose, and flew down to join them. *Kack!* He settled by the first, or leading, heron, who cried harshly and flew up and pitched by the second; and in turn the remaining three had to shift down the line. I have seen this happen many times, and usually each move is loudly resented. The heronry is in the wood below the church—if a solitary nest each season may be called a heronry. One of the nesting herons is ancient, and one of the local fishermen, who uses a fork with barbed prongs to transfix dabs in the mud at low water, calls him Old Nog.

It is pleasant to sit in the sunshine, and to watch the business of others. It is summer again, for awhile—but stay: where are the swallows? They were here yesterday; such excited twittering on the roof of the tiny church! For all the blue sky and the flipping grasshoppers, it is not summer without the swallows; and Hope, or the longing for full life, must wait with the seeds in the trusted earth until the celandines come again.

Chapter Twenty

THE FIRING GATHERER

The last wave of the high tide leaves a wet riband above the smoothed sands—a riband of corks, sea-weed, and pine bark; of corpses of gulls stricken by the peregrine falcons, of auks and guillemots and puffins smeared with dark-brown oil-fuel; of sticks, tins, and bits of boxes. At night the shore-rats come down to the jetsam, sniffing for potato peel or cabbage stalk, and gnawing the bark of green ash twigs. The jetsam has its human prowlers, too, who come for the driftwood for firing.

One old woman was to be seen on the beach (except on Sundays) almost as regularly as the lapse of the high water. She used to wheel a ramshackle perambulator down Vention Lane, leaving it at the bottom of the hill, where a ridge of loose dry sand was piled by the winds before the cottages of the deserted lime-kiln. Then with a sack over her shoulder she would traipse along the wavy edges of the tide-line, her feet sinking in the damp sand. When I followed her footmarks when she had gone home, I would see how one track wandered to distant objects which to her dim eyes had held the possibility of treasure—a broken lobster-pot, a bottle, a paint-pot, the embedded roots of a tree borne by floods to the estuary and carried along the coast, a mattress or straw palliasse, the swelled carcass of a sheep, a ship's fender, a round glass float of a submarine net—which were being rolled up by the waves several years after the end of the Great War. The tracks of feet approached these unwanted objects, and branched away about fifteen paces from them, when the old woman's eyes, sunken in red fallen lids, had seen that they were not firing. Sometimes the footsteps circled an object that had aroused her curiosity: there she had stood awhile, speculating on the meaning or origin of a broken black rubber thigh boot, spotted with red repairing patches; on an oval tin with the figure of a dapper little man wearing bowler hat and eyeglass upon it. She could not read. The toffee tin had been picked up, carried a short distance, and cast away.

So she padded along the tide-line to the end of her daily prowl—a jagged mass of rock rising out of the sand, on which thrift and samphire grew with lichens, called Black Rock—where she would turn back, collecting the driftwood of broken boxes, herring-barrel staves, and sticks which she had claimed by flinging above the tide-line on her outward way. She was a shrivelled old woman, wearing a flattened shapeless hat that might in some past year have been found half buried in the sand. The torn folds of her many hanging clothes hid her like the black fragments of withered mushrooms. Her voice was a cawing whisper; her hands, with the long chipped nails, were more battered than the bits of roots and branches they grubbed up. She lived in the hamlet with her only grandchild, whose parents were dead, a beautiful fair-haired little girl, thin and shy as she peered through the curtains of the small closed cottage window, her eyes in her pale sharp face blue as borage flowers. To this little maid old Grannie gave all her life; every stick gathered and brought home was a token of hope. For the old woman believed that the child's strength would remain, and even increase, only if she was always before a warm fire.

The little maid was usually behind the closed window: for Granmer was "turrible afear'd" of cold air, and kept her well wrapped up beside the fire. If she sweated, so much the better.

Sometimes, when the sun laid a bright triangle over the threshold, I saw the child loitering by the open door, looking up at the gulls or curlews passing in the blue sky, or down at the fragments of mussel-shells and small brown pebbles set in the lime-ash floor by her feet. From the confining space of the cottage room she saw and wondered on many things. Even in the gentlest days there was a shawl hiding her mouth, so careful was Granmer.

Once a visitor told the old woman that it was the worst possible thing for a tubercular child to remain in a stuffy atmosphere, all her frail strength leaving her in perspiration; but Grannie would not listen to such clitter-clatter. She set her little dear in the tall-backed wooden chair before the wan yellow flames of the sullen driftwood fire; but it did not improve her. One evening she was "took turrible bad wi' coughing", and after that she was kept in bed; and out of this darker room "the dear Lord took her for His own purpose" soon afterwards.

The old woman pushed her rattling perambulator down Vention Lane as before, except that now she went every day (but never on Sundays), heedless of the stormiest weather. The front wheel spokes of her firing-carrier broke through the rims, and she fitted on the rusted spindles a pair of cast-iron wheels off a lawn-mower, and pushed the tilted perambulator front-to-back, to prevent it tipping out its load. Her outward track wandered more, and she remained longer staring at useless objects; and one day she was seen pushing the perambulator on, or rather through, the soft sand, in which the narrow rims of its tall wheels cut deep lines. She spoke strangely to some children, who laughed at her for awhile, then became frightened and silent, and hurried home to tell their mother.

The old woman was found by the Black Rock, where she had fallen beside the perambulator, and they led her homewards, and put her to bed, and sent for the parish nurse. The perambulator was not worth fetching, but the children had fun with it, pulling it up the slopes of sandhills above the tide-line, and trying to ride down on it. Then they took it on the harder sand, and left it in the sea; and the tide came in and knocked it over, sands scoured and settled where tiny naked feet had jumped, and silted it up. By chance the waves of a later tide lifted it upright about the same time that its owner died; and in gentle summer weather the odd wheels sank down, until only the handle of iron and cracked china was visible. This too vanished in time, leaving the wide shore to the gulls and the curlews, and the tide riband to the rats, whose feet and dragging tails left marks in the dry loose sand above, where grew the flowers of the sea-rocket, beautiful and sturdy in their native sunshine.

Chapter Twenty-one

"DEVONSHIRE CIDER"

Having been given several sacks of apples one autumn morning, I thought I would make some cider. I had a 9-gallon sherry cask, and the wine-soaked oaken staves would surely add richness to the apple juice. I had often had glimpses of a cider-press in a barn on my way to the sands, but this was some distance from the village. Peering through the barn door into cavernous gloom, I saw the massive oaken engine, with a great screw running up through its centre, hand-cut from the trunk of an ash tree. The screw was six feet tall, and nearly as thick as a man.

Possibly it had been there since the reign of Elizabeth. Alas, it was derelict; the platform of the press was rotten, and the whole thing was loose. Chickens used it as a perching place.

While I was examining it a cottager came out and told me that Farmer Rodd in Ham had a cider press, and she was sure he would let me use it. So I returned to Ham and saw Farmer Rodd, who had a brother staying with him from Taunton to help him with cider-making—he was a clerk in a lawyer's office, and spent his holiday every year helping him to make cider.

While I was talking to them outside the pound house, a small brown-faced, brown-eyed boy arrived, staggering under a sack half-filled with apples. Throwing them down he said, with a merry smile,

"There you be, farmer. They'm yours, midear."

"For the last two years this boy has been giving me apples," said the farmer to me. "A kind-hearted li'l tacker. I haven't the heart to tell him I've got enough of my own already. Here you are, Tikey, here's threepence."

"Thank you, sir," sang out the boy, taking the money, and running away immediately.

The boy was telling the literal truth when he said that the apples were the farmer's; for unknown to him, the boy had gathered them from the farmer's orchard during the darkness of the night before. A month before he had removed flowers placed on graves as tributes to the dead, and, after a little rearrangement, had smilingly reoffered them as tributes to the living. He was a merry, brave little chap; and did things "for devilment", as we all knew.

"Yes, I think I can manage your little lot," said the farmer dubiously. "Us'll grind them up now, and get them out of the way."

So saying, he picked up one of the sacks I had brought down in my wheelbarrow, and with the help of his brother, tipped the apples into the cutting machine.

While the brother turned the handle, the farmer pressed the apples down with a spade, and made a remark which he repeated regularly for the next ten minutes.

"They'm 'oppin'; they'm 'ard," he said.

"Yes, they are hard, so they're hopping," said his brother, and began to turn the handle faster.

The *bob-bob-bobble* of the hard apples against the blunt revolving knives rose in pitch, and with more determined face Farmer Rodd pressed on a shovel and said again:

"You see they'm 'oppin'; they'm 'ard."

"You're right," said his brother. "They are hard, so they're hopping," and then began to turn very slowly.

"Please let me turn," I said, and the puffing bowler-hatted brother yielded the handle to me.

My determined turning made little difference to the cutting, for the apples continued to hop.

"Let me give you a breather," said the brother, a determined look in his eye. Was I cheating him of his annual exercise?

Five minutes, ten minutes went by, and I began to feel embarrassed, for sweat was beginning to appear from under the hard black rim of his hat, and the farmer was looking as though he would welcome a rest.

"They'm 'oppin'; they'm 'ard," he said for the twentieth time, pushing back his less fashionable bowler.

"I'm most awfully sorry," I said. "Look here, let me take them . . ."

"Don't 'ee worry," replied the farmer, "they'm 'ard, that's why they be 'oppin'; but us'll get'n through in a while, when the acid eats into the knives."

At last we had to smash the apples with a wooden mallet. They were a mixed lot, including pippins and large hard-skinned Canadian keepers. Once broken from their smoothness, the crushed apples were drawn into the knives, which were rusty and very blunt, and then chewed into fragments. Shovelfuls were then placed under the press, and built up into what was called the cheese. First a layer of apple fragments, then a layer of straw, with the ends turned up and tucked over the layer, then more apple fragments, then more straw. Farmer Rodd's press was, he said, a modern one, put there by his grandfather, with twin-screwed rods of iron at each end of the press. The rods were an inch and a half thick, and allowed the press to run up and down with level ease on their greased threads.

The cheese was squeezed down, then the oak press was spun upwards and more layers of straw and apples built up. So it went on, until all that remained of three sacks of apples was a flat and hard wad of pulped straw, pips, cores, and skin, which was lifted off and thrown to neighbour Billy Goldsworthy's chickens waiting round the door outside.

The clouded apple juice in the kieve or trough below was then poured into an oaken butt to be left to settle, when it would be racked, or syphoned into a barrel lying on its side with the bung-hole open at the top. As there was not enough of my apple juice to fill the barrel, the farmer said that if I liked he would add some of his old stuff until it was filled. It was necessary that the barrel be bung-full for the scum of the first fermentation to froth up and dribble itself away. In a week's time this first fermentation should have ceased, when the cider would be ready for racking off into my sherry cask. I must then tap the bung well home, said the farmer, and put the cask in the cellar.

I don't know what happened to my cask of cider, which, in my absence from the village, was very kindly brought to my cottage and put in the cellar by Billy Goldsworthy; I say I do not know what happened to it: but when I tapped it six months later on a hot March day, a thick brownish-bubbling stream like varnish ran forth, silently, amidst a swarm of unburst bubbles. Seeing Billy Goldsworthy pass, I called him in and told him I was anxious that he should be the first to taste the cider which he had so generously transported, free of charge, in his wheelbarrow.

Billy Goldsworthy said certainly, thank you very much, he could manage a jug just then, it being a very hot sun he had been digging in. I gave him the jug. He looked at it. He sniffed at it. Then he said that as it was a new barrel, the landlord should taste it first. So I had a sip, and passed the jug. He had a sip, and put the jug down. Had I put an old iron chain into it, or a bag of old nails? No, I hadn't. Ah then, that was the trouble; the cider had missed its meal of iron. Also, I must pardon him telling me, if I understood, but my cellar was too cold. Cider couldn't abear the cold, his dear soul, that was the trouble. A cold cellar, and no iron to ait! Why, no wonder it was like a swarm of bees about the tongue!

I told him that the so-called cellar was only a damp and dark cavern between the kitchen and the living-room, and that the temperature and dampness of all three places was equal. Ah, there it was, the cider had eaten itself into bubbles, and 'twas no use keeping it; 'twould only go ropey, and sour the barrel. Gone in, my cider was, in his opinion.

Feeling disappointed, I rolled the barrel outside the gate and pulling out the tap, watched it gurgling and grumbling out of its prison. The sun was very hot in the March sky. Spider gossamers were gleaming in the warm air. Constellations of celandines shone out of the wayside grass. The cider ran in a wide delta over the dusty road, which in those days was untarred. Very soon I began to notice a strangeness in life, as though the sun had swung the earth into the fourth dimension. I began to sing. Meeting my wife on the stairs, with an empty baby's bottle in her hand, I noticed how her eyes were brighter than usual, and her cheeks were like apple blossom. Spontaneously, without the least feeling of remaining my calculating male self, I kissed her. She kissed me too; we smiled; and without a word, ran away from each other. Then Gwennie the maid came out of a room with a duster, and also looked very pretty; without any effort I found I was saying that it was a lovely day. The dreary winter was gone, and I was actually happy! I ran into my writing-room, determined to begin a new life, to be more methodical than even Arnold Bennett.

I found I did not want to work in such sunlight. Peeping round the window, I noticed Billy Goldsworthy standing outside his barn, and actually laughing as he talked to Widow Lovering; and this day, I am convinced, was the beginning of Billy's courtship.

After a while the children came out of school and stood in the road looking at the drying runnels, and the little pools under the tap-hole. They stood there and increased in numbers; I don't know what I said, but I can still hear their massed shouts of instant laughter. Presently Clib the gravedigger came ambling down the road, and after greeting me very staidly, with many nods of his red head, he began to giggle, to prod me in the ribs, and to tell me that I was a naughty man. Why? I asked. I had merely washed the ditched wall of the glebe field outside the

Lower House with a watering can. It had, as I knew, created a lot of indignation among people going to church on Sunday morning; for on the previous Saturday evening I had assumed the office of the Sanitary Inspector and had thoroughly washed the wall where men stood after coming out of the pub; and the marks of numerous runnels of the water down Church Street had been misinterpreted on the Sunday morning. Was that naughty? The children shrieked almost hysterically with laughter.

When Clib and the other children had gone away, the yard doors of Hole Farm rattled and opened, and out came gaunt, sparrow-beak-nosed "Stroyle" George with a bunch of daffodils for my baby's birthday. He was nearly a month late, but still he had remembered that the baby had been born at the beginning of the previous year. We talked amiably for some minutes, and then remarking that I had wasted some very good cider, he went away.

Cider is a difficult drink, even when it is really cider; one pint can make you feel fine, but two, perhaps three pints can entirely throw your world out of its orbit, into a dimensionless space.

About half an hour later I was going to have influenza; and Gwennie the maid said she had a headache; and my wife was saying that she *had* repeatedly asked Gwennie not to put the egg-shells into the ash-bucket, and that she didn't care a hang if she was adjutant, and I was a rotten colonel anyway, all my men would mutiny, anyhow, this wasn't the Army and when was I going to pay back the housekeeping money I had borrowed? While we were arguing, and the baby was crying, a bang on the door announced the second visit of Stroyle George; who with bloodshot eyes and scaly-finger shakings accused me of telling someone that he had borrowed a new hurdle from me eighteen months before, and had not returned it. I was a bad neighbour, and a liar; for I knew very well that he had offered to buy it from me last month, but not at its cost price of 2s. 6d., for it was now second-hand. I told him to keep the hurdle on condition that he kept away from me; and he left with dragging boots and grumbling voice-

"DEVONSHIRE CIDER"

We were trying to eat an unappetizing meal when Billy Goldsworthy began thumping in his barn. The old fool was still trying to split, with an axe that had not been sharpened since 1880,
sections of an elm tree which he had allowed to season until the
grainless wood was tough as leather. It was a good opportunity
to go and tell him that his unpleasant banging at night must
cease, for it woke up my baby, and interfered with my work. (I
had done no work for three or four months; still, I was always
meaning to begin again.) Billy Goldsworthy retorted that I
could not stop him as he was on his own property. I replied that
if the noise did not stop he would no longer be in a position to
be on his own property. Overhearing our voices Stroyle George
flapped from out his farm door and told Billy Goldsworthy that
if he did not bliddy well stop his knocking at night, he would
bliddy well take him before the judge. Billy Goldsworthy retorted that if his, Farmer George's, dog didn't stop howling at
night, he would see a lawyer about it. Stroyle George retorted
that he could see all the bliddy lawyers in Devon if he liked, for
his dog was locked up at night, and it was my dog—pointing at
me—that was wandering about keeping folks awake at night.
I probably replied as rudely as I could, and left them to it.

Their argument continued, the one angry and shouting, the
other quiet but persistent. At two o'clock it was still going on,
when from the bedroom window I called down curses on both
their heads.

Clib, coming from his dinner to resume work in the churchyard, complained to me that he had a headache. I had one too.
It must be the influenza, I said. He said, as he bowed several
times from his heels, he thought it was the cider, the smell of
the cider, the cider, it was all over the village, all over the village,
and people were complaining, complaining, people were complaining. While he was bowing and speaking in his unique
rhythm, I noticed a most peculiar thing—half a dozen wasps,
all of them large queen wasps, were crawling over the damp
cider marks in the road. When I touched one with a stick, it was
unable to fly. One or two sluggish bluebottles were there as well,

called from their winter torpor from thatch-eave and hole in dry cob wall.

Other people in the village told me that the smell of the cider had given them a headache; and to this day I don't know what was wrong or right with my cider. The village butcher, who posed as an expert ever since he had made me sick with the pale, thin, Sedgemoor acid, told me that I should have put a few pounds of steak, or several clean dead rats as an alternative, into my barrel. I told him not to mix up the making of sausages with that of cider. Ignoring my insults, he persisted that the cider "aits all the time—you want to put some maet in for it to ait. It will ait all away by the time you come vor tap 'n."

With a grin he told me that once a small man had fallen by accident into one of the great hogsheads in the rectory outhouse during Parson Hole's time. The small man, he said, was a cooper who had come up from Crosstree to repair leaky staves, and finding a bottle of brandy, he had drunk it, and apparently fallen asleep inside the hogshead. His mate, not knowing that he was there, had gone on with his work, and had completed the putting in of the new staves. The blacksmith had riveted up the iron hoops. The man was missing from his home, but the mystery was not solved until some years later when, the hogshead being too sour for further use, its top was knocked in, and within was found a brandy bottle and a gold ring which the man had worn. Everything else—nailed boots, clothes, flesh, hair, had been "ait up by the cider", declared the butcher.

"It's a dirty lie!" I cried, feeling myself to be, at last, a proper villager.

"That's what they always say hereabouts," he grinned.

"Cider is just filthy poison," I said. "Only degenerates like it."

"Now would you like a nice little glass of cider," he wheedled. "I have just opened a barrel I ordered, all the way from Sedgemoor. Come on, just a glass. Bootiful stuff!"

"I don't want to be eaten alive," I said. "Or to look like you," I added.

"Cider be a bootiful drink," he went on, reaching for two

glasses, "just one. Look, do you see that man going down there with the coal cart? Now if I was to ask him to have a drink he would empty my barrel by the evening. I minds the time when he drank eighteen pints in an hour—'twas down to South Hole Farm. He took some coal there and they gave him a 3-pint jug as it was a very hot day. When he had finished it he said he had forgotten to drink the health of the man who had drawed it for 'n. 'Go in and get another jug,' he said, 'for the drawer.' He swallowed that one and then said to the labourer, 'Go in after another jug, for the master.' He drank that, and said, 'Go in after another jug, for the missis.' He put down that one, and said, 'Go in after another jug, for the young master,' and when 'a had swallowed the fifth jugful, 'a said, 'Now go in after one for me.' He was a proper daddy for cider," said the butcher. "A dad for cider, he was. Mind you, it was palatable cider. None of this yurr sweet bottled stuff, which is just kid's drink." *Palatable*: it seemed a strange word in village talk.

A day or two later I was talking to Stroyle George about cider, and he told me that it was no good putting meat or iron in a barrel. "You want to put some ginger in for it to ait," he said, "and a beetroot, and a handful of raisins. A proper daddy for raisins is cider. You see cider is vegetable, and ginger and beetroot and raisins is vegetable too, and it ban't natural for vegetable to be aiting animal. Animal to ait vegetable, yes, look at the bullocks aiting grass; but you don't see the grass aiting the bullock, do you? Tidden God's purpose. Vegetable to vegetable, but not vegetable to animal, not likely!"

"What about the sundews?" I asked.

"What be they?"

"Plants that ait vlies."

"Vlies? Well, vlies ban't animals, be'm? Noo-mye!"

"Sundews be proper daddies for vlies," I said.

"Aw, I don't know naught about what you'm telling," mumbled Stroyle George. "I'm dealing with natural facts, not kid's talk or all they lies you read in books! There be no gettin' over natural facts, you know!"

"You'm right," I said.

The only other fact I got from him was that cider is "ropey" when it is old—probably a kind of fungus.

Well, I have made my first and probably my last cask of Devonshire cider.

But before I leave the unpalatable subject for ever, I must record an evening spent in a barn beside the stream in Cryde, during those first wonderful months in the village following the Great War. I was drawn to it by chinks of light coming through its double doors. Inside, two candles shining in tobacco smoke lit the faces of many men. The great oak press was shadowy against the wall; the iron shovel, shaped like a three-sided box, was silver-bright, worked upon and ensculped by the juices of crushed apples which for days and nights had been shovelled from the cutting-machine to the cheese under the press. A circle of boys and youths was gathered around the kieve into which the juice was running. Each boy had a straw in his mouth through which he was sucking the yellow liquid. This apparently was an old custom in Cryde, or in this pounding-house; for at all other cider-making in that barn I saw boys in there sucking at the juice.

It was here that I first met Colonel Ponde, clad in rubber waders, and wearing a fisherman's hat stuck with flies. Being then a newcomer to the village he was watching anxiously the level of his own apple juice in the kieve, for six or seven boys sat there, all silent, all with straws in their mouths. Colonel Ponde had been the first to pound his apples that year; the next season I noticed he was the last, when no boys were remaining.

Even now, when I have determined to dislike cider for ever, certain misgivings arise like ghosts in sleepless midnights. What did I do wrong? I had a sweet sherry cask, and the juice was good, for I tasted it. Did I murder the innocent young wine by tapping the cask before it was grown? If I had kept it for a year, for two years, would it have grown slowly in beauty and become nectar? Ah! I know. The farmer had filled up the cask with his own cider, to oblige me; and that cider had been the ancient, pale, acid stuff they call "hard" cider—and it had corrupted my own lovely maiden wine. Farmhouse cider! Heroine of a thousand suburban ballads, praised by a million suburban voices, all thick, throaty, and hooting *fortissimo*, "Devonshire cider!" Sour and bitter termagant, garrotrix of its own offspring—ropey fungus—for even that stifles in its watery, yellow, gulls'-eyes acids. Eater of men and rats, old boots and iron bedsteads, thou thin juice of all vileness, worshipped by the winnicks and loobeys of Ham, what was it Revvy used to sing, as his forefathers, all rheumaticy farm labourers, sang before him?

> *Brown bread with holes in it*
> *Skim cheese with eyes in it*
> *Hard work and no beer*
> *Hanged if I bide wi't.*
>
> *But hard cider much as you please*
> *Loose your teeth and bow your knees*
> *Sour your gut and make you wheeze*
> *Turn your words to stings of bees*
> *Thin your blood and kill your fleas*
> *Hard cider much as you please.*

Now, pavement poetasters, musical morons, and maundering mannekins, sing your suburban "Devonshire Cider" ballads! And let me get back to my work as the serious historian of the village.

Chapter Twenty-two

CONSECRATION OF
THE NEW BURIAL GROUND

The rooks wheeled high in the autumn sky, looking down on the procession of human beings winding its slow length under the trees of the rookery. The birds had ceased to caw. Had a rook human intelligence, what would it have made of the noise arising from the slow procession led by the white-haired, white-surpliced bishop? Like a human rook— or better, like a crow—I was watching what the pamphlet put into my hand by a smiling choirboy described as

THE FORM AND MANNER
of
CONSECRATING
NEW OR ADDITIONAL
BURIAL GROUND
in use in
THE DIOCESE OF EXETER

The Burial Ground is to be properly enclosed, fenced, and completed with gates and churchways.

An intimation of the Bishop's intention to consecrate the Burial Ground, with the day and hour appointed for it, is to be fixed on the Church door at least three days beforehand.

An awning or tent should be erected on the ground to be consecrated, and provided with table, chair, footstool, pen and ink.

The procession, led by white-surpliced priests and choir, wound slowly up the path through the hillside coppice. First the Bishop declaimed one verse of the 16th Psalm, then the followers responded with another. So they came to the hilltop, where brambles had been cut and rough paths made in the scrub. An owl, which for years had awakened to hoot every day at noon and at four o'clock, flapped away in dismay from its roosting place amidst the thick foliage of a holm-oak.

I stood just behind William Gammon. He was wearing his best suit of black cloth, like the other older men. At the top of the slope by the wall of the rectory kitchen-garden some of the older people, having left the procession, were resting in the warm beams of the early autumn sun. A plum tree, straggling with wild wood, grew by the rugged cob coign of the two walls.

"Well," said Willy Gammon, in his croaky melancholy voice, "they ringers up in the tower gived us some beautiful pealing to cheer us before the service, didn't'm?"

Willy's brother Ernest, a white surplice over his neat dark suit, passed with his fellow churchwarden behind the Rector and the parson of a neighbouring village. Willy had been sitting in the Higher House from 12.30 to 2 o'clock as was his Sunday custom. His brother Ernest never went near a pub. Willy was frowned at as brother Ernest passed, but Willy's brown child-like eye remained unperturbed. There he stood, a man entirely without pretensions, physical or spiritual, a mason who had never saved a penny, father of a large merry family; there was Ernest Gammon, employer of labour and owner of increasing property, whose two children had been given a superior educa-tion. Willy had a deep and tender sympathy for all human actions, as I knew. It was impossible to talk with Ernest as man to man, for he seemed to find so much to disapprove of in the behaviour of others. His eyes were never limpid like Willy's, but always guarded. Under that guard, perhaps, lurked the younger brother of Willy.

"What, did 'ee manage vor climb up here, midear?" said Willy, with tender concern, going forward to shake the hand of an old woman. "Why, Grannie Carter, I be pleased vor see 'ee looking so well, midear."

Widow Carter, mother of Revvy, shook Willy's hand. She had been ill in bed for weeks.

THE NEW BURIAL GROUND

"I mind the time, Grannie Carter, when Revvy and I were boys in this very place, come yurr to stale (steal) the plums off this same tree. Aiy, forty year ago. Passon Hole's gardener used to come out of the door round th' corner and chase us with a long stick, but us boys could run in they days. Aiy, us could." The words were like music, soft and melancholy as the autumn sunshine.

Thou shalt shew me the path of life; in Thy presence is the fulness of joy—disapproving glances and frowns were given to Willy by the chanting Rector and chanting Rector's warden. The procession was wending slowly downhill again.

"Aiy, I'd like to be buried up yurr at the top, among the brimbles an' all, near th' old plum tree, 'tes the prettiest spot in Ham," went on Willy, serenely. His pink patch, concealing an empty eye-socket, was turned to the procession; he was ignorant of the effect of his words, otherwise he would have remained silent out of politeness. Willy was speaking his thoughts aloud.

Willy's nephew and niece, both in the choir, glanced askance at the reprobate as they slowly passed down the hill again.

"Aiy," sighed Willy, "when the dear Lord calls, us'll go happy, won't us, Grannie Carter, midear?" He belched discreetly, for he had drunk an extra pint of beer for the occasion.

Below, by the tent, Willy's churchwarden brother, pale with nervousness, was reading the Petition to the Bishop.

"What be'm up to now?" asked Willy.

"Ssh! The Rector's warden is reading the petition!" whispered Mrs. "Vanderbilt" Will Carter, anxiety and disapproval in her attitude. "Do be careful! The Bishop might hear what you're saying!"

"Poor brother Ernst, he hath no more voice than a dipchick," replied Willy, despondently. "'A was always a timid boy, was Ernst."

The Rector of Ham and the Vicar of Crosstree followed his Lordship into the tent, and the whisper went around, "They'm signing th' papers!"

It was pleasant under the trees, in the company of Willy

Gammon and Granmer Carter, with the sun-maze shuffling on
the woodland slope. Across the streamlet and the graveyard wall,
beyond the gaps where two of the nine old elms had been
thrown, stood the grey church tower. I felt suddenly happy that
I knew all these people—if you smiled at them, and were
friendly, they always responded. One creates the world, as it
were. How many thousand vanished worlds lay buried under
the uneven turf of the old churchyard?

At last, it seemed, the long controversy over the burial ground
was ended. It had gone on for nearly five years, from Church
Council to Parish Council, and back again to Church Council.

Eventually there was a combined meeting of the Church
Council and the new Parish Council—Jonathan Furze was its
Chairman—and the representatives of the Chapel. At last they
were all in agreement—to accept an acre of ground adjoining
the churchyard as a gift from an old gentleman, a retired lawyer
settled at Cryde, who had also agreed to pay all "the expenses
incurred by the abortive negotiations". In addition, the donor
had given a pair of silk stockings to every girl in the Church
choir; and there was anticipation of free sacks of coal and even
of turkeys at Christmas! A proper gennulman, plenty of money!

"Well, why shouldn't 'a give th' money?" said Tom Gammon, who worked less hard than anyone else in the parish.
"'A hath plenty of money! 'A's got it, surenuff—and how did
'a get it? Ah, a lawyer knows how to get it all right!"

Most villagers, however, thought that he was "a proper
gennulman" for his gift. Certainly he appeared to have what
the village seemed entirely to lack, for in giving the money, he
used this style of speaking, "I thank you for enabling me, with
your help, to carry out the extension of the Churchyard, and I
hope and believe it will be all that is necessary for parish-burying
for the next fifty years. The part I played has been very small,
for it is almost entirely due to your kindness in unanimously
accepting my small offer that I am enabled to ask you to accept
this ground. I offer my sincere thanks to the Parish Council for
the kind way in which they have met the deputation of the

THE NEW BURIAL GROUND

Church Council in these matters. I hope this will be the beginning of a new era in Ham, and that now all will live harmoniously together and do what is best in the interests of the Parish."

Had he any premonition that he was to die soon afterwards, and to be the first buried in the "new extension"? The village was to see Clib the sexton, in his postman's trousers, hacking at roots with a mattock, only a few weeks afterwards.

The parish, content that it had been saved a 2½d. or even 3d. rate, forgot the matter; and the controversy of *Cemetery, or Burial Ground?* was ended by an address from the Bishop.

The Bishop came out of the tent, while a neighbouring squire took a Kodak photograph of him.

The crow is not a gregarious bird, like the rook; rooks quarrel and squabble and try to filch one another's property in their treetop villages: the crow is aloof, suspect, observant, unsocial. My mind was a crow that wondered what cawing of indignation would have arisen in the Churchgoing consciousness if William Gammon had produced a Brownie camera from under his black coat, and pointed it at the gentle-faced old man while he was addressing us? William stood still, smiling with happiness, sometimes saying, "Proper! Proper! Proper li'l old graveyard th' dear old gennulman have gived th' parish!"

"Ssh! Ssh! Be quiet! Ssh!"

The Bishop, who bore the name of Trefusis, was preparing to speak.

"We are come together with one heart and one soul to dedicate this ground to God: for we are giving it to God this day. You are called to present to God what has been provided after many difficulties and trials. There are always difficulties in this mortal world, my children: nevertheless, while you are here on earth, you must always remember that you have duties to perform to your neighbours. No man can live for himself only, and be a happy man; for man is so made that he attains serenity and strength by working with and for others."

The Bishop spoke in a throaty voice, for he was very old; but there was sweetness in his face and gestures. His words fell slowly in the wan sunlight among the trees. We were silent within ourselves.

"I, who am old, and soon to die, have seen the graves of those I have buried pass away in time, forgotten or lost, until nothing is left but grass, and a lessening mound. Such is God's intention for all living things: to be, to bloom, to mingle in earth and air, in the hope and faith of resurrection in radiance beyond the hills of our mortal mornings grey. All of us have the journey down into darkness, even as the lonely hero of all, the Man among men, our blessed Jesus, whom we call the Christ."

So the wise and gentle words ceased, and the white head was bowed in prayer; and in the moment of silence following, while our thoughts prayed for us, we were glad that we had listened.

Last Chapter

SURVIEW AND FAREWELL

On a morning of St. Martin's Little Summer I climbed the circular stone steps of the church tower to take my last look on the village. Over the glebe field the sun rose up, melting the first thatch-rime of the year—for the year truly begins with Spring. With the Spring man is resurrected; his consciousness is the world. Man leases the world from the sun, the great landlord; a landlord that one day—the sun knows only day—one day will fall from its orbit into the twilight of star-travelling space. That time, said Mr. Clib the sexton, industriously toiling with shovel and mattock in a pit below, that time would be Judgment Day, when the graves would yawn, and the dead walk. How deep did they now lie in waiting, how many tiers since even the Saxons?

The elms, or their forefathers, standing east and west of the tower, had nourished themselves on those tiers, and the grass had grown and faded, more than a thousand seasons; the sun had drawn up vapour, the rain washed away salts of phosphorus and nitrogen, compounds of carbon, oxygen, and calcium—each corpse but a few ounces after a century—yet the ground below and around the tower was many hundreds of tons heavier by the hope of resurrection . . . the dust of earlier pagan villagers was on the hills, or fire-salt in the sea.

There was Clib working in his postman's trousers, hacking roots with a mattock, and pausing to straighten his back and scratch his red poll, as I had seen him a score of times.

Thoughts of soil and roots and ash were soon borne away by the wind murmuring round the tall square tower. The sun was the sun, and it was pleasant to be alive. Gone the yellow elm leaves of the coloured autumn; the winds of the equinox strewed them among the gravestones and over the rectory lawns north of the tower. Soon Clib would have to get his long ladder and clean out the gutters of the church roof. Summer was gone, and without regret; the young man's identification of self with Nature was gone with all that early happiness, and unhappiness.

Down in the street below a three-year-old boy, his glance following a stooping mother's arm pointing upwards, cried in a high, tiny voice, "You be up there, Dad? Me come too! Yass!" Distinctly in the autumn air I heard the word *Chocolate*, and the journey to the shop was immediately resumed.

There was tranquillity on the tower. I thought of the changes which had come since first I, a beardless boy, arrived in this country almost as remote and romantic as Crusoe's isle. It was a dry May month in 1914, the sun always shining, the sea ever blue from misty early morning until eve's greying purple of the far-lying Atlantic. O, those Atlantic sunsets from the high down above the sea, where the evejars churred! They weighed the heart with wildest longing, an immense tranquillity of sadness. That was just youth, perhaps, a youth more solitary than most. And how wonderful was the journey to romantic Devon! That last part in the train from Exeter, beside a river that went away under hillside oakwoods, and returned suddenly as the wheels thundered over bridges! Mile after mile beside the lovely river in the valley: rocks, waterfalls, pools, and glittering fast shallows; then, at last, after many stops at stations where flowers grew, it was the village of Crosstree, where I got out, and looked about in a quiet sun-dusty street of small thatched shops, with an apple orchard in bloom opposite the level-crossing. There was a man with a brown moustache standing up in a carriage, grinning, a straw in his mouth, his cap peak pointing up at forty-five degrees to his forehead. He called my name. He told me his name—Arty Brooking, sent to fetch me. Green-heart fly-rod and patched black bag were put in the cab, and I sat beside this most amiable fellow, and off we went up and up a long hill, the steepest I had ever seen, and then up and up an ever steeper hill, at the top of which we stopped, and looked back over an immortal tract of sea and land and sky, more infinite than anything my eyes had seen. A tract of sandhills and lines of breakers, a tiny white lighthouse in the remote distance, beside a narrow estuary gleaming azure as it widened into the sea. All that dark length of land ended at Hartland Point, and beyond, under the westering sun, the sea stretched without land-fall until the coast of America. We looked in silence. *Makes you think, don't it?* said my companion at last, shifting the straw in his mouth.

(That was four months before the horizon suddenly dropped away, and the earth became a place with an unreal, harsh-bright sky.) The journey in the old black cab lasted an hour and ten minutes, but it was timeless in the sunken red lanes with their tall hedges and ferny banks. Towards honey-light, as the roof-shadows spread across the dusty road, I came to Ham and saw the quiet grey tower rising over the silent graves and the tall elms, and heard the murmur of a tiny stream, and saw a white owl floating silently over the tall grasses of the glebe field. O blessed place, O sweet swallows and cornfields, O hills and the sea!

Seven years afterwards I was back again, to live solitary for all time, as then I thought. Haggard and thin, rejecting the harsh-bright mentality of the human world, I sought again in wave and tree and bird that land beyond the lost horizon; avoiding my fellow-men, whose lives seemed to be based only on self-interest, on the little ego which did not even understand itself, let alone its neighbour.

From the skiey stance on the church tower I recalled the ten years of the post-war which I had known. The spiritual, or imaginative, or illusive search of the years before and after the war was written in several books: disprized, not to the age they were written for: perhaps to the next age, after another purging more terrible than that which youth had known; perhaps after all to no age, since the logical end of dream is negation of life. It is finished: all I would recall now is the actual, or concrete, changes in the village, before I depart.

In the year after the Great War, there was an attempt to run an omnibus service from Ham to Crosstree, thence to the market town of Barum, on market day, Friday. It failed, as farmers had their jingles, and folk were dubious about the steepness of Noman's Hill. The iron-roofed garage, standing in a corner of "Thunderbolt" Carter's field opposite the shop, became a carpenter's store, where coffins and doors were made. The transport pioneer, a young ex-airman, failing to pay the balance of the purchase price, forfeited both land and money; Vanderbilt Willy, twitted with his meanness in Higher or Lower House, became more deaf than before.

Two years passed, and Harry Zeale, who had rebought the land from Vanderbilt Willy, purchased a motor car for use as a taxicab. This vehicle, of pre-war make, seemed very black and tall and slow. One day a wheel fell off, and the axle was reforged by the blacksmith. Soon afterwards, on returning from Crosstree station with a jet of steam arising from its radiator, the gearbox, lacking grease, began to scream, and reforged itself beyond motion. Thereafter, pulled by a horse into the carpenter's shop, it became a night-roost of chickens.

About this time the lime-washed cottage walls facing the lanes from Crosstree and Cryde became red-dusty from the passing of motor cars in summer. The first charabancs thundered past from Combe on their way to Santon and Barum, forcing smaller cars to get into the ditch or be crushed. Several dogs were nearly killed; but they soon learned, without hurrying, to avoid the dust-streaming wheels. Then came a nearly-regular daily service of an omnibus with wooden seats; this was put out of business by a regular service of horsehair-and-spring-seated buses run by a district company. The district company was soon absorbed by a county company, whose red buses were considered most comfortable, as they had coach-built roofs and windows instead of canvas hoods and celluloid screens. The red buses in turn were absorbed by a national company, whose green double-decker, six-tyred monsters glided discreetly through the sunken lanes and were courteous to all smaller traffic.

In 1925, when three flying-boats of the Royal Air Force haared and throbbed overhead, Ship the cattle-dog of Hole Farm fled tail-down into the farmyard, and the blacksmith's hens beat their wings in terror and ran into the darkness of the forge.

Thinking of the hens, I recalled Revvy's duck, which loved my spaniel. There were four ducklings, but rats ate three; and the duckling grew up alone, a friendly creature that knew only a life bounded by a few yards of stream, a small enclosed garden, a passageway or drang, a dark shed, and Revvy's kitchen. When it was grown its feelings led it to be happy whenever it saw the dog. To this indifferent being it would waddle, quacking happily, and after bowing, would prostrate itself until its bill was pressed on the ground before the squatting dog. Groaning displeasure, the spaniel would get up, stretch itself and yawn, and walk away. The duck would follow, quacking to it, not knowing why it must follow. One day it followed the dog into Stroyle George's farmyard, from which it returned quacking feebly, while the dog limped home whining. All the next day it lay in a basket before Revvy's fire, neither eating nor drinking; but it raised itself and tried to quapp its bill when it saw the dog, and then the narrow head sank down, and the watching eye became as though contemplating something not of the life it had hitherto known. It grew colder, and when the dog sniffed it scarcely moved; and when Revvy came home his "poor li'l old duckling" was gone.

Leaning against the lichened embattlements of the Norman tower, I recalled how such an act of kicking or striking dog or duck or other beast used to agitate me to angry indignation when I was younger. Later, I perceived that a happy or harmonious man would never kick or wish to hurt a friendly or confiding creature straying on his land. And if a man were unhappy, there was a cause for unhappiness. Often such a state grew with a man's life, as a trout grows thin in poor water; and who would blame a thin fish.

How easy, how thoughtless, to use the word *cruel* in application to the deeds of others! There was the lawsuit of a son-in-law against his father-in-law and brother-in-law, or it may have been the other way round. A sheep had broken from one field into another; the enraged owner of the invaded field did not impound the sheep, as he was entitled to do by law if he chose, afterwards demanding damage-money; but he vented his rage against his marriage-relative by kicking the sheep, which died. Now I knew the cause of the rage: an inharmonious union, a quick war-marriage of young people, later causing sour looks and bitter words. Very occasionally such bitterness ends in a man lying under a hedge, a gun beside him, the top of his head blown off. Alone and harmonious on the church tower, with the gilt wind-vane making a light jangled music as it moved, I knew that the inflammation of despair was the original cause of such acts so easily condemned as cruelty: so easily inducing righteous anger, so facilely calling forth condemnation—and thus, sadly, helping to perpetuate the original cause.

Can it have been five years ago that I intended to write that unhappy story of a poor sheep: the broken leg, the broken ribs, the staring grey-yellow idiot-eyes in the long and woolly face; the white-lipped curses of the young husband; the wife supported by father, mother, and brother—who lived in an adjoining cottage—showing the sullen hate of sexual disharmony.

There was to be comic relief, too—when, after a truce or temporary cessation of the unhappiness, the ferret of the young 6-acre farmer got out of its cage one night, and entered the fowl-house of the father-in-law, where ninety-seven white spring chickens, a dozen hens, and two stag-birds (cocks) were roosting. The fowl-house was enclosed in a wire-netted grassy space; and in the morning it looked, said a villager, who had gone there to buy eggs for his shop, as though thousands of white rags had been torn up and scattered on the trodden grass. Curled up in a corner of the silent fowl-house was the ferret, its hair clotted into spikes by dried blood, and blinking its mild pink eyes.

What was the truth about the missing pages of the Minute Book of the Parish Council, that incident in the bitter controversy of *Cemetery or Burial Ground*, which lasted four years and four months—the period of time of the Great War, of which it was a microcosm? The old clerk, Charlie Tucker, told me that he had spoiled a page, and in cutting it out with a sharp pen-knife, he had inadvertently cut several blank pages. That was all: no records were missing, all had been there. Yet with what eloquence had Mr. Jaggers, in his speech which had destroyed finally the old Council, convinced us of the significance of cut-out records! As for the new clerk, he was Mr. Jaggers himself who took the place of Charlie Tucker: and within a year the new clerk had lost the entire book, missing blank pages as well as the year's records: Charlie Tucker built his houses of local stone; Mr. Jaggers built his great boarding house of asbestos sheeting, on the flimsiest deal framework. A leary (light) cart maketh the most noise: that was the old saying in the village.

Other stories of the happenings of the village, which will never be written. Billy Goldsworthy's courtship of Widow Lovering; the secret smiles of the sixty-five-year-old bachelor as he worked in his barn. "A woman about the place makes all the difference, don't you see," he told me once. "So I'm told," I replied, superior with my four married years. "It be true what I'm telling you," he went on, in a rapid whisper. "My dear soul, a nice woman has a power of good over a man, that's my way of thinking." Every night the neat little man called at her door in the dusk, sometimes with a small basket of pears, or peas, a pail of limewash, a few dry sticks for the stove. The marriage was taking place; it was off: it was on once more. Billy's sister, who since the death of old Mrs. Goldsworthy had worn her mother's clothes—period 1880—looked odder than ever, as she padded white-faced and unspeaking behind the cows to and from milking. At last, after a year of courting, Widow Lovering declared she preferred to remain a widow.

Not even Shakespeare would have gathered with greater zest the remark of Bale the trapper in the Higher House one evening, giving the reason why the courtship had failed—but such roistering wit is of the air, not print.

And there was to have been a story of the old belfry; and of the old lead roof which was scored and cut with hearts and outlines of boots, with dates, and initials of those long since gone under the grass below. The six ringers used to sweat as they pulled at the coloured sallies, for the six old bells swung unevenly in their oaken cage. It was said that the cage was infirm. The death-watch beetle had bored into the pale streaks of sap wood until they were like miniature rabbit warrens in sand; but the hard cores of the centuries-old oak gave no nourishment for the white grubs which tapped and tapped to each other in their dark galleries when the wood had ceased its humming after the last clash of the great tenor bell. So the small brown beetles ceased to lay their eggs in their ancestral warren, and taking wing, flew out of the belfry.

Salt-wind moaned in the slats of the tower windows; swallows' wings fluttered by their mud nests; voices and village noises came up remotely in the dim and murmurous loft: then the tower trembled with the ponderous inharmony of the bells, prisoned in their cage.

Up the damp stone tower, feeling its way in growths of blackening streaks and pallid smears, came the enemy and conqueror of even those iron-hard oaken cores, wraithlike, seeming weaker and less substantial than the rottenest leaf, yet possessing

275

in its ghostly lace the power to possess with evil spirit the hardest wood. It settled there, after its climb from the ground; and the bell-cage was doomed unless creosote or some other exorcising chemical were used immediately to kill the fungus called dry-rot. Then it was found that the cage was loose in the tower, and there was danger of it falling when the bells were being pealed.

The Rector suggested raising money for a new cage by a summer gathering in the glebe field, with tugs-of-war, a jumble sale, side-shows like climbing the greasy pole, judging the weight of a live sheep, fortune-telling—all the fun of the fair, to be opened by the Member of Parliament. Bills were printed announcing a Fete in the Glebe Field in Ham Saint George, Ye Olde Englishe Fayre, for the Bell Fund.

"I minds the time," said an old man, staring at one of the bills nailed under the lych-gate, "when ould Pass'n Hole held the Ham Revel in thaccy glebe viel'."

It was a lovely day, and the village revelled in the Feet, as the foreign word was pronounced in Ham. I gave an autographed copy of each of the books which had recently been published—*The Beautiful Years*, and *The Lone Swallows*. Put up for auction, the highest bid for the brace was twopence; and the Rector, wishing to save the feelings of one of his parishioners, withdrew them and bought them himself, paying to the Bell Fund fifteen shillings for them, the published price. Seven years later, when I saw that some unautographed copies had fetched five pounds each, I reminded him of his purchase; he said he had kept them until recently, when someone, possibly with a knowledge of first editions, had taken them from his library, where they never reappeared.

The Bell Fund Feet, or Ye Olde Englishe Fayre, was remembered for several occasions.

(*a*) A side-show called SEE THE SWIMMING SEALS, 2*d*., which was a small tent, containing a basin of water with bits of sealing wax in it.

(*b*) The sight of the Member of Parliament being pursued and finally accosted by a parent, who presented a boy with a yellow school cap and a yellower face, with a request that Mr. Peto, Conservative M.P., should help the lad to enter a political life.

(c) A boy falling off a pole in a pillow-fight and breaking his neck.

(d) The prize for the hogget weight-guessing competition—a saddle of mutton—being won by the labourer who worked on the farm whence the sheep had been borrowed.

(e) The excellent tea for a shilling in the old disused rectory coach-house.

Ye Olde Englishe Fayre, or Feet in the Glebe Field of Ham Saint George, was successful; and many gifts of money added to the Bell Fund. One man, who had recently acquired a small manorial property in the neighbourhood, gave the price of a bell on the condition that his name and address were cast around the rim.

Soon a lorry arrived with the tackle, which was fixed to a steel girder grouted under the lead roof. A whirring endless chain on several wheels slowly lifted the bells from their Jacobean cage and swung them humming towards the small square of tiled floor far below, where despite continual warnings tiny faces peered up. Among the grassy mounds the bells rested, while the children ran round them and tried to chip off the pennies, florins, and crown-pieces annealed to the rims. Soon the word went round that they were not real coins, but only the castings; meanwhile the treasure hunt continued, and each bell, green when it was lifted into the six-wheeled lorry, bore a hundred scratches.

With invisible and appalling strength the endless chain, hooked to the massive cage, tore beam from beam amidst creaks and groans of the oak which had endured the elements within the high loftiness of the windy centuries. A man in shirt-sleeves kept the chain whirring on its pulley wheels by a series of flicks with the finger and thumb of his right hand, using only wrist and elbow, while talking to another man beside him about the chances of Canonbury against the Arsenal in next Saturday's football match. *Crack! Ah-aa-aah! Crack!*—the shrieking beams were slowly torn apart from their ancient claspings, while the star centre forward was declared a dirty player, pretending to fall on one knee when he missed the ball, and shooting out his leg to trip an opponent.

Then while the belfry, hollow and gaping, was being set with the steel girders of a post-war cage, and the bells were waiting to be recast into a peal of eight in a distant foundry, a meeting was held in the schoolroom to decide what motto the new tenor bell should bear around its mouth for the next few centuries. The tenor bell is the biggest of a peal, with the deepest note; his the stern tongue which calls alone at the end of the ringing before the Sunday morning service. A dozen Church-people were present at the meeting, and in the absence of the Rector on a tour in the Holy Land a letter was read asking them to choose suitable words. There was neither suggestion nor idea, so eventually, with diffidence, I submitted mine,

MY IRON TONGUE DOTH BID MEN COME

After discussion a variation on this couplet was put forward by, I think, George Miles, who kept the lanes "clean" of grass under contract from the Parish Council. The schoolmaster approved his variation as being better poetry, and as everyone voted for it, the following inscription was eventually cast:

MY MORNING RING SHALL CALL THEM IN

I thought this more suitable for the lighter treble bell, but said no more, feeling myself to be an outsider.

A long time ago—and yet, it was yesterday; and yesterday the youth rode up from Crosstree station, and saw the first buzzard soaring over the pinewoods of Anneswell, and watched, with aching breast, the moon rising over the glebe field from this very tower.

Yesterday, when Mr. Jaggers and his daughters built their hut overlooking the solitary sands of Vention, where I used to bathe naked and alone until midsummer; yesterday, when their summer boarding house arose grey with asbestos, for fifty or sixty people; yesterday again, when a rival hotel, for maybe two hundred and fifty people, arose farther along the hillside, amidst heather where once the merlin nested, and the evejars churred their songs at night.

So my book is nearly ended, and I have climbed to-day to see the village from the church tower, whence in the olden time the rooks could be seen sitting in their nests. Woodlice used to have their colonies in the corner of the old leads—how long did it take them to crawl up from the ground below? There they lived and raised their families, grazing on leaves and sticks whirled from the elm-tops by the gales and eddies of wind; and lichens grew there, with the green round-leafed pennywort plants. Once, disturbing a damp heap of rotting leaves in a corner, I found a thin red worm. How did he get on the tower? On the sexton's boot, from the earth of a new grave dug in the compost of human hopes below?

There was the Great Drought of 1921, which lasted from April until late summer, and was general over England; then there was the Great Winter seven years afterwards, when plover were found frozen in the snow, and I went ski-ing on the downs, and the beech-clump of Windwhistle Cross was hidden in a snow-drift. O joy, to be as a bird gliding alone and free in a new white world, silent but for the wind in my ears and the soft slur of the waxed wood in the snow.

Another year there was the Great Gale, throwing thousands of elms by the roadside, and ruining inland spruce-plantations, which looked as though they had been shelled by howitzers.

And the Great Flood at seven o'clock one morning towards midsummer, when it began to rain from a heavy sky which flashed and rolled with thunder. At 7.40 a.m. Revvy came out of his back door to look at the stream, which was running very fast, brown-red, and a foot deep. Hearing a strange noise beyond the new extension of the burial ground, "a sort of roaring crash", he peered over the new masoned wall, and saw a wave six feet high surging over the ground. The wall collapsed, and Revvy was swirled down under the old churchyard wall, to the garden wall across the way. The suck of water in the culvert by Hole Farm broke his clasps on the wall, and he was thinking (he told me) "there goes my hat, shan't see he again", when a greater volume of water overcame the local suck under Hole Farm and carried him down the street towards Billy Goldsworthy's barn. He was wearing an old coat given him by the Admiral, and the air enclosed by this against his chest kept him afloat. He was choking, for the surge along the churchyard wall had several times turned his feet up where his head should have been. Seeing the white faces of his three children peering from the bedroom window, he struggled to his feet, and pushing against the flow now setting through the farmyard—the double doors of which had been carried away—he managed to crawl out of an eddy lapping Billy Goldsworthy's barn doors. He had been in the water less than a minute.

Meanwhile his cousin and neighbour, Thunderbolt Willy, had stumped downstairs on his club-feet to get the money kept in the cracked teapot in the dairy. Sister Bessie was before him. She screeched as the back door fell in and the muddy water knocked her down; thereafter she was silent, swirled around the room with floating chairs, tables, and the dresser. Brother Willy managed to wade against the flood, to reach the teapot, and to put the money in his pocket; then he pulled his sister out of the water, and set her on the table. The pink back of a drowned or drowning sow heaved through the room, and lurched away through the window, taking glass and frame with it, followed by a string of floating coke from the Rectory. Then what looked like Mrs. Revvy's old-fashioned iron mangle came tipping and sliding through the house, followed by some shrubs from the Rectory garden, some oil-cans from the engine-room, and one of the water-closets from the new brick lean-to built against Revvy's cottage.

An hour later the water had gone down, leaving a foot of mud in the low-lying cottages. Some of the sexton's raspberry

canes had been uprooted; but Providence had not been entirely
unkind to the gravedigger, for most of the Hole Farm dung
dump had been left on his ground. A violent rain or cloud-burst
falling on the hill by Windwhistle Spinney had poured over the
sloping fields, had gathered behind the high cob Rectory wall,
which then burst, releasing many million gallons down the
valley, to Cryde and the sea. Channels four feet deep were cut
through the metalling of lanes; drainpipes were choked, exposed,
torn up, and rolled into the waves two miles away; ploughs,
stone rollers, harrows, trees, all were taken along. The old
clapper footbridges over the stream at Cryde stood, however—
and the dam in Ponde's Mash.

Revvy's garden wall was swept away, with his garden, his
closet-house, and his wooden washing-house. The Rectory
electric light plant—the former Rector's "horrid engine",
wobbling dynamo, and earth-leaking batteries, which he had
sold for £40 on leaving a year previously—were "gone in", and
insurance provided for his successor a nice new modern set. The
Rectory garden was a rocky winter-bourne, and for weeks the
main gate bore a notice in large shaky characters

NO ADMITTANCE

TO SIGHTSEERS

I understood how a blend of sympathy and curiosity, when
multiplied several thousand times, became merely colossal
impertinence; so a peep through the hedge at the new Rector
wearily scrubbing a carpet with a stable broom was enough for
my imagination.

A fund was started, and thousands of pounds were subscribed
by strangers. The administrators of the fund were said to have
been surprised by the extraordinary number of sets of silver
forks and spoons and new knives which had been washed into
Cryde Bay. Soon all lower Ham walked about in new clothes;
all the older garments had been buried secretly at night, to give
them the sorriest appearance of ruin. Tons of coal, wood, onions,
potatoes, gallons of oil, many lamps, sets of dinner plates and

cups and saucers had been washed away, all of the best quality. Many farm implements, which were never seen again, for the simple reason that they had never been seen before, appeared to have disappeared from the valley farms—in fact, everyone who could cashed-in in true local form from the Flood Relief Fund.

Stroyle George's farmhouse became a museum. For days and weeks afterwards the gaunt farmer repeated the words of his ill-fortune. Not for him to forbid the curiosity and sympathy of sightseers! There the mud was, just as it had been left by the Great Flood. And there a collecting box was, on the table.

At length, the Sanitary Inspector having declared several times that the place must be put right, the museum was closed, and cleaned at the Parish Council's expense. During that time a neighbour had given the use of one of her cottage rooms for a dairy, for most villagers helped one another in time of trouble, and the holiday season was beginning. For three months the milk was scalded and the cream scooped from the clome pans in the neighbour's cottage, and then the neighbour asked for her room. With bad grace the dairy was removed; and at night the neighbour's kind action was repaid by having the contents of an earth-closet slopped against her front door.

The new constable, being informed, called up the sergeant of police, who persuaded the outraged widow not to take action. He said that it was a thoughtless act, done on the spur of the moment, the imaginative effects of which were far greater than the act itself. The insulted widow agreed eventually; meanwhile Church Street had been renamed by some villagers.

It is said that after thirty years of age parental traits begin to develop in a son or daughter, traits which perhaps have been disliked and even hated by them when younger. Certainly the village was surprised at the action of the daughter. Someone in the village, feeling sorry for the farmer, lent him the money to pay his half-year's rent. Soon afterwards the farmer, meeting his helper in the village street, began to abuse him in a loud voice, declaring that he would have him up before a judge and jury for defamation of character. "Why don't you go and tell folks about your own whoremongering ways, instead of telling about other people?" he shouted. "What do you mean?" "You told the parson I borrowed half a year's rent from 'ee!" "Come with me and see the parson," replied the other, as calmly as he could; "then you will see you are mistaken." The Rectory bell jangled in the hollow house; no door was opened. "The parson is either hiding, or he is out. I repeat, I did not tell the parson, or anyone," said the man who had lent Stroyle George the money free of interest or security. Later, he learned that the farmer, going to the Rector to borrow money, had been told, "You should not borrow if you already owe money, for then you will not be happy." In a rage the farmer had slandered his helper about the village. The money was never repaid.

The farm came up for auction; the old tenant quit. Charlie Tucker bought it, and made it a better place to live in, with bigger windows and a wet-proof cement floor, with a kitchen range for hot water. Soon there would be electric light, and a new tenant keen to clear the fields of stroyle grass and other weeds.

The memories of unhappy things are fewer than the laughable ones. There was the week-end visit to Sedgemoor with the butcher who said he would show me some proper cider. Sedgemoor was a flat tract of marshy land, intersected with withy-bordered dykes called rhines; set with scattered cottages, all of them damp, and many of them flooded in winter. In summer the clay of the marshy fields hardened and cracked; mosquitoes sang at night, rising out of the sluggish sewage-bearing waters of the river. The dimmit-light or dimpsy of the hills was called dumpsy in that lurdan land. I recall many fleas in a bed, and the matter-of-fact statement, "Always fleas where there's chickens." I recall the pale and bitter cider in the hogsheads, an acid drink that blenches the honest stomach and is thrown up before it is warm; and my host, whose inside must have been harder than the oaken staves of the sour hogsheads, bending double with laughter at the sight of myself rejecting the apple vinegar. I recall the double bed wherein I found to my dismay that I was expected to sleep with him, and his request that he be allowed to cuddle me.

"I've slept with my wife every night for a dizen years, and feel sort o' cold and lonesome without her, if you understand."

I did not understand, especially when he began to tickle me, while laughing an inane cider-laugh; so I slept on the floor, wrapped in my leather coat and some newspapers, while he chuckled at intervals throughout the mosquito-singing night.

The next day we visited acquaintances of his early manhood. There was a cottage with a privy by the back door, over a stagnant ditch, a place of accumulated horror with lean pigs snuffling there, animals with wild-boar heads and the pendulous bodies of bloodhounds. He told me how in these parts they killed unwanted cats by stamping on their heads. Four small children, and the child-like wife carrying another one; the cottage with a damp earth floor covered with flat stones, and flooded every winter, sometimes for two months. The cottager was having trouble with a neighbour, at whom he had shouted and cursed when he passed by the cottage; he had put a mommett (effigy) in an apple tree in the orchard, as a protection against the ill-wishing of the neighbour. The wife was terrified, believing that her baby would be stillborn, or a winnick (idiot). They were convinced that the neighbour was a hag-rider. We stood by the ditch again, amidst the coarse buzzing of flies in the brassy sunshine, and I assured the mother that baby and herself would be all right; but I dared not say what I thought.

Perhaps it was the "hard" cider that made me want to return home as soon as possible; and my host was treated to a ride at midnight in a sidecar which swayed and lifted at the corners, while he cried in terror for less speed.

"Aw stop, will 'ee plaize to stop, us be doing sixty miles an hour, aw stop, my gor, I'll never zee missis again!"

"The brakes are broken and the throttle's jammed wide open," I yelled. "You laughed when I was sick! The sidecar connections are loose, too!"

SURVIEW AND FAREWELL

We did the forty miles of the twisting road in an hour. I never drank cider with him again; he never rode with me again.

The sexton below, digging a new grave: another world has passed away; soon my world, of which this book is a part, will sink into the earth again. I have an equal mind about death: I have planted a tree, made a child, and written a book. But to our history: the new burial ground wall was being rebuilt stronger, and the rock plants were back again on the ditching of the paths. The coffin of the old gentleman who gave the land almost went back to Cryde where he dwelled when alive; for the coffin was nearly washed out of the grave.

Clib below, digging a new grave; another world had passed away—the world of Emma the Maltese, mother of Hen-ry, who was always being beaten for playing in the water and making dirty his clean clothes.

The Maltese came to Ham with her husband and baby boy when Harry Gammon returned, a time-expired Class A reservist, to his native village. Harry worked as a mason; he had been a sapper in the Royal Engineers, and the Army had trained him. The first thing Harry did was to fill up with stones and mortar the dark angle-shaped opening under the thatch of the cottage he moved into—the cottage which I had occupied for seven years, and the white owls for possibly more than seven times seven that number of years. He left a tiny hole for the outlet of the birds—but whether they escaped or not, I do not know; at any rate they were not seen there again. I watched the work being done, feeling that my spirit—that part of me which seemed alien to the village—was being suffocated. Thereafter Harry settled down to village life, but after a year with his wife Emma and baby Hen-ry, he was called up and sent to Shanghai with the Engineers: the revolutionary struggle, with its kaleidoscopic and conflicting visions of a fairer life, was beginning in China.

Left even more lonely than before, the Maltese lived with her little boy in the cottage immediately below the churchyard—in the shade and silence of the elms. Occasionally, when the sun was shining, her voice was heard singing arias from Puccini's operas; and the village said, Oh my, did you ever hear anything like it? The Maltese was a fat woman, more noticeable because of her second baby, which was born three months after her husband's departure. To the village, she was always The Maltese —she had no friends. Hen-ry had all the Gammon vitality; his mother, with what unknown despair and anguish behind her rages, used to scold, wheedle, kick, wallop, and chase him—in vain. The boy screamed; then he grinned, and went back to get dirty in the water again.

When I used to pass the cottage, I felt that one lived therein who was being slowly stifled; sinking in an eddy where the slow muddy stream of village ideas left all the silt of its superficial consciousness.

After a year Harry returned, and his wife wept with joy; but she was still The Maltese, rootless, but alive, breathing through the leafed branches of her two children. Another year passed, and then a daughter was born. Once or twice, on passing the cottage, I heard again fragments of the Puccini airs, while I glimpsed her holding the baby girl before her, and singing to its pale face and solemn brown eyes. One day you will be a good friend for your mammy, won't you, baba?

One day, in a rage, The Maltese picked up a knife, and threatened to kill her children, and then herself. At once the stream of the village consciousness was in flood. They always knew The Maltese was queer; The Maltese was a foreigner, after all, they foreigners was always dangerous; something ought to be done; tell the policeman; tell the parson; fetch the doctor; The Maltese ought to be put away; remove the children out of danger; Harry Gammon, you ought to do something, don't stand there grinning, like a mazed fool, she trimmed poor li'l Henry like a proper bully when you was away; her be mazed, shouldn't be at large. Well, I mean to say, we might all be murdered in our beds, don't you think? Don't you think her mind should be examined by a lunacy expert? I never did take to her myself, I must say. Awful, isn't it?

Somebody ran for the doctor. The policeman was near. The

Maltese saw him. She ran upstairs, clasping her baba. She cried out wildly; she threatened to kill herself if they took her away. Don't take me away, don't take me away, I won't do it again, O God, don't have me put away. Then she screamed, and beat her head, and screamed.

She was taken to the Infirmary to be watched. She would not eat. She was melancholy. She said, again and again, Where are my children? They are quite safe; now you must be quiet, and get well quickly. You must do what you are told, and eat your food, please.

I want my children. O baba, baba, come to Mamma!

After a week in the strange room, not having eaten, not seeing a friendly face, she tried to escape. She failed. Soon afterwards she began to weep and moan, to beat her head, always asking for her children, and especially for baba. Then she threw herself in a fire, and was badly burned. After this, she was quiet, just lying in bed and staring at the walls or ceiling, as though she had wept all the tears of her life away. So The Maltese died, like something walled-up; and Clib was digging her grave below.

As I listened to the chink of Clib's shovel, I wished vainly, weakly, that I had gone to see her more often when her husband had been away—now why didn't I help her with Hen-ry? If only . . .

Down in the village street a tiny little boy was returning with his mother. One of his hands held two of her fingers, and with the other he held a bar of chocolate.

"You up there, Dad?" he asked in his feeble treble.

"Yes."

"You come down, naughty boy!" he squeaked. The term naughty boy was a joke. There were no naughty boys.

Yes, it was time to come down from the tower, this place of isolation, this airy wilderness, and to say good-bye to the village. A last hasty glance around. New Council buildings to be erected in Vanderbilt Willy's field: he protested, but soon got used to the idea. There he was, leaning up against Billy Goldsworthy's barn, lighting his pipe, come out to stand awhile in the sun, as a trout comes out of its hover to rest awhile in the stream. I must go and shake his hand, for I'm fond of the old fellow.

Once I thought his close-fisted reticence was a terrible thing. All things change; oneself with them. Stay a moment—a last moment—a farewell glance, a pang for so much neglected, so much left undone. Ah yes, there was Granfer Jimmy Carter, who, ruptured at 80 years, was told by three doctors that he would die if he didn't have an operation within twelve hours. Who thereupon put on his best 1875 hat and black tail coat and trousers, and went down to vote in the school, it being Election Day. Dang they Whigs, or Liberals, he was Tory through and through, farmers no good, nothing like a gennulman! Who on returning up Church Street, wheezing, bowed legs and clumping stick, was asked by Clib the postman, somewhat dubiously, "How be you, Granfer Jimmy?"

"LIVING!" cried Granfer Jimmy, in a loud voice.

The next day Revvy's father was working in his garden; and the next day; and the next. Either his twisted gut untwisted itself, or, having broken, joined itself together again. He lived for two years afterwards, and just before he died he said to me, in answer to a question why he thought the church was empty to-day:

"I believe there be a God, and I believe there be a Devil: but I don't want any man vor tell me his opinion of either!"

Now it is time to quit my solitary stance overlooking the village. Now what is my finest memory, outside the elements of earth, sea, and sky? LIVING! cried old Jimmy Carter, at the verge of the grave. LIVING! shone the great landlord of the sun, burning bright over all. I would see all things as the sun sees them, without shadows.